op'88

S. edition

The Concorde Conspiracy

Boeing SST USA

Length: 298 ft.
Speed: 1,800 mph
Range: 4,000 mls.
Capacity: 298 passengers

Cancelled: 1971

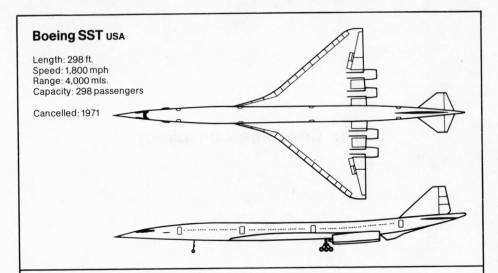

Concorde Britain & France

Length: 202 ft 3.6 in.
Speed: 1,350 mph
Range: 4,000 mls.
Capacity: 128-144 passengers *

First flight: 2 March 1969

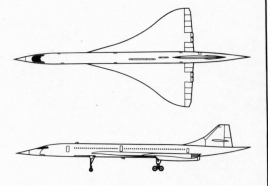

Dependent upon interior layout and seat pitch

TU-144 USSR

Length: 215 ft 6.5 ins.
Speed: 1,430 mph
Range: 4,000 mls.
Capacity: 140 passengers

First flight: 31 December 1968

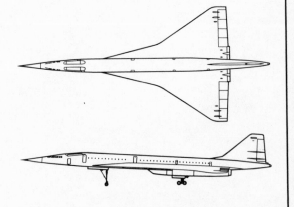

The
Concorde
Conspiracy

by John Costello

and Terry Hughes

Charles Scribner's Sons
New York

Library of Congress Cataloging in Publication Data

Costello, John.
  The Concorde conspiracy.

  Includes index.
  1. Concorde (Jet transports) I. Hughes, Terry, joint author. II. Title.
TL685.7.C7   387.7′33′49   75-20394
ISBN 0-684-14374-7

1 3 5 7 9 11 13 15 17 19 c/c 20 18 16 14 12 10 8 6 4 2

Printed in the United States of America

Contents

I thought you
were making ...
the tail

1

Champagne in Toulouse

Early on the morning of 29 September 1972, a fleet of white vans
drove into a hangar at the St. Martin factory of France's national
aircraft constructor, Aerospatiale. Instructions were given in the
crisp autumn air and the unloading began. Boxes of succulent
grapes followed a veritable mountain of pâté de foie gras into the
hangar; trays of médaillons de boeuf and côtelettes d'agneau
were carried in, followed by several hundred cheeses—Port
Salut, Camembert, Brie, Pont l'Evêque, and Roquefort. Then
came the wine: white wines from Bordeaux, and hundreds of
bottles of "vin de pays," the local Corbières. To crown the feast
came mandatory champagne—each bottle bearing a Concorde

1

insignia on its label. It was going to be an impressive spread, even by French standards.

Outside the hangar, on the vast tarmac, it was already growing hot as the sun rose into the clear blue Languedoc sky. Clouds hovered far away over the distant peaks of the Pyrénées. It was a perfect day for the celebrations to mark the roll out of Europe's two most advanced and ambitious commercial aircraft projects —the huge A300B Airbus built by five European nations, and the graceful airline version of Concorde, a dazzling product of the Anglo-French technological entente.

The gleaming white Concorde had been towed from its hangar the night before; the floor had been scrubbed and polished by the squads of blue-coated workers who hovered around enviously as the small white-jacketed army of waiters began to lay out the vast banquet for over a thousand guests. At the head table, amid the gleaming silverware and framed by banks of flowers, Pierre Messmer, prime minister of France, would play host to ministers and leading industrialists from half-a-dozen countries representing the top echelon of Europe's aerospace industry. Male chauvinism still held sway in France; ladies would be sitting some distance away at another ornately decorated table.

Opposite the Concorde hangar a long blue canvas stand had been erected, with a small dais before it, reminiscent of a Punch and Judy booth. Here the inevitable speeches would be delivered. The long lines of European flags hung lazily from their flagstaffs as the first guests began to appear. Bernard Dufour, the thirty-nine-year-old director of the Aerospatiale plant, wandered imperiously among the stands checking all arrangements.

A graduate of the elite École Polytechnique and the University of California, Dufour was a short, immaculate man with the penetrating brown eyes and swarthy complexion of the Midi. As controller of the 10,000 designers, engineers, and skilled workers of the St. Martin factory complex—and carrying one of the most demanding jobs in French industry—Dufour's bearing was understandably Napoleonic. His role extended far beyond Aerospatiale. As a key executive in the French management hierarchy, his decisions could immediately affect hundreds of other companies spread out across Europe. The two projects which were coming together in the huge assembly halls towering behind him were examples of a new European phenomenon, "the multinational airplane."

The events of that morning had been carefully planned to tell the world that the Europeans were determined to carve out a future for themselves in the prestigious areas of aerospace. It was an act of faith, but also a challenge. World aviation was already dominated by the United States which since the Second World War had captured more than 80 percent of the global market. Even within Europe, which accounted for a third of the world's passenger market, the aircraft industries had been losing ground. American companies were equipping many of the national flag carriers—Alitalia, KLM, Sabena, Iberia, Lufthansa—as well as a substantial proportion of the British and French air fleets. The United States held over 80 percent of the market even inside Europe. The only answer to the challenge of the American colossus was for the Europeans to band together, pooling resources, know-how, and markets. In this way they could build aircraft to compete with the transatlantic giant. If the great companies of Europe failed with the Concorde and Airbus being rolled out that morning, then world aviation could become an American preserve for the foreseeable future, and her grip on all branches of advanced technology would be unshakeable.

Concorde's French manufacturers were sparing no effort in extracting the maximum public relations benefit from the Toulouse presentations. The world's press and VIP guests were already converging on Toulouse by air.

Shortly after nine o'clock the first specially chartered airliners filled with guests began circling the city. Those who peered out of the cabin windows at the sprawling red roofs below could see why Toulouse was called "la ville rose." One of the first planes to touch down was from Amsterdam, loaded with delegates from the German–Dutch firm of Fokker-VFW, which was building part of the Airbus wing. Far away to the northeast, a DC-9 headed toward Toulouse from Munich, carrying a delegation of top planemakers from Messerschmitt-Bolkow-Blohm, led by the former German defense minister, Franz Joseph Strauss. The Spaniards, too, were flying in across the Pyrénées from Barcelona, carrying a team from CASA who was constructing the Airbus tail.

The British contingent was still a long way off, high over the Bay of Biscay in a new BEA Trident 3. On board, Sir Arnold Hall, the chairman of Hawker Siddeley Aviation, Britain's biggest aircraft company, gave the signal, and the first champagne corks of the day popped.

The champagne miraculously banished the early-morning blues, and the atmosphere was mildly euphoric as Sir Arnold hauled himself to his feet. Journalists from Britain's leading newspapers looked up expectantly. After all, someone had to mention the British in what was promising to become an all-French occasion.

"Today is a European occasion," said Sir Arnold. "We are going to celebrate one of the great events in Europe's proud aviation history. Two marvelous aircraft will be rolled out. In these days of high costs and massive marketing effort, no one country, no one industry can stand alone. We have worked together." Sir Arnold continued, "We in Hawker Siddeley are proud to be a part of this. Look out of the window and you will see a stout pair of British wings. We are designing the wings of the European Airbus and playing our part in the great adventure."

Sir Arnold sat down. Those who were peering out at the Trident's wings might have momentarily believed that no aircraft had a right to fly unless it sported a stout pair of British wings.

The British press contingent aboard, happily bubbling with French champagne, was still a little skeptical about the true reason for the day's events. Riding in the first-class compartment was Britain's minister of aerospace, Michael Heseltine, together with his civil service and industrial advisors. They knew all about painful in-fighting and how each European nation fought to protect its own interest, while acknowledging the virtues of cooperation. Britain still held a valuable share of the world aviation market, won in the teeth of American competition. Many in the British industry were desperately anxious that Britain should not give away all her hard-won experience, secrets, and skills.

Hawker Siddeley might be happy enough to work with Europe on the Airbus project but the British Aircraft Corporation, Britain's other major aviation constructor, had really pioneered the way into Europe. For nearly ten years the company had worked with Aerospatiale on the Concorde, and as a result some BAC executives were rather cautious about the benefits of cooperation. Concordes were being built to a common design in both BAC's factory at Bristol and at Toulouse. An extremely elaborate system of manufacture had evolved in which parts for the two assembly lines were made in plants scattered throughout the two countries. In addition, the research and development had been carried out on a completely integrated basis in the various government research establishments. But during the decade of close operational working the French had sometimes badly upset their British counterparts. In terms of public relations, the French seemed to have taken over the show. They had flown their prototype 001 first; they flew at Mach 2 well before the British, and had flown Concorde to South America in a blaze of publicity.

The Trident joined the BEA jet fleet parked a short distance from the long, blue stand. Elegant Aerospatiale girls in bright pink escorted the British visitors to their seats. Almost at the same time, a French Air Force jet brought Premier Messmer from Paris. Flanked by two stiff generals and the slight, wiry figure of his host, Henri Ziegler, the president of Aerospatiale, Messmer strode across the tarmac. The Air Force band broke into an uneven salute and the premier treated them to a top-speed inspection which revealed, rather too obviously, his true feeling about their turnout.

The prime minister had arrived, and the stands were now full. Everybody was beginning to feel the heat. French officials began to look anxiously at their watches, Bernard Dufour discreetly consulted Ziegler. The assembled heads of the great European aircraft companies—Rolls-Royce, Fokker, Hawker Siddeley, Aerospatiale, BAC—waited and chatted as if in anticipation of a football match. But where were the Germans? Discreet jokes rippled down the length of the long benches.

There was a whine of a taxiing jet. Moments later, like a medieval army advancing behind its leader, the Germans marched across the tarmac, headed by the bull-like figure of Franz Joseph Strauss. Puffing his apologies, he took his place alongside Ziegler and the French prime minister.

On a discreet signal, the band broke into a mildly discordant salute. The last notes had all but faded as Henri Ziegler marched across to the small boothlike dais. It was one of his big moments. His purposeful stride, with the sun glinting from his steel-rimmed glasses made him look exactly what he was—an extremely tough man. A former engineering general in the French Air Force, Ziegler had learned how to stand up to any of the political bosses of Gaullist France. Even more, he could talk back to the formidable French civil service, particularly the Ministère des Finances. His moral fiber was legendary, and at sixty-two he prided himself on physical fitness and took his holidays climbing in the Himalayas.

To men like Ziegler, the United States had illegitimately seized Europe's aviation inheritance and "colonized the sky." Since the end of World War II, European aviation, although renowned for its originality and discovery, had never been able to turn its promises into hard cash in the way that the United States industry had done. For evidence, they had no need to look any further than the fleet of planes that had brought them to Toulouse. The Americans had already seized a substantial lead in the new generation of wide-bodied jets with the Boeing 747, Douglas DC-10, and the Lockheed Tristar. Even Europe's challenger in this field, the Airbus, was going to fly by courtesy of American General Electric engines, a fact tactfully overlooked in the Toulouse celebrations.

Many British engineers shared Ziegler's belief that the American hegemony was unfair. But they realized that, in part, this had stemmed from a fragmented European effort when the United States could wield huge economic wealth and had a home market as large as the rest of the western world. It was not simply a question of sharing construction costs that had made these European projects possible, but the anticipation that they would have ready access to a very big and united market.

But they also knew the Americans would not take such a challenge lightly. The giant aerospace industry of the United States would draw on its extensive reserves of skill to cling to the lion's share of world aviation. This moved Ziegler to end his address with a call for Europe to keep its nerve. Like all Frenchmen, he was well aware of the British tendency to be tempted by the lure of blandishments by fellow Anglo-Saxons.

After all, BEA had recently announced its decision to buy the American Tristar, instead of helping the Airbus to get off the ground with a string of orders.

When the blond-haired Michael Heseltine, Britain's minister for aerospace, came to make his speech, he knew that the audience would be listening for any signs of weakness in his government's attitude to join European projects. After all, Britain did well in exporting aerospace products, including the RB-211, to the United States. Heseltine was one of Heath's youngest ministers.

A successful businessman with a flair for publicity, Heseltine with his Savile Row suits and well-groomed hair breathed success. Heath had chosen shrewdly in picking him as the man most likely to sell Concorde. His brief had been simple; he could go anywhere and do almost anything to sell the airliner. When he took over the ministry, Concorde was coming to the critical point where the deadlines on the options were approaching. Heseltine had to inject official enthusiasm and a measure of marketing skill into the whole Concorde operation. Already that summer he had flown halfway round the world on the British prototype, drumming up interest and orders.

As he stepped in front of the expectant multinational audience, Heseltine knew he was batting on a very good wicket. Politically the aircraft industry was becoming the most integrated in Europe, and the British government, about to become a full member of the EEC, wanted to demonstrate its full conversion to "Europeanism." Concorde and the commitment of Britain's large aircraft industry were regarded as a technological dowry for the marriage planned three months hence, on 1 January 1973, when Britain would finally become part of the European Economic Community.

Heseltine began with the familiar Churchillian trick of speaking in heavy French. He thanked his guests and then suddenly switched to make his main points in English. It did not quite work, and Heseltine had to recover while the old political pros like Strauss and Messmer looked on. But his theme was trenchant and to the point, surprising even the hard core of pro-European industrialists and civil servants in the British contingent. Heseltine urged more international projects and suggested that the European members should be thinking even farther ahead

than the Concorde and Airbus, to closer integration. "My government has authorized me to take every step to encourage the
integration of the British aircraft industry with that of Europe."

For Britain—which had for so long a "special relationship"
with the United States that had led to the heavy commitment and
eventual bankruptcy of Rolls-Royce—his words sounded like
strangely good intentions.

Then came the French prime minister, walking briskly to the
dais. Everyone expected a long piece of Gaullist rhetoric. In fact
he said surprisingly little, except to wish the European industry
well. It was an anticlimax for those who expected a traditional
Gaullist attack on the iniquity of the Americans.

As Messmer stepped down, the Air Force band crashed out a
fanfare which was soon drowned by the roar of aircraft engines.
The fragile stands vibrated as the mammoth Airbus, tall as a
hotel, wheeled round the left end of the stand. It advanced down
the tarmac, displaying its bulk. At the same time, with a precision
and a higher-pitched scream, the long, needle-nosed Concorde
wheeled in from the right and surged forward. Like medieval
knights at a tourney the planes charged toward each other at
alarming speed, their paint sparkling, their turbine blades racing.
Even the hardened pressmen began to sense a sensational story
in the spectacular drama of a multimillion-pound collision.
Gendarmes yelled at a lone British film crew calmly filming in the
oncoming Concorde's path. They escaped decapitation by a
millimeter as Concorde's sharp wing brushed their scalps. Just
before the crunch, brakes screeched and, noses feet apart, the
great machines stopped. As their turbines moaned to a halt, a
wave of applause broke across the spellbound audience. It was
an awe-inspiring spectacle. Here for all to see was the European
challenge to American domination of the skies.

Concorde was the spearhead. Flying at more than twice the
speed of sound, it would cut the Atlantic crossing to a mere $3\frac{1}{2}$
hours and bring every spot on the globe within a maximum of 12
hours flying time of every other. More than a billion pounds had
been invested by Britain and France to get Concorde into
production. Fifty thousand men were deployed across two
countries, with BAC and Aerospatiale jointly sharing the airframe, Rolls-Royce and the French company, SNECMA, building

the engines. Salesmen were already working steadily to gain vital orders for this new-generation airliner. The assembly lines at Bristol and Toulouse were gearing up for full-scale production, ready to work off the long list of over seventy options held by more than a dozen of the world's major carriers. First in the queue, alongside Air France and BOAC, would be the United States flag carrier Pan Am. If Pan Am gave the thumbs up, it could lead to an avalanche of orders and a massive return for Britain and France.

The spectators came down from their stands to inspect the aircraft. Cameramen and photographers filmed the airliners from every angle. The official party of ministers was led forward proudly by Ziegler.

Suddenly a hooter sounded. The doors of the giant hangar slid silently apart revealing row upon row of tables laden with food, wine, and mineral water. No other cue was required. To a man, the thousand guests surged forward, hurrying to their places at table. Framed by the cool hangar, the Concorde gleamed outside in the midday sun, as glasses were raised to toast the airliner which would fly across the Atlantic faster than a rifle bullet. The Concorde was the triumphant symbol of two nations' engineering skill and faith. Europe's heritage in aviation would at last be regained.

A brutal shock was in store.

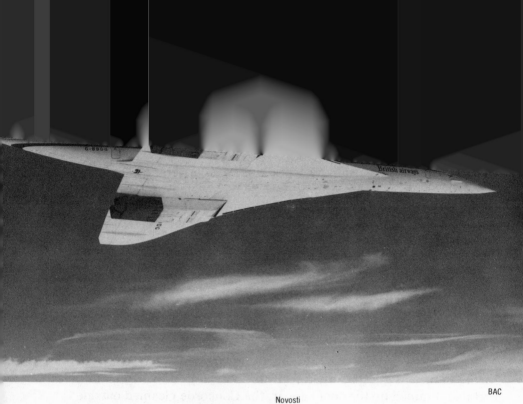

BAC

Novosti

THE SSTs

The Anglo-French Concorde 002 in flight over the Atlantic.

A prototype of the TU-144 at Sheremetyevo Airport, Moscow.

The Boeing 2707-300 mock-up at Seattle.

AP

ALL LINED UP BUT NOWHERE TO GO

"A hell of a setback." Sir George Edwards, chairman of the British Aircraft Corporation, tells the grim news of Pan Am's cancellation to the British press, 1 February 1973.

The production line at BAC's Weybridge plant, where inevitable cutbacks were expected as the option list collapsed.

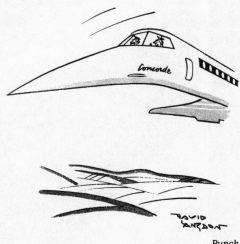

Punch
"Flight Deck to Sales Deck—where to now?"

2

A Very Clever Hand of Poker

On Thursday, 1 February 1973, a cold drizzle fell from the leaden London sky. The September sun and fiery speeches were just a memory to the journalists summoned to a press conference at the Belgravia offices of the Institute of Directors. Their views on Concorde were equally depressed. Hours before, news had come from New York that Pan Am would not be ordering Concorde, nor indeed would Trans World Airlines. Other American carriers who held options on the airliner were expected to follow Pan Am's example. It was like a defeat on a far-off battle front. The spearhead of the European attack on the American market had been turned and blunted. There were serious doubts about the survival of the billion-pound Concorde enterprise. The Americans had not merely rejected Concorde, they had virtually wrecked it altogether. TWA's Charles Tillinghast had spoken of its "dismal economics" and the cool statement from Pan Am damned with faint praise, "Pan Am studies indicate that the airplane will be capable of scheduled supersonic service, but since it has significantly less range, less payload, and higher operation costs than are provided by current prospective wide-bodied jets, it will require substantially higher fares than today."

Inside the Institute of Directors, there was no champagne atmosphere. What had once been a smart saloon overlooking fashionable Belgrave Square was now showing signs of wear and was lit by a dusty chandelier. Portraits of some of the better-known captains of British industry looked down, almost in sympathy, on the plight of Sir George Edwards, chairman of the British Aircraft Corporation. Sitting behind a green baize table, as the TV lights clicked on and the microphones were adjusted, Sir George looked very tired. Well over sixty, he had just returned from an exhausting transatlantic sales mission that had failed.

After a lifetime in the British aircraft industry, Sir George had faced setbacks before; this was perhaps the most disheartening and public. The pressure was beginning to tell, and as he drew himself up to speak, many noticed the fatigue in his voice. Yet beneath it all there was that grit and toughness which characterized a famous generation of British planemakers. Known affectionately but respectfully as "Uncle," Sir George was the last in a long line of famous names—de Havilland, A. V. Roe, and Handley Page—who had built up a major industry by personal endeavor. Famed for his down-to-earth aphorisms, Sir George claimed that he had been born "with a slide rule in one ear and a spanner sticking out of the other." All his working life, since starting as an apprentice, had been devoted to "defeating Isaac Newton." Concorde was the culmination of a career that had begun with biplanes, had passed through the era of the brilliant aircraft which had defeated Hitler, and had seen the remarkable post-war success of the Viscount and the elegant VC-10. Many were wondering whether the Pan Am decision would crown this brilliant career with a bitter defeat.

As soon as he started to speak in his clipped, dry tones, those who knew Sir George ceased to worry. Beneath the weariness there was the characteristic ring of steel. "What we have to do now, makers and governments together, is to approach this situation with common sense and without panic." Sir George went on, "We shall not regard this—as somebody described it—as a 'mortal blow.' It is a hell of a setback. Anybody who has been in this business as long as I have gets used to it, but you may learn to live with it." The answer to this problem, Sir George continued, was simple; government and people had to "keep their nerve." It was a part of the price of being out in front.

In Sir George's view, the American airlines had not wanted Concorde because of their very bad balance sheets. If the Americans believed that they could not operate the aircraft profitably, others held very different opinions. He strongly reaffirmed his faith: "I don't believe that this airplane is any different from any others. I think when it gets itself into service it will go. The standard of comfort and the saving of time will make it attractive to the customers."

He made no secret of the difficulties of selling to the Americans. "It's not even like getting up the north face of the Eiger—you no sooner get up one than you find you have got three more." Referring to the situation with the other airline customers he said: "There will no doubt be lots of people who will say, 'Oh my God—if Pan Am and TWA have not bought the airplane, what the hell are we going to do with it?' " It was largely a matter of keeping faith: "Those of us who put a lot of our life into the project and a lot of faith into it will be either right or wrong."

Sir George's grit and determination were supported on the other side of the Channel where there was no doubt that Concorde's rejection was an American plot. It was a perfect situation for Henri Ziegler, who sprang to the attack. "I remain convinced that Concorde is a good aircraft . . . and that commercial supersonic flight will be with us in two years." Then he went on with his customary temerity, "People will be obliged to realize that Concorde exists and cuts the world by half." Air France dutifully followed Ziegler's lead. President George Galichon claimed that "Concorde can allow us to give the businessmen the kind of service they no longer obtain from the buses of the air. Concorde will be full-up most of the time." He even said that the fare structure had been worked out, which showed a healthy profit.

The British journalists, however, saw that it was far more complicated. Taking on the Americans would produce no easy solutions. But how could the government go on pouring resources into a project costing over a million pounds a week and which had no apparent sales market in the world's biggest travel market? Many of them pondered these questions as they raced by taxi to Westminster, where Michael Heseltine held his own press conference.

Flanked by his aides, the minister appeared confident and even bouncy. The government had made its decision. It was continuing to back Concorde. It believed in it. "I support wholeheartedly the continuing development and production of Concorde. Our determination is to continue to give every support to the manufacturers in their sales efforts. Supersonic travel is, in every way you can forecast, with us." Later he repeated his bromide for the benefit of the British television audience. In his experience as a salesman he claimed that "there were good times and bad times. This was one of the bad moments." Later in the House of Commons, he told a silent and anxious chamber that the government was continuing to back the project, but admitted, "This is a serious setback and must be seen as such."

Behind the confidence and determination, however, there were nagging doubts.

The American rejection of Concorde had thrown the Anglo-French supersonic gamble into frightening relief. The stakes were alarmingly high. The British industry was highly vulnerable. Apart from Concorde there was no other major civil project, and failure of the supersonic airliner could bring drastic unemployment to Britain, affecting more than 25,000 skilled men in hundreds of factories. They would be forced to seek less skilled work, damaging Britain's earning capacity in the world. The aerospace industry, whose workers exported more per head than almost any other industry, would be reduced in size and efficiency.

The effects of the disaster would not be confined to the big aircraft companies. It would spread like a tidal wave and affect hundreds of subcontracting companies in both countries. A 1970 survey by the British Centre for the Study of Industrial Innovation had shown that over 700 companies were involved in supplying Concorde with everything from ash trays to automated flight systems; many firmly believed that Concorde had helped to raise their technical standards. This technological spinoff would die, and morale in Britain's most forward-looking companies would be shattered.

France too would suffer. The dynamic thrust of her new aerospace industry would be slowed down. Designers, engineers, and technicians would be dispersed. The dream of an advanced European technology under French leadership challenging American industrial power would be dimmed. Billions of francs would have been spent chasing an illusion, and as the *Times* was quick to observe, there was another danger; failure of Concorde could deal a savage blow to Anglo-French relations.

Cancellation of the project would gravely affect the political and industrial relationship between Britain and France, and would therefore threaten the coherence of the EEC. On the other hand, perseverance with the project could lead to very difficult trading relations with the United States and tensions might arise as a result of an Anglo-French monopoly of supersonic passenger capacity.

Many French and British citizens saw the decision of Pan Am and TWA as a deliberate conspiracy to kill the plane. Workers at BAC's Bristol plant were in no doubt that the Americans were determined to throw them on the scrap heap. Lou Gray, a Filton shop steward, began to organize a defense campaign. His view was simple. "If the Americans wish to boycott Concorde it can only be for political reasons. It is the opinion of every man in this factory that the Americans are trying hard to sabotage our supersonic project for the benefit of their own."

BAC's management privately agreed with their shop stewards, but felt it tactful to remain silent. The views of the shop floor were supported by a flood of letters pouring into the newspapers. The *Times*, a barometer of middle-class British opinion, carried many protests. Mr. F. Dent of London believed the decision was surprising only to "those who are unfamiliar with the American businessman's ability to play a very clever hand of poker." Two Oxford booksellers, Miles and Richard Blackwell, claimed that they were growing weary of "being bundled into Boeings" and would not "be blackmailed into paying first-class fares for an over-priced service. We should be proud to ride for a change in a plane with the Union flag on its tail."

But there were other angry voices. Some sections of the British press called for a halt to the project, labeling it as a "greater folly than the South Sea Bubble." The sniping and questioning which had bedeviled Concorde's progress now welled up again. Why, some newspapers demanded, had the project ever been started? How on earth had the costs risen from a 1962 estimate of £150 million to a figure of £1,070 million ten years later? And finally, they wondered whether anybody would ever buy the airliner in sufficient numbers to make the whole thing worthwhile. These three issues had run like a cross-thread throughout Concorde's development.

The fact that the answers were either unconvincing or proved wanting stirred many articulate people to see the Concorde project as a totally different kind of conspiracy. Unlike the Bristol workers, they did not believe that the American airlines and aircraft manufacturers had plotted to deprive Europe of its heritage. If there was a conspiracy, it involved Whitehall mandarins, French elitists, and irresponsible technocrats who had successfully foisted their Utopian scheme on an unwilling taxpayer. They saw Concorde as a mind-boggling waste of resources which should have been devoted to hospitals, schools, roads, and other socially desirable objectives. The anti-Concorde camp believed that the public had been repeatedly hoodwinked by the bureaucrats. They pointed to the enormous bill and the excessive secrecy surrounding the project. According to William Rogers, M.P., a former Labour minister, if there was widespread skepticism and worry, Concorde's sponsors had only themselves to blame. They had "consistently concealed, even from Parliament, much of the detailed information which would have allowed others to share their sense of pride. Instead of dialogue there has been silence. In place of frankness there has been mystery."

These opinions were not confined to Britain. None other than the former chairman of the Gaullist party's Foreign Affairs Committee, Charles de Chambrun, was severely critical. He accused the technocrats of misleading de Gaulle, obtaining huge credits for their favorite projects, and "short-circuiting any possible Parliamentary control by submitting a mere fraction of the true cost and keeping their real objectives well hidden." According to de Chambrun who, as deputy for Lozère, had considerable influence in the National Assembly, the old president had been duped by arrogant technologists into reinforcing France's prestige with a "technological Austerlitz." These misgivings were shared by the deputy from Nancy, the voluble Jean-Jacques Servan-Schreiber. He saw France mesmerized by Concorde's beautiful shape and immense prestige; the project was being continued at the expense of other more important technological programs. He claimed that facts were being concealed about Concorde's range, performance, and profitability, all of which he believed fell far short of specification. In the view of Servan-Schreiber, the radical French publisher and politician, Concorde was a gigantic white elephant which would only be used by "a few millionaires."

In 1973, at the time of Pan Am's rejection of the supersonic, each man, woman, and child in Britain and France had contributed £100 to the Concorde project. Most politicians and media men realized that the loss of such an immense investment would produce a monumental scandal, questioning the efficiency of government and its ability to make technological decisions on behalf of the people. Many of the decisions committing the government to supersonic air travel were made at a time when the scientists, civil servants, and politicians could not possibly forecast with any accuracy the end result. Ironically, many of the taxpayers now contributing were not even born when the scheme was first broached. From deceptively simple beginnings, the whole undertaking gradually acquired a life of its own embracing many far-reaching considerations of high diplomacy, industrial needs, and technological policy. Sometimes, the whole project, which rivaled the scale of the American space program, seemed beyond the control of officials, industrialists, and even governments, with powerful interest groups pressing it forward or threatening extinction. The life of Concorde can be explained in terms of two broad conspiracies, as alternate sides of the same conflict.

On one side were the technocrats and industrialists of the

French and British aviation industries, encouraged and protected by their political masters. Their motives were only partly concerned with building a supersonic airliner. They were equally interested in the reestablishment of fading national prestige and the regeneration of European industry so that it could withstand dynamic American pressure. Their motives may have been muddled, and they were certainly not dishonorable, but they seemed primarily concerned to extract all kinds of political advantage from the project, particularly in relation to the changing politics of the Common Market and attitudes toward the United States. Beneath the maneuverings of the Concorde lobby was the underlying conviction that Britain and France, and indeed Europe as a whole, had to live on its brains. The overcrowded continent of Western Europe did not possess the technical or the natural resources of the United States. If Europe did not live on her talents, she was nothing.

The Concorde lobby brought into being an antiparty, which single-mindedly conspired to kill the project at any cost. For the anti-Concorde party the decision to build the aircraft was grossly mistaken and neglected other avenues of technological advance of more obvious social benefit. It believed that Concorde represented a monstrous insensitivity to the physical environment in the name of progress and survival and that it was being narrowly justified. The "anti-Concordists" argued that the sonic boom would make life miserable for millions upon earth merely to satisfy a few wealthy travelers. Large sums of money would be invested by taxpayers who would never travel on the plane. The anti-Concorde party did not accept that Britain was engaged in a technological race with the United States. In its view, there were common interests among all people, on both sides of the Atlantic, to resist the SST. Concorde was far too high a sacrifice to offer on the altar of technical progress.

These same dilemmas spread to the United States, where the conflict developed its own distinctive style; there it was the anti-SST lobby that won the day.

Poppe

Popper

THE LEAP AHEAD

Britain's De Havilland Comet 1 inaugurates the world's firs[t] regular airliner service from London to Johannesburg, [2] May 1952.

Lord Brabazon, the pioneer aviator who masterminde[d] Britain's post-war aviation strategy with Sir Frank Whittle[,] inventor of the jet engine.

Pedigree of a supersonic. The evolution of Concorde's win[g] shape illustrated in wind tunnel models at the Royal Air[-] craft Establishment.

Keystor[e]

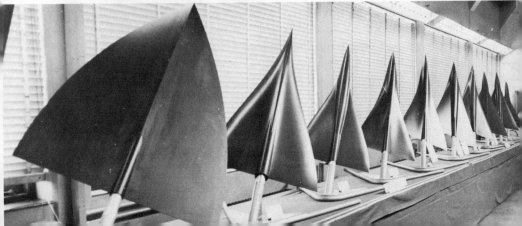

BREAKING THE BARRIERS

The Mach-3 North American B-70, dubbed the "Valkyrie," which the Senate Armed Services Committee believed could become the forerunner of a supersonic airliner.

President Truman congratulates Captain Charles Yeager, USAF, the first man to crash the sound barrier in a Bell X-1 rocket plane, 14 October 1947.

Punch

"Nothing is being left to chance—we even have a team working on the most advantageous time to cancel."

3

It Was Farnborough's Plane

The genesis of Concorde can be traced back three decades. In the spring of 1944, as the Allies were preparing their assault on Fortress Europe, Churchill's War Cabinet had already begun to consider the problems of peace. The aircraft industry figured prominently in their reconstruction plans. One million people were working in factories spread throughout Britain, turning out front-line aircraft like the Lancaster, Spitfire, and Mosquito. New skills had soon been developed by Britain's craftsmen. Plants which had been making saucepans in the 1930s now specialized in metallurgy; radio companies became adept at producing airborne electronic equipment; and watch companies learned how to make aircraft instrumentation. The war had given Britain a national asset, ideally suited to her engineering skills. As the War Cabinet committee met to consider how this new-found knowledge could be exploited Britain's greatest contribution to aviation technology, the jet engine, was about to go into Royal Air Force squadron service.

It was already obvious that only Britain and the United States could meet the post-war demand for new commercial aircraft fleets. The rapid technical strides made in long-range bombers and transport aircraft foretold an immense boom. The Atlantic had been mastered by ferry pilots, and millions had become air-minded whether they were on U-boat patrols or flying on bomber missions. The American industry was performing prodigious feats, turning out thousands of Flying Fortresses, Mustangs, and Dakotas, but Britain would have to compete with her immensely powerful ally after the war. She was already at a disadvantage; the Americans had a virtual monopoly in the production of transport aircraft as a result of an agreement made in 1943. The only way in which the Americans could be seriously challenged was by the exploitation of the brains and skill of Britain's scientists. The vast aircraft plants in Seattle, Santa Monica, and Burbank could not be outbuilt, but they could be out-thought. If Britain could take a technical leap ahead, she could corner an important share of the post-war aviation market.

A special cabinet committee was set up to examine the necessary policy to secure Britain a future in the post-war civil aviation business. Its chairman was Lord Brabazon, a pioneer aviator who carried the distinction of being Britain's first licensed pilot. His committee studied many options and plans. If the Americans were going to build big aircraft, Britain would build them bigger, and a scheme was drafted for the mighty one-hundred-ton Brabazon airliner, a "Queen Mary of the air," which would carry passengers in great luxury for distances of fifty-five hundred miles. Other smaller projects were examined, but perhaps the most important and exciting was the plan to exploit Britain's breakthrough in jet engine technology, with the construction of a transatlantic mail carrier. This, the origin of the world's first operational jet airliner, the De Havilland Comet which flew in 1949, was the key step in the direction of Concorde.

The Brabazon committee could approach these ambitious ideas

with great confidence since the instrument that was to play the main part in Britain's bid for commercial air power was at hand—the Royal Aircraft Establishment at Farnborough. This institution was the "Vatican of British aviation research." The brilliant team of scientists had been greatly expanded through the exigencies of war, and now the unprepossessing collection of huts and hangars on a Hampshire airfield represented perhaps the greatest concentration of aeronautical expertise in the world.

The Royal Aircraft Establishment would be needed to continue work on defense requirements, but its scientists could also be used to provide background research and initiative for the development of advanced commercial airliners. The Farnborough influence was immensely strong, through its network of contacts in industry and the civil service; this was to become an important factor in launching the European supersonic project. Under the pressure of war the concept of faster flight and the ways of achieving it had dominated Farnborough thinking. Sir Morien Morgan, one of the Royal Aircraft Establishment's most celebrated scientists, recalled that the teams had "worked intimately together for years when speed was of the essence and rules were often made to be broken." Shortly after the war, Farnborough had seriously begun to consider the methods of achieving high-speed commercial flight, as "supersonic bombers were being energetically evolved and technical people all over the world were beginning to wonder what civil spinoff would come from their deepening confidence in designing really high-speed military aircraft and missiles." Britain's most powerful aircraft establishment had concluded that supersonic flight was inevitable, and that Britain should be in the vanguard.

In the immediate post-war years, much of the technical progress in high-speed flight sprang from defeated German technology. The Reich's scientists had made the first important theoretical steps that were to take man toward his supersonic goal. When the Americans stumbled upon the secret Messerschmitt factory at Oberammergau they were amazed to find a prototype jet fighter whose wings could be preset to different angles of sweep. This, together with complete research data on the advantages of the swept-back wing for high-speed flight, prompted one of Boeing's engineers attached to the United States Army to send the information back to Seattle as fast as possible. He knew that since 1941 Boeing had been working on a jet replacement for the famous Superfortress, and in the spring of 1945 the design had been finalized with straight wings. In just ten days from receiving the German data, the company had built wind-tunnel models, checked out the results, and had incorporated swept-back wings into their bomber design. The project was the B-47, the direct ancestor of the Boeing 707 passenger jet. In this way German technology influenced a whole family of aircraft right up to the jumbo jets, which all rely on the swept-back wing.

The Allies hustled off to their own drawing boards all the top scientists who did not "disappear" behind the Iron Curtain. One of the leading Messerschmitt aerodynamicists, Dr. Dietrich Küchemann, was "invited" to Farnborough. It was to be his original theory that convinced the British government that an efficient supersonic airliner was within the realms of possibility. The Cold War conflict hastened faster-than-sound flight and on 14 October 1947, an American, Captain Charles Elwood Yeager, piloting the experimental Bell XS-1 rocket-plane, became the first man to break through the mythical sound barrier. As he streaked at more than 700 miles per hour 70,000 feet above the Nevada desert, through the initial buffeting of the transonic speed and into the calm zone of supersonic flight, the world's first man-made sonic boom struck the desert sands nearly ten miles below. The stubby rocket-plane, which was carried aloft slung in the bomb bay of a Superfortress, proved that controlled flight was possible above the speed of sound and that the so-called "sound barrier" could be relegated to works of popular fiction and feature films. But the stresses imposed during an aircraft's transition to supersonic flight could not be ignored. In the same year, a British plane, the De Havilland Swallow—piloted by Geoffrey de Havilland—broke up as it passed through the barrier and plunged into the Thames estuary. John Derry became the first European to fly supersonic, piloting a redesigned and strengthened Swallow a year later.

Such was the strategic importance of supersonic flight that within five years of Yeager's achievement, the United States had squadrons of F-100 supersonic fighters in service. The Russians produced the famous MIG 21, and the British were close behind with the Hawker Hunter. Fighters, with their relatively light airframes and powerful engines, were a comparatively straight-forward proposition, but as the designers got down to building a supersonic bomber, the problems mounted. Fighters need only a short burst of supersonic speed to carry light payloads for a short time, but the faster-than-sound bomber demanded a massive airframe, large payload, and a sustained period of supersonic flight. The requirements were of the same complexity as those of a supersonic passenger plane. But in spite of the massive resources devoted to the supersonic bomber for defense purposes, no satisfactory solution emerged. The first military aircraft relied more on the concept of "brute force and bloody igno-rance." The only solution, according to one leading American designer of the time, was "give me an engine big enough and I'll give you an ironing board that'll fly supersonic."

When the Farnborough team first got down to their drawing boards and "began to collect their scattered thoughts on super-sonic civil aircraft," the task was frightening.

In the aviation research centers of the West and in the Soviet Union, the aerodynamicists wrestled with the problems associ-ated with a large supersonic. This demanded an airframe design which could surmount the fundamental problems of high-speed flight. The first of these was that the supersonic had to take off and land at low speeds. Yet the ideal wing design for low speed was the straight wing, whereas high-speed flight, as the Germans had calculated, demanded a swept wing that kept well within the turbulent cone of airflow generated around the fast-moving aircraft.

When a plane moves through the air at, or above, the speed of sound the air particles in its path receive no warning of its impending approach. Instead of parting smoothly and passing cleanly over the wing surfaces, thus generating the lift that keeps the plane airborne, the air becomes turbulent and detached from the aerofoil wing surfaces. This causes severe stress and loss of vital lift. The swept-back wing was evolved to cope with precisely this problem: to remain inside the smooth airflow, inside the V-shaped shock waves that spread out from the aircraft's nose, rather like the bow wave of a ship. These inevitable shock waves not only cause considerably increased drag on an aircraft moving faster than sound, but also the characteristic sonic boom.

Swept-back wings become increasingly sharp, the higher the Mach number. And although sweepback is used in this way to "cheat the Mach number" it is at a price, because aircraft with a high sweepback do not perform well at low speed and have to land fast, "like bats out of hell." Highly swept-back configurations are satisfactory for small fighters, but less suitable for large bombers—or supersonic transports. The penalty to be paid for the increased drag at supersonic speeds on large airframes is at the expense of larger engines and staggering fuel consumption.

This was, perhaps, the basic problem to be solved. If the aerodynamicists failed to solve the problem of the supersonic's wing configuration, there could be no faster-than-sound airliner. But the scientists wondered what other difficulties lay beyond the first barrier. Man would be entering a completely new domain. Were there new hazards, such as unsuspected turbulence, that could shake a plane into disintegration? Would new materials and flying techniques be required? Would it make commercial sense? Although technical solutions could be found, would a supersonic airliner be profitable enough in operation to attract the world's airlines?

The first meeting of the Royal Aircraft Establishment's committee to consider formally the question of supersonic transport design took place on 25 February 1954. The assembled scientists minuted that "the coming generation of civil aircraft will travel at a high subsonic speed, and the question arose whether their successors should fly at slightly higher subsonic speed or at supersonic speed." The minute concluded by noting that "serious thought" should be given to "seeing if the requirements of civil supersonic aircraft tend to give any different guidance to research." The results of the initial research were not encouraging at all. As Sir Morien Morgan remembered, "Some horribly large airplanes resulted for quite small payloads, even when one cheated a little by skinning down on fuel reserves and using quite a lot of reheat for takeoff. In fact only silly airplanes emerged if one attempted the full non-stop London–New York range. One could get only fifteen passengers for an all-up weight of about 300,000 pounds at takeoff, giving a direct operating cost five or more times that of the then subsonic long-range machines." In his own words, "Our efforts momentarily ran into the sand."

When the report was issued, its main conclusion was that "no thin, straight-winged layout could get passengers across the Atlantic at anything like competitive economics" and "that a search should be made for more attractive aerodynamic shapes." Like their American colleagues at the same time, the Royal Aircraft Establishment shelved their first attempts, and it was back to the Farnborough drawing boards.

If the scientists began to flag in their determination, their spirits were raised by Sir George Edwards, then head of Vickers airplane company, who played a key role in the birth of the project. "I nailed my colors to the mast. Shortly after I came back from a trip to Moscow in 1956, I advocated strongly that we should abandon any more subsonic airplanes and go straight ahead and build a supersonic." Some companies were trying to get the government to put money into subsonic airliner projects, and as Sir George recalled, "Other leaders of the industry did not show much enthusiasm at the time and I got into hot water. But I came out strongly in support; so although the lead came from the government side, the fact that I was putting my weight into it at the time that I did—well, let's say it was helpful."

The support of Britain's leading aeronautical industrialist was especially significant in launching Concorde, as Sir George had already been successful in marketing a technical breakthrough with the turboprop Viscount, bought in substantial numbers in the United States. He had other subsonic jet airliners on the drawing board, including the VC-10. But Sir George Edwards was convinced that airline passengers would always buy speed, and that "there is a definite connection between industry, population, and speed of transport." In 1956 he called on the British industry to abandon any future subsonic designs and to concentrate on high-speed markets. If it did this, the industry could build up an unassailable lead in commercial aviation. This was music to the ears of the scientists at Farnborough, where, after a year of deliberation, an influential group led by aerodynamicist Philip Hufton believed they were getting near the breakthrough point with a combination of swept wings and waisted fuselages. Such was their enthusiasm that they persuaded the director of the Royal Aircraft Establishment to go to the Ministry of Aviation to establish a joint Industry/Farnborough committee to report on the practicality of supersonic flight. The Conservative government, in the midst of the Suez Crisis aftermath, was readily persuaded to give its blessing. The Supersonic Transport Aircraft Committee was born. It was to be a real blockbuster of a committee. The man chosen to lead it was Morien Morgan, well qualified by his work with supersonic fighters and bombers. Members were nominated from across the industry—every major aircraft firm and engine group, men from the Ministry of Aviation, the various research establishments, even the Air Registration Board and the state-run airlines BOAC and BEA. If they could not hammer out the basic proposals for practical supersonic flight—and no *one* team in Britain was better qualified than they were—then no one could say that the effort had not been well made.

If there was one point in time where the Concorde could have been said to have officially started it was at the first meeting of the STAC in London on Guy Fawkes Day*—5 November 1956. At this meeting, Farnborough research polarized around two clear proposals: the slender, delta Mach-2 aircraft and the swept M-shaped wing, with the waisted fuselage, flying at Mach 1.2.† It was the original research of ex-Messerschmitt designer Dietrich Küchemann and his colleague, E. C. Maskell, that unraveled the aerodynamic mystery of supersonic design and which led to the successful Concorde delta shape.

The bold aerodynamic adventure which Küchemann and Maskell initiated, in simple terms, was the revelation of the secrets of the paper dart. Traditional theory, with its emphasis on round leading edges to encourage a smooth attached airflow over the wings to generate lift, had never really offered an adequate explanation of how the paper dart, with its sharp leading edges, manages to fly. According to theory, sharp leading edges create

* Guy Fawkes Day is the British celebration of the foiling of the gunpowder plot of 1605, when Fawkes, a Roman Catholic nobleman, unsuccessfully tried to blow up Parliament. It has been traditionally marked by the lighting of bonfires and setting off fireworks.

† A Mach number is the accepted way of relating an aircraft's velocity to the speed of sound which is not constant but which varies according to the temperature of the atmosphere. Named after Ernst Mach, an Austrian physicist, Mach 1 is normally 760 mph at sea level. Concorde's design speed of Mach 2.2 is about 1,430 mph at 60,000 feet.

turbulence and a detached airflow which separates from the wing surface, causing loss of lift. This led to premature stalls and disaster in flight. Küchemann and Maskell reasoned that the slender delta wing, the paper dart, generates its lift from a hitherto unexplored airflow—in fact, from the detached airflow, the vortex rolls of air that the sharp leading edge generates over the wings on a slender delta shape. Not only did this provide a unique stability at all speeds, but as every schoolboy knows, the paper dart has a surprisingly good performance if the right relationship of width to length is achieved.

There was only one snag, which the Farnborough team had always known about and had dubbed "the road block." American research led to the conclusion that slender deltas were extremely unstable at incidences above a shallow angle. This would prevent a normal landing and takeoff, especially as the instability was thought to occur at all angles of incidence greater than 3 degrees. To get a delta down at this angle would mean landing at over 500 mph! Even "bats out of hell" hardly achieve this, and certainly a planeload of passengers never would. If the American research were accepted, then the Küchemann approach to supersonic flight looked like hitting the "road block," and supersonic passenger travel could be decades away. One man at Farnborough was determined to prove the Americans wrong. With remarkable tenacity and ingenuity an ex-World War I fighter pilot, W. E. Gray, began his own series of experiments. Ignoring the wind tunnels and all the expensive paraphernalia of Farnborough's labs he assembled his data with a lash-up model launcher worked by elastic, a camera, and a set of hastily constructed models flown from the top of a stepladder. Graduating from the stepladder to the roof of the Farnborough balloon shed, and eventually to a helicopter, his brilliantly simple free-flight experiments with models enabled Gray to discount the American research results. Confirmed by extensive wind-tunnel tests and experimental aircraft like the Handley Page 115, the "road block" was utterly demolished. The slender delta was shown to be stable up to angles of incidence above 20 degrees. Farnborough's scientists now knew that a supersonic airliner with dartlike wings was a practical possibility.

On 9 March 1959 Sir Morien Morgan submitted the STAC

Report to the controller of aircraft at the Ministry of Supply, Air Chief Marshal Sir Claude Pelly. It represented over two years' work, and no less than 500 separate studies were attached, going into all problems associated with supersonic flight from the sonic boom to ozone, radiation, and airfield noise. The key recommendation of the report was that the Farnborough scientists were now so confident that Britain had the secrets of a supersonic transport that the government should embark on a project for two airliners as soon as possible—one capable of carrying 150 passengers over the 3,450-mile transatlantic range at "not less than 1,200 mph" (Mach 1.8), and a second medium-range plane carrying about 100 passengers over a stage length of 1,500 statute miles. This aircraft would have a cruise speed of about 800 mph (Mach 1.2), and success depended on "the right compromise between supersonic and the subsonic part of the flight plan." The slower medium-range transport was seen as the next logical step in subsonic flight, and Farnborough obviously had the problem of the boom in mind. The transatlantic plane was to be the second priority since it raised so many complex technical problems.

The STAC humbly admitted that cost was difficult to estimate, but they set out a table for the minister's guidance. The development of one short-range prototype was estimated at £25–40 million; the long-range version would require a further £40–50 million. If developments were pressed ahead and five more aircraft were built in each class, costs would double for the medium-range plane to between £50 million and £80 million, but would rise less steeply for the transatlantic version (£75 million–£95 million). Thus the total investment needed according to the STAC's 1959 estimates was anything between £125 million and £175 million for the two. This was only one fraction of the £1,000 million plus bill which emerged ten years later.

The committee urged the government to act quickly. Failure to start work could mean "a decision to opt out of the long-range supersonic transport field altogether." Britain would be unable to regain her competitive position. Sir Morien Morgan's committee continued with a passionate statement of faith:

> Since this country's future will depend on the quality of its technological products and since its scientific manpower and

resources are less than those of the U.S.A. and U.S.S.R., it is important that a reasonable proportion of such resources are deployed on products which maintain our technical reputation at a high level. A successful supersonic aircraft would not only be a commercial venture of high promise but would also be of immense value to this country as an indication of our technical skill.

Farnborough could justifiably be proud of its achievement in the technical area of supersonic flight, yet in the 500 reports sent to the ministry, there was perhaps less attention to detail over the "high promise" of the commercial aspects of a supersonic airline.

A few paragraphs suggested that there would be a market for between 120 and 175 aircraft, "assuming that the economic and operational problems associated with supersonic flight have been solved, by the time they are due to enter service." One vitally important rider in the sales paper was whether "airline finances would permit the enormous outlay associated with these aircraft."

The men of the STAC were brilliantly right in their technical assessments, but their cost estimates were wildly out. They certainly totally failed to calculate the immense capital investment in research and development facilities. They also failed to relate the likely costs of the supersonic aircraft to the kind of airline fare structures that could evolve in the next decade. To them this appeared almost an irrelevance against the prospect of building the world's first supersonic airliner.

"SST"

4

Paper Planes in a Cardboard Sky

The report on President Eisenhower's oval-office desk read like a sales brief.

"Ever since the Wright Brothers' memorable accomplishment in 1903 the military establishment has had a vigorous development program. For over fifty years commercial aviation has had the advantage of leaning on a strong military development program." General Elwood Quesada, chief administrator of the Federal Aviation Authority, was alarmed about the news that Britain and possibly France were planning to launch supersonic airliner programs. As self-appointed guardian of the American aircraft industry, he wanted the president to act. The American lead in commercial aircraft, resulting mainly from the war, was already substantial, but it was not preordained to be eternal. Quesada was trying to overcome a major obstacle in American government thinking: that civil aircraft development was in no way the responsibility of the federal government. This was a thorn the White House did not wish to grasp, especially with an election on the horizon. However, as everybody in American industry knew, it was always possible to prime the pump of research and development with government military contracts. Manufacturers such as Boeing or Douglas could then quickly adapt the research, whether the Pentagon espoused the project or not, to developing commercial airliners.

Eisenhower was not convinced. His economic advisors were urging an immediate cutback in government spending. The supersonic bomber projects, including the controversial B-70, all lacked credibility, and his Service advisors were writing off the manned bomber in favor of missiles. Boeing and Douglas were successfully dominating the field in civil aircraft, without government aid or interference. They had always produced planes for the market stimulated by a huge domestic demand. In the early 1960s the airlines were clamoring for subsonic jets to equip their rapidly growing fleets. The need for a supersonic seemed far away as the 707s and DC-8s rolled off the production lines in Seattle and Santa Monica. They had seen the British try to beat them with the Comet 1, which, in 1952, was five years ahead of any United States competitor, but the unfortunate technical failure of the Comet 1 had meant that although the American manufacturers had come up from behind, they now virtually monopolized the world's jet market, and "had come up smelling of roses." The Europeans might try to be first with a supersonic, but as one Boeing executive put it, "We can develop hell out of anything; we may not be original, but we sure know how to put it into production."

The supersonic airliner presented a major problem for the United States industry if there were no supersonic bomber project to precede a civil airliner. Boeing and all the other manufacturers knew that it was going to be a tough task raising the development money without some form of federal aid. Preliminary studies had shown them that the supersonic project would be enormously expensive; pessimists estimated development costs at over $1 billion. The airlines were understandably reserved. As one airline boss put it, "We are all buying airplanes costing $5 million each! We can't afford to throw them away overnight."

If the United States industry could not afford to take the far-sighted view of the supersonic, the Europeans with their different system could. It took true, determined vision to predict the time when the world's airlines would need to reequip with supersonic fleets.

The American industry, hearing leaks and rumors from Europe, began to sense their vulnerability. Farnborough had engineered a technical breakthrough which the British government would certainly try to exploit. Even worse, they might join up with the French to create a strong industrial base from which to launch a whole new generation of advanced airliners. The American companies had tried to solve the problem of building a viable supersonic transport through a range of bomber projects, but they had all fallen short of technical promises. In spite of their immense resources the Americans were not as advanced as the British and French in their knowledge of supersonic transports. The "brute force and bloody ignorance" principle had been applied with gusto by American designers in attempts to solve the problems of faster-than-sound flight. This had led to some strange ideas and equally old-fashioned reactions from the United States Air Force.

In the 1950s, to keep ahead of the Russians, General Curtis "Bomber" Le May, commander of the United States Strategic Air Command, commissioned work on a supersonic replacement for the B-47. After four years, he asked to be shown the designs but was not impressed. Relying on the brute force and bloody ignorance concept, the designers had projected a 500-ton monster, whose enormous engines needed so much fuel that each plane would have to carry two jettisonable tanks, each as big as a small fighter. The general is reported to have almost choked on his cigar and bellowed, "This isn't an airplane—its a three-ship formation!" The project took a nose dive into the nearest wastepaper basket.

The next attempt was less ambitious and actually found its way into service with the U.S.A.F. This was the medium-range B-58

Hustler, designed to "dash" on its target at a maximum speed of Mach 2.2. Its costs were a salutary warning to those who wanted to build large supersonic planes. Although it was built of aluminum and had a large delta wing, its development costs were three times the estimates. The Hustler's appetite for fuel was voracious, and many Air Force chiefs seriously doubted its capability as a strategic bomber.

Another American attempt must surely rank as one of the most unique airplanes in the history of aviation. The B-70 was a monster designed for the exorbitant speed of Mach 3. Because of the searing heat produced by the friction of rushing air at such great speed, it was built of steel and titanium. Shaped like a praying mantis, it had downturned delta wings and squatted on a massive four-engine power-plant. The B-70 was designed to ride its own shock wave, like a surfer on a Pacific roller. To Boeing and North American, who were vying for the privilege of building this futuristic monster, aptly named "Valkyrie," it was a supersonic transport in embryo. Here was the ideal proving ground for the nation's SST, with government research and billions of federal dollars all ready to be poured into its development in the name of national defense. When Boeing lost the contract to its rival, North American, in 1958, it must have seemed that the Seattle company which had given America the jet transport had been dealt a body blow. But the B-70's days were numbered. Militarily, it had attracted the fatal Pentagon tag of "the paper airplane which would fly in a cardboard sky." The United States Chiefs of Staff had become totally engrossed in the missile race with the Soviet Union. Bombers were out.

On 30 November 1959 a fateful Telex clattered through to the headquarters of North American Aviation: "CEASE ALL STUDY, DESIGN, DEVELOPMENT, AND FABRICATION WORK TOWARD THE B-70 WEAPON SYSTEM." With this message the Pentagon defaulted on its traditional role as patron of United States civil aircraft development. It was now clear that getting a United States SST in the air was going to be a herculean task.

The B-70 cancellation appeared to threaten the vital long-term interests of American superiority in commercial aviation. If the B-70 stopped, then effective research and development of any

United States civil transport would stop as well. Senator Lyndon Baines Johnson leaped into the massive row that boiled up on Capitol Hill. "Transportation of people and cargo at three times the speed of sound, and above the weather, could be attained through the utilization of B-70 technology," Johnson argued, in a forceful document prepared by the influential Senate Committee on the Armed Services. "The impact of a supersonic cruise transport on world traveling habits and on the entire field of transportation is expected to be far greater than the impact that accompanies the introduction of jet transports. Our leadership in commercial aviation will almost certainly be lost unless the nation continues the development of Mach-3 technology and applies it as promptly as possible to air transportation adaptations." So outspoken was Johnson that some people wondered whether his subcommittee was more concerned with the issues of national defense or the cause of civil aviation. But the Air Force backed him. Its chief of staff, General White, told the congressional hearings, "The B-70 is not just an airplane, it is a national aeronautical development."

As a result of the furor, the two prototype Valkyries were allowed to survive as "experimental" prototypes, but if there was any doubt about the cost of going to Mach 3, the staggering $1.5 billion that it cost to get them into the air for their brief experimental flights was an ominous pointer. Misfortune dogged the Valkyrie. One suffered a spectacular mid-air collision, and the survivor was soon relegated to a museum. Johnson was right—supersonic-scale investment was impossible to find from conventional commercial sources. The only way in which an SST could come into being now was either through a joint aviation–industry effort or as federal funding. In 1960 neither looked like a remote possibility. As Europe prepared to launch its challenger, the American SST was stillborn.

Elwood Quesada tried hard to impress the president with the fact that the Europeans, not to mention the Soviet Union, were determined to mount a challenge. However, this was a crucial election year for the Republicans, with Vice-President Nixon nominated as a presidential candidate. The electorate came first and budget cuts were more important than a future SST. If Eisenhower's reaction did not dampen the spirits of General

Quesada and the SST lobby, a report commissioned by the FAA in 1960 and compiled by United Research Inc. of Cambridge, Massachusetts, was even more disheartening. In a thorough assessment of the SST concept, it pointed out that even if the B-70 program were maintained, it would cost the Administration at least $1 billion to develop a transport version. Even more damaging was the assessment that the technical and financial risks were "greater than ever known before." The report also suggested that the market could only stand one SST to be manufactured in the free world.

The report received a mixed reception. *Fortune*, the influential business magazine, noted, "The concept challenges the imagination and at this stage almost everyone associated with aviation has good reason for being frightened of it." But it went on to add, "If pushing ahead with the SST is a risky proposition, the risk of not doing it may well be greater." The decision on the SST was to face President John F. Kennedy following his victory over Richard Nixon, when he entered the White House pledged to the New Frontier and getting America moving again.

There was a fundamental difference of approach to aviation on each side of the Atlantic. At the same time that the United States was canceling the B-70 and jeopardizing the future of an American supersonic airliner, the British and French governments were on the brink of pouring millions into the development of a project started without any military base, and which was civil from the outset. Perhaps it reflected the different political philosophies, with the Europeans backing a civil project they knew to be in the national interest, while the United States could only do this under the guise of national defense. It was this difference in philosophy which was to prove crucial to Concorde's survival and fatal to subsequent attempts to launch an American SST.

Europe was raising the stakes, but opponents of an American SST received help from a rather unexpected source. In the spring of 1961, as the British and French were drawing together and President Kennedy was considering American SST policy, the world's airline bosses let it be known that they did not exactly welcome the prospect of supersonic flight, whichever side of the Atlantic it came from. In 1958 the arrival of the subsonic Boeing

707 and Douglas DC-8 had forced them to write off huge fleets of obsolete Super-Constellations and DC-7s with much operational life left in them. Pan Am had forced the pace by introducing the big jets on the North Atlantic, and, in less than a year, the effect had been dramatic. To the delight of Boeing and Douglas, every major airline was forced to follow or see itself go out of business. The flying public wanted speed and, with profits just beginning to recover in 1961 after the huge investment in subsonics, the airline bosses saw the danger of it all happening again with the premature arrival of supersonics. "Premature," in their terms, meant before the end of the decade, since the subsonics had a good fifteen years of life in them.

The notice board outside the conference room in the Queen Elizabeth Hotel in Montreal announced: "IATA—14th. TECHNI-CAL CONFERENCE Subject: SST PROBABILITY." The world's airline bosses now took a long hard look at the SST at the conference. As *The Economist* recorded, "Brash optimism has given way to something nearer humility. . . . They have not put the SST on trial so much as on a psychiatrist's couch. It is not surprising that this meeting is being held behind closed doors guarded by hotel detectives. Who knows but that one of the little gray nuns, attending the next-door gathering of the Quebec Hospitals Association, might not leak to the outside world the fact that none of the manufacturers present expects to deliver an SST before 1970 and many of them are thinking in terms of 1975? This is quite early enough to suit the airlines who are determined not to make the same mistake they made when they introduced the big jets three years ago."

The feelings of the airline delegates were bluntly summed up by the former IATA chief, Sir William Hildred, who wondered, "Am I square in suggesting that even for the young 550 mph is not too bad? The international industry will fall back on evil days if the jets are thrust to an untimely end by the onset of the supersonic." With a deafening air of finality he concluded, "I hope I shall not live to see the damned thing."

For a grueling six days the delegates grilled the planemakers of Britain, France, and America. "Psychiatrist's couch" was too gentle a definition of the exercise that the determined IATA delegates conducted as they probed every detail of supersonic flight. It was a daunting new area for them, encountering everything from the problems of micro-meteorites to turnaround service time, from the physical strain of supersonic travel to the sonic boom.

One important new fact emerged at the conference. The airlines and the builders realized that the supersonic transport would not necessarily be popular. Public opinion might actually question the technical brilliance of traveling faster than sound. A scathing attack was made on the concept of supersonic travel by Professor Bo Lundberg, a former test pilot and director of the Aeronautical Research Institute of Sweden. For the first time assuming the mantle of the "Cassandra of the SST" in public, Lundberg showered doubts about the supersonics: Would the structures of the aircraft be safe at such heights? Would there be catastrophes arising from supersonic hailstones? Would radiation have dangerous effects on pregnant women? And what about the sonic boom? Surely it would be intolerable to expect people to live with that noise. He also reminded the profit-conscious airlines that the passengers had not been asked "whether they wish to be shot through the air, rather than flown." He handed out a dour Swedish warning to the planemakers: "Supersonic transports cannot be built without introducing a host of similar features simultaneously. An aircraft designer can normally do a great deal to minimize foreseeable risks . . . but he can do nothing about the risks he fails to foresee." The planemakers from Europe and the United States listened, but paid Lundberg little attention and wrote him off as a Nordic pessimist. It was an indication of the public relations battle ahead; but in 1961 they were more concerned with impressing their future customers. The market was their audience in Montreal. The manufacturers even listened in polite silence to a naturalist who, in the midst of the elaborate technical presentations and with undisguised nervousness, proceeded to deliver a lecture about the supersonic threat posed to the whooping crane. This endangered species could well become extinct if the sonic boom shattered its eggs.

Dr. Russell headed the presentation for the Anglo-French project, issuing a warning to the Americans who were set for the faster Mach 3 aircraft: "The advocates of Mach-3 airliners seem to be confronted by a formidable array of self-inflicted difficulty. The Mach-2 solution offers close competition on similar financial arrangements to the subsonics, while the Mach-3 "hot rod" needs a very indulgent backer." The American Convair engineers had an answer for this and everyone else; it was Mach 3 or nothing, because "there is some chance that the Mach-2 vehicle will be obsolescent before the first one is delivered. Faced with this outlook, few airlines are likely to buy the aircraft in fleet strength. The market would be highly speculative." *The Economist* put the matter more bluntly, in its self-appointed role as the mentor of the British industry: "The Ministry of Aviation must be wondering whether one British company can be right and the entire American aircraft industry wrong." But as the airline bosses went home, they must have reflected long and deep on Lundberg's gloomy prediction: "Once supersonic aviation has been introduced it will grow and continue to grow indefinitely, if it is at all an economically sound proposition; but ultimately found to be a mistake because of protests from the public, it will not be possible for the airlines to turn back to pure subsonic aviation without economic disaster."

After the Montreal conference the airlines' attitude to the SST was noticeably less euphoric, and this change might have been the signal to prompt the British and French into a reappraisal of the project as they moved into partnership. But since commercial market considerations had played a minor part in the calculations so far, it is hardly surprising that they were barely considered in the final stages of the decision to go ahead. What was more important to Europe was to get the first supersonic into the air. Rumors were reaching the West that the Russians were preparing to build their own supersonic airliner.

Yet as the British and French were coming together, and with the Russians joining the race, the Americans continued to vacillate about how to fund an SST in the absence of the supersonic bomber. They knew that they were being dragged slowly but surely into the race "like a limp civil rights protestor being hauled off to jail," which was the graphic way in which Najeeb Halaby, former test pilot and President Kennedy's new head of the FAA, described the process. But what many Americans really feared was expressed in the words of the president of American Airlines: "One of the worst beatings we'll ever get is if we have to look up to a Soviet SST, the way we had to look up to the first Sputnik!"

Le Canard Enchaîné

"Si les Anglais me laissent tomber, je le ferai avec Franco! . . ."

5

The Reluctant Entente

Duncan Sandys, Britain's minister of aviation, looked across the table at his cabinet colleagues, assembled under the chairmanship of Harold Macmillan. "If we are not in the supersonic aircraft business," he told them bluntly, "then it's really only a matter of time before the whole British aircraft industry packs in. It's obviously the thing of the future. It may pay. It may not pay, but we cannot afford to stay out."

Sandys had decided to back the Supersonic Transport Aircraft Committee recommendations. Indecision could be disastrous; time should not be wasted on long-winded studies or economic analysis. He pressed his point, "If we miss this generation we shall never catch up. We will end up building executive aircraft."

Sandys' advice had to be taken very seriously. The handsome, auburn-haired minister, who had been badly injured in the war, was a powerful member of the government with a strong following in the party. Tory to the core, he represented one of the last links with the great days of Churchill and was known for his ruthlessness and unyielding determination. Sandys had been used by his famous father-in-law as a troubleshooter and had been entrusted with the vital war-time mission of tracking down and neutralizing Hitler's "V" weapons and gingering up the D-Day organization. Harold Macmillan had employed Sandys in his traditional troubleshooting role, particularly where there were obdurate issues and strong power groups to be handled, as in the defense industries. It was perhaps ironic that Duncan Sandys was proposing a new role for the aircraft industry, since he had been responsible for removing most of its advanced projects. His 1957 White Paper had decreed the end of the manned bomber and supersonic fighter. As minister of aviation, he had the specific brief to rationalize the fragmented aircraft industry. Even if Britain had wanted to undertake a supersonic airliner program, the aircraft industry made up of over fifteen medium and small companies would have been unable to carry it through. The STAC proposals presented Sandys with an ideal carrot with which to persuade the companies to accept unpalatable mergers with their deadly rivals. In November 1959 he had started the massive haggling session.

> I got the aircraft manufacturers together, there were about fifteen of them. I said, "I think there is only room for two." They agreed there ought to be amalgamations of some sort and felt that it would no doubt take a number of years to achieve it. I said let's see whether we can do it by Christmas. So what I did was set up a marriage bureau in my office. Every week I suggested that firms come and see me. I would propose marriages and they would tell me how they got on. It went very well. We didn't achieve it by Christmas but we did achieve it by Twelfth Night.

The fifteen came down to two—Hawker Siddeley and the British Aircraft Corporation.

In considering Sandys' supersonic proposals, Prime Minister Harold Macmillan expressed some disdain toward the idea of faster-than-sound travel. He prided himself on his Edwardian style and elegance. It was hard to imagine him in a hurry, which would have seemed a slightly vulgar eccentricity. Although Macmillan might accept Sandys' proposals to start design studies as some sort of answer to the aircraft muddle, there was a far more powerful argument in his mind. After a decade of false hopes and disappointments, Macmillan had decided that Britain could no longer stand alone in a world of superpowers. The only sensible alternative was to make some accommodation with the rapidly growing European Economic Community, made up of France, Germany, Italy, and the Benelux countries. As Macmillan knew, this meant a deal with his wartime friend, President Charles de Gaulle, who saw himself as gatekeeper of the new power grouping, and news had come that France too had started work on a supersonic airliner.

Across the Channel in the Fifth Republic, issues of national prestige were interpreted in direct terms. De Gaulle had decided that the technological challenge to "Atlanticism" was to be rooted in military independence and had initiated a colossal development program for missiles, warheads, fighter aircraft, and nuclear submarines. The ending of what the general liked to call "American colonization of the skies" was a natural part of this philosophy, and the supersonic airliner project the way of achieving it. Even to Harold Macmillan, who was directing his considerable powers of statesmanship toward the European objective, de Gaulle's views lacked a certain reality. "He spoke of 'la gloire' and cried that France should lead the world, almost reliving the state of Louis XIV." The fact that France too was engaged on a supersonic project pressed the British government toward action.

The decision to start on the preliminary design studies toward what was to be Europe's biggest technological venture passed easily through the cabinet. There was hardly any anxiety about where it would lead, or what it would eventually cost Britain.

Contracts had already been passed for long- and medium-range design studies. Hawker Siddeley, somewhat predictably, was given the medium-supersonic project, and to the surprise of the industry, the long-range contract was granted to the West Country firm of Bristol Aircraft. Although it had been in the aviation business for over fifty years, the company had suffered a very bad run since the end of the war. The mammoth Brabazon project which it had been awarded had ended disastrously in recrimination, bad publicity, and a £13 million loss. Even its successor—the turboprop Britannia—met with little success on the world market because of its late arrival. Now the design teams and engineers were gloomily facing the future. They grasped the supersonic project eagerly. As one executive put it, "We were on the poverty line. We didn't want to starve to death."

If Bristol had to thank one man for its reprieve it was Dr. Archibald Russell, the chief designer. A stocky West Countryman himself, who was unafraid to speak his mind in a strong rustic accent. Russell had been a member of the STAC and possessed one overwhelming qualification for the job of designing the long-range supersonic: he had built an experimental Mach-3 plane known as the Type 188. It was far from graceful and had been constructed of stainless steel to resist temperatures above 2,000 mph. He saw it as a "real brute of a plane," but it had taught him one important fact: the heat barrier was far more crucial to supersonic flight than the sound barrier.

As the STAC report made clear, and as Russell knew from his T-188 experience, heat was a major problem. If supersonic aircraft were to be built with metals in current use, then there was a strict and finite limitation on their speed. Above Mach 2.2, the heat from friction becomes so great that the crystalline structure of aluminium degenerates. A decision had to be made between starting a practical project using familiar and well-tried techniques and materials, or leaping into the new field of engineering required for making planes out of less conventional materials. Dr. Russell decided to stay within the state of the art, building his design out of a new aluminium alloy developed by Rolls-Royce. This could give a maximum speed just above Mach 2. To go faster to Mach 3, which is what the Americans were expected to do, meant accepting the complex problems of titanium and stainless-steel construction, for only a short time advantage over the North Atlantic route. It might well be possible to solve these problems in the course of time and at a price, but it was doubtful whether the airlines would foot the bill, and precious lead time over the American competitors would be lost.

Once launched on the supersonic project, Russell and his team made another important decision that would make supersonic flight a practical proposition: they selected an existing engine to power the plane to twice the speed of sound. The engines are the very heart of an aircraft, and as far as commercial operation is concerned, the key to its operating economics. It was known that a supersonic would need engines of high thrust. To push an airframe to Mach 2, even with sophisticated aerodynamics, required the expenditure of considerable energy. In a happy coincidence, an existing engine, the Olympus turbojet, was being developed by the Bristol Siddeley Company (later to be taken over by Rolls-Royce) in their plant down the road from Bristol's Filton works. The original Olympus design had been in service with the R.A.F. for many years in the Vulcan bomber and was being uprated from a 10,000- to a 20,000-pound thrust for the R.A.F.'s TSR-2 bomber. Bristol Siddeley engineers believed it could be pushed even further. Rolls-Royce, anxious for the prestige of being part of the supersonic project, proposed building a new engine for Russell's design, quoting development costs of £17 million, which in the light of what happened on the RB-211 must be counted as one of the most unrealistic costings ever made—even for the aircraft industry. The design team, however, saved considerable investment by opting for the Olympus.

Russell's team began to draw up proposals for a six-engined transatlantic supersonic to meet an August 1961 deadline while Hawker Siddeley began working out plans for the 800-mph medium-range airliner; but while the British sorted themselves out, France had already begun work on her own supersonic.

At the Sud Aviation plant in Toulouse, a French team was busy drawing up plans for a four-engined Super-Caravelle, which would take over the medium-range market of its successful subsonic namesake. Backed by ONERA,* the French equivalent of Farnborough, Sud Aviation was coming up with similar designs, but of smaller overall size. The company's designer, Pierre Satre, believed, rather like the British industry, that "we had to make something new and original. We had to try and innovate—to lead from the front!"

* ONERA: Office National d'Étude et de Recherche Aérospatiale.

Actively encouraged by President de Gaulle, the French industry was beginning to feel its muscle. It had already shown its resilience after virtual extinction during the Nazi Occupation with the Caravelle medium-range jetliner, which had been sold into the American market. It had been impossible to suppress the immensely strong French aviation tradition which had played an important role in the development of flight. Although they had been reduced to servicing Luftwaffe transports, the French engineers had kept their eyes open and had gained experience from handling German jet engines.

After the war, some of these were "conveniently" left behind by the Germans and enabled the French to start new research work. By the late fifties, skies above France echoed to the roar of strange research aircraft like the Sud Durandel and the Nord Griffon which exceeded Mach 2 in 1959. Above all, however, France had more experience than any other Western country with delta-wing forms, used not only in experimental aircraft, but also for the highly successful Mirage. Sud was now ready to take the next dramatic leap. They had settled on the slender delta approach for their new Super-Caravelle, and according to Sir Morien Morgan, had "evolved broadly the same approach to civil supersonic design. In the event, this proved fortunate, since it paved the way to a united front of benefit to both parties."

The first contacts between the British and French were on an industry level. There had always been a measure of subcontracting between the two industries and the Caravelle owed much to British technology. The designers, engineers, managers, and workers began to grow accustomed to cross-Channel working, realizing that they had a community of interest in developing a strong European industry. The reason for cooperation on the supersonic became very simple. As one BAC engineer put it to his French partners, "You want to do a supersonic transport and don't know where to find the money. We want to do a supersonic transport and don't know where to find the money either. If we both use the same engine and use the same hydraulics, electrical systems, and air-conditioning, we can both save money." The idea appealed to Satre and his team, and when he returned to Sud Aviation, the practical details began to be explored. But the French took a long time to adjust to the idea that cooperation with the British meant building a common airplane, not just swapping the interchangeable parts of a medium- and long-range aircraft.

If the advantages of Anglo-French cooperation were to mean anything at all, it was necessary to build a genuinely common aircraft—one product which could be aimed at a united market. At the same time this would be the most efficient way to pool resources of skilled manpower, money, and technical facilities. For two highly qualified design teams to agree on a breakthrough aircraft would be difficult enough, but when one was French and the other British, skeptics could be forgiven for expressing disbelief that any common view could possibly emerge. Encouraged by the two governments who would be putting up the finance, BAC and Sud Aviation began to come together more hesitantly into a form of partnership.

The growing relationship between BAC and Sud delighted the British government. By 1961 both British and French aviation ministries were pulling strings behind the scenes as BAC and Sud Aviation started on their final designs. The French government, anxious about cost, was keen to find a partner, but at first Sud Aviation, particularly the man at the top, was not. Georges Héreil, boss of Sud, was a dynamic French extrovert who easily upset his British colleagues. Many of them thought Héreil far more interested in a political career than leading French aviation into the Mach-2 age.

In attempting to resist what he regarded as a shotgun wedding, Georges Héreil planned to steal a march on both the French government and his British rivals. At the 1960 Paris Air Show he unveiled a model of a medium-range, all-French supersonic airliner which he christened the "Super-Caravelle." On TV he told the world that it would come into service in 1967 and would take France and Sud Aviation into world leadership. After this, the British were naturally upset, and high-level diplomatic exchanges in London and Paris began to work for a change in attitude. It was not an easy task. Héreil was known to his British contacts as "that impossible man" and exhibited the traditional Gallic trait of confident stubbornness that brings out the worst in Anglo-Saxons. But Héreil was one of the most powerful men in French industry and had arrived at Sud Aviation charged with the task of clearing up the company's finances—by liquidation if necessary. Instead of being forced out of business he had started the Caravelle. "Monsieur Caravelle," as he was politely called, now believed that his team had all the answers. There was no question of surrendering the design leadership or even sharing it with a British company.

The farthest that Héreil was prepared to go was to consider sharing engine development, parts of the airframe construction, and production techniques. He knew that the British held an ace card with the Olympus engine. Millions had already been spent developing it for TSR-2, and the French would not get the project off the ground without it. The alternative was to purchase an American power plant, a solution hardly likely to appeal to the general's philosophy of technological independence of the United States.

The two governments, both mindful of a higher political purpose, continued to work on the companies. A joint plane had to be thrashed out between the engineers, but it was a long way off. The Sud Aviation supersonic was a medium-range aircraft that could not cross the Atlantic. It was Héreil's philosophy, incomprehensible to his British opposite number, that by getting the smaller plane into production first, the Americans would stay out of the market for medium-range supersonics. He even tried to interest the Americans in a gentlemen's agreement when he gave the Spellman Lecture at Delft in 1961. It was greeted with stony indifference. According to Pierre Satre, later to play a leading design role on Concorde, "The people in Boeing, Lockheed, and Douglas were well aware of this proposal. But American contacts at the time thought that the American industry would cover the whole field."

The British, from bitter experience with their Comet 4, realized that only a long-range plane could sell; an aircraft that could not cross the North Atlantic was a nonstarter. They knew, too, just how unreceptive the Americans were about giving any support or agreement—gentlemen's or otherwise—to the idea of a European supersonic. Sandys, who had tried to interest them in some cooperation with the British industry, had met cool indifference. Having no plans to build a supersonic airliner, the United States was far from interested in encouraging the Europeans to take a technological leap in a field they regarded as almost their exclusive preserve. General de Gaulle was right to a point; he realized that Europe must challenge American technology or become its subordinate. The British were about to discover just how seriously the American aircraft industry took the challenge and the pressure that they would apply through all available diplomatic channels to stop the project before it had started.

In 1961 the British government concentrated its diplomatic efforts in an all-out bid to enter the Common Market. They still had to gain the acceptance and cooperation of France. Whatever France's partners in the EEC believed, it was General de Gaulle who would ultimately decide the fate of the British application. Macmillan's government badly needed a dramatic gesture toward Europe, but on the one front where this was possible, the engineers and designers were exasperatingly far apart.

In late December, a new minister of aviation, Peter Thorney-croft, was dispatched to Paris to meet the French minister of transport, Robert Buron. They decided to exert greater pressure on the companies. The result was "an important step forward": an official request to both companies to "cooperate in formulating a joint outline project." The deadline for the request was early the following year. Meanwhile, Britain's application to join the European Economic Community was moving to a decision.

In Brussels, the New Year saw the British team under Edward Heath embarking on the last rounds of the negotiations; but between Bristol and Toulouse, the hoped-for "entente" between the aero-engineers ground to a halt over major differences of approach. Sir George Edwards, not a man to give in easily, "sometimes doubted whether we would ever see it through together." The joint designs did not appear on schedule. To disguise lack of progress, the governments issued a statement that "the two companies had arrived at a preliminary design" and were "to be invited to jointly undertake a design study and other preparatory work to enable the governments to reach a decision." This time, July was given as the new deadline. But still the arguments dragged on, and by the autumn they had still not reached a final proposal.

Time was running out, and the Macmillan government badly needed its gesture of European commitment in the face of increasing French coolness. A new minister of aviation was appointed, Julian Amery. As a Francophile, he could be expected to ease through the final stages of the Franco-British negotiations. Even so, the constant persuasion, argument, and altercation that were slowly bringing the two concepts together dragged on. The manufacturers were not even ready by the 1962 Farnborough Air Show, where it had been planned to announce the supersonic to the world.

Meanwhile, in the United States, interested observers were divided between those who predicted that the British and French could never agree about anything—let alone about a highly complex project like a supersonic airliner—and those who saw a potential threat developing if the European project got off the ground. A pressure group led by Najeeb Halaby at the FAA began to quietly push schemes for an all-American SST. The materialization of the Anglo-French project would give a much needed impetus to President Kennedy to launch an American project. It was no surprise to Julian Amery to find that the FAA lobby, led by Halaby, was a fervent supporter of the Concorde; it was as anxious as the British government to get the project under way. What concerned him was the lead time over American competition. His conclusion was that the European plane, with a head start, would have a two-year lead on coming into service. That, in the view of his experts, was enough.

It was in the formative months of 1962 that the Americans carried out the first of their attempts to affect the future of the whole project. In the final stages of the negotiations with the French, the United States Administration decided to intervene. Perhaps this was understandable, since it was now becoming clear to the United States aerospace industry that the British and French governments were committed to a supersonic airliner in the interests of national policy, and that their aviation interests would have to toe the line. The Americans knew enough from their frequent contacts with the British aero-engineers just how much research had been done and the advanced state of the planning.

Seen against the perspective of later American attempts to influence the Concorde's future, this first direct effort was clumsy. Julian Amery found none other than the former president of the World Bank, Eugene Black, dropping into his Whitehall office for a chat. This unusual emissary tried to persuade the British minister of aviation not to embark on the project. Amery was astounded; he knew the project was now a part of British foreign policy and, in his view, vital for the survival of aviation technology outside America. If this was American influence at work, it strengthened de Gaulle's argument that Europe must unite to stop it. But the pressure continued with a constant diplomatic offensive mounted from Washington. Almost every visiting American official would raise the question of the wisdom of the supersonic project. It did not shake his confidence, but it added to the minister's workload. "Almost every week I had to answer an inquiry from some minister or other that came from American questions about the continuation of the project."

In view of the important national interests involved, including the massive funding, the British and French governments decided that the only effective way of creating a legal basis for the supersonic aircraft was by international treaty, formally registered at the United Nations.

There have been many treaties between Britain and France, some ceding territory, some making trade agreements, others expressing mutual defense obligations, but never to build an airplane. Under normal circumstances an agreement to build an airliner would have been the subject for a business contract, but the conclusion of a formal treaty meant that any breach would immediately bring a confrontation of national interests. However, with such large sums being invested, and the stakes so high, an old-fashioned treaty was the method chosen by the Foreign Office and Quai d'Orsay. It was to provide Concorde's salvation.

Waiting for that vital treaty to be signed taxed everybody's patience; but until the aircraft companies had hammered out a common design, not even the Macmillan government could make its final commitment to Europe. They did manage to find a temporary substitute by offering an obsolete military rocket project—the £multimillion Bluestreak—to the European Space Research Organization. Like all political gestures, not only was it an expedient, but it saved several thousand jobs at the British Hawker Siddeley plant, consoling the company while its rival, BAC, collected the backing for the Concorde.

The final breakthrough that led to agreement between the British and French manufacturers and which opened the way for the Anglo-French supersonic treaty came in an unconventional way. Tiring of all the endless meetings over the size and shape of the common plane and overburdened with officials, Lucien Servanty, the senior Sud Aviation designer, called one morning at the Paris hotel of Dr. Strang, BAC's chief designer. The company Citroën sped through the autumn avenues of the Bois de Boulogne to a factory on the outskirts of Paris. The two men were complete opposites: Servanty a grizzled, peasant-like man, endlessly smoking his French cigarettes, while Strang was a product of British grammar-school meritocracy—cool and rather clinical. There, overlooking the Seine, in the old Bleriot factory at Suresnes, they locked themselves in a drawing office. Nobody knew where they were; bureaucrats panicked. Working hour after hour on the basic drawings in a building which had produced thousands of French fighters for the First World War, they ironed out the remaining differences. Through a haze of Gitanes they both sketched the draft designs of Concorde. At the end of the day the designers signed the drawings, copied them, and headed back to their own managements. It was a first draft, but it was enough. To the Englishman it was a new style: "It's very unusual to do it in this fashion. It's very much the sort of thing you think of as a schoolboy. It very rarely happens in real life."

At the beginning of October 1962, the long-awaited draft arrived at the Ministry of Aviation. It was just twenty pages long, hardly an accurate blueprint, and in aviation terms, little more than a sketch. But to the politicians on both sides of the Channel it was enough, and it became the much needed plan for their immediate political objectives. Without actually digging the Channel Tunnel there was no better way of symbolically linking the two countries. France could now go ahead to build a bigger aircraft industry, with British support, and Britain could secure acceptance into Europe with French goodwill. The cost was put at £1,000–£1,500 million, which sounded a politically convenient figure to be split between the two countries. The treasury was naturally unhappy with such a broad estimate which it was asked to endorse. It began multiplying the figures by at least three; but the cabinet was only too happy to go ahead at last. In any case as one minister later pointed out, "Everybody knew at the time that it was almost impossible to assess the exact cost of a scheme which was at the frontiers of technology."

No time was lost in preparing the treaty, which was seen as a "Passport to Europe" and an enormous boost to Britain's Common Market hopes.

To anyone who examined the agreement it was obvious that more than the Channel separated the British and French. It was little more than a political document, and even its clauses reflected the still unresolved argument about what range the plane would have. Some leading French engineers even thought that they would have to build two versions, since Article 6 specified "equal attention to medium- and long-range versions." If so, their partners would be underwriting this dilemma, as Article 1 made it clear: "The principle of this collaboration shall be equal sharing of the work and of the expenditure incurred by the two governments and of the proceeds of the sales." The really far-reaching nature of the agreement, however, was shown in Article 4, which stipulated that "*integrated* organizations of the airframe and engine firms shall be set up." This was a revolutionary proposal that was significant not just for European aviation but for a whole range of advanced industries. It was what the European technological challenge really meant: industrial reorganization on a continental scale.

The Anglo-French Supersonic Aircraft Agreement was signed on November 29 in the plush surroundings of Lancaster House, London. Julian Amery, minister of aviation, signed for the United Kingdom. Geoffroy de Courcel, France's ambassador in London, signed for the French Republic. De Courcel was an appropriate choice. He was called "First Gaullist" because as an aide-de-camp he had been the General's sole supporter in the dark days of 1940. As the signatories signed and smiled before the gleaming wooden model of the new aircraft, it looked like the beginning of a new entente.

In the heady atmosphere of that morning's press conference no one noticed that there was one vital section missing from the agreement. There was *no* break clause. Neither party could opt out. It was an absolutely binding document, an exceptional agreement to be made between two nations. The break clause had been omitted for a very good reason. Julian Amery had insisted on its being left out—and had persuaded the cabinet to support him. The diplomats pointed out the possible consequences, but their political masters were determined not to allow the French any opportunity to wriggle out at a later date. At the same time it demonstrated Britain's total commitment to the project. It was a shrewd maneuver, and by insisting that it be omitted, Julian Amery insured the survival of Concorde.

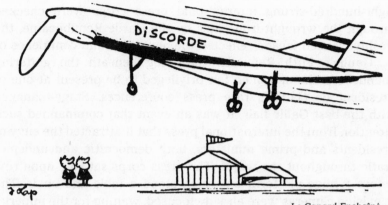

"Vous avez remarqué le nez?"   *Le Canard Enchaîné*

6

Passport to Europe

The British government was cock-a-hoop about the new supersonic treaty. It could hardly be a more serious earnest of Britain's intent than to commit £75–£85 million, spread over eight years, on an aircraft project aimed at challenging the United States. Surely this would please de Gaulle and wipe away any mistrust of the Anglo-Saxons. So confident had the British government become that on the same day as Julian Amery and Geoffroy de Courcel were signing the treaty in London, the British ambassador in New York was confidently predicting that the Brussels negotiations would end in success with Britain inside the Common Market by the New Year of 1963.

Eleven weeks later the answer came. In Paris on Monday, 13

January 1963, journalists from all over the world were summoned to a press conference at the Elysée Palace, the official
residence of the president of the French Republic. As the
eight-hundred-strong international press corps were checked
through the wrought-iron gates by the Garde Républicaine, the
freshly cleaned façade reflected the new pride and confidence of
de Gaulle's Fifth Republic. Gathering beneath the glittering
chandeliers, the newsmen felt privileged to be present at one of
President de Gaulle's rare press conferences. Stage-managed
with the best Gallic flair, it was an event that commanded such
attention from the international press that it attracted the envy of
presidents and prime ministers, both democratic and undemo-
cratic throughout the world. The press corps sat row upon row
before a huge platform on which stood a table and chair. The
television cameras were already focused, waiting for the imperial
entrance. The president's cabinet, led by Prime Minister Georges
Pompidou, took their places in the front row of the audience.
Everybody already knew what the subject of pronouncement was
to be: General de Gaulle's final judgment on Britain's application
to join the Common Market.

For over fifteen months now Britain's team led by Edward
Heath, the Lord Privy Seal, had been negotiating entry terms in
Brussels. Prime Minister Harold Macmillan was determined to
lead Britain into Europe as his last great political mission, even if
it meant facing the hostility of some of his own party who sought
an independent role for Britain in world affairs.

But Macmillan, who had come to power in the wake of the
Suez disaster, knew that there could be no post-imperial glory.
Britain's ailing economy and her declining industries demanded
membership in a wider group—the Common Market. Particularly
important were the needs of the technological industries—elec-
tronics, computers, atomic energy, and aerospace—where access
to a large market was important, not only in making these
industries more competitive, but also in creating bigger investment resources necessary to fund research and development.

In a historic broadcast on September 21, five weeks before the
Anglo-French supersonic agreement, Harold Macmillan had already told the British nation that it was "no good pretending that
we can go back to the old world before the war." He spelled out

his reasons for joining Europe, and at the heart of them was a plea for British technology, a dowry he knew he could offer Europe. "Britain," he said, "should make not just the things which anybody can learn to make, but the difficult things which need precision and highly skilled workmanship." He went on to catalog the special skills which Britain possessed: "nuclear power stations, computers, *supersonic aircraft*." Much of what he said in his gently reassuring Edwardian style about Britain's need to enter the European Economic Community sounded like a merger proposal between two well-established, respectable cor-porations. "Well, it's been a great success up to now. They form a great economic group . . . and so you see western Europe is quite different from the Commonwealth. They are both going concerns, but different."

Toward the end of his script, the prime minister who, as Lieutenant Macmillan, had witnessed the slaughter on the West-ern Front in the First World War, allowed a personal note to enter. "Many of us"—he paused a moment—"especially those who are young in heart or in years, are impatient of the old disputes, intolerant of the obsolete conceptions, anxious that our country should take its part, and if possible a leading part, in all these new and hopeful areas." Here was a clear plea to Gaullist France, as much as to a bright new British technology which could not grow in a walled English garden.

Despite Macmillan's eloquent pleas, and the supersonic agree-ment, everyone sitting at the Elysée conference on that afternoon of 14 January 1963 knew that the key to Europe was in de Gaulle's hand. The general disliked the Common Market with its gray bureaucrats arguing endlessly over the price of olive oil. For him, history demanded a more glorious style of leadership.

De Gaulle believed that France should lead Europe to a new position of power and influence against the superpowers, espe-cially the United States. If Europe did not reassert herself, she would be "Atlanticized." The rekindling of Europe's technology was essential to de Gaulle's scheme. Britain with her strong technological industries—spending more on scientific research and development than any other European country—could play a part in this grand scheme to regenerate a continent.

In the middle of the twentieth century, national prestige was judged no longer by armies and dreadnoughts but depended on computers, atom smashers, and jet airliners. Scientific prowess had in some ways replaced the older military glories. Russia had brought this home to the West when she launched her first Sputnik in 1957 and raced ahead with a manned space program. The United States which had got off to a disastrous start in the space race—Khrushchev had contemptuously dismissed the first United States satellite as a "grapefruit"—was by the early sixties chasing Russia hard. Both de Gaulle and Macmillan had been at the summit of politics in two of the world's most nationalistic countries too long not to understand instinctively the national need for prestige projects. Yet it was in some ways ironic that the decisions on such complex and far-reaching matters as technology should lie with two leaders who seemed so much a part of a vanished world.

In cabinet, Macmillan had drawn the analogy between the supersonic airliner and his great-aunt's Daimler, which traveled at the "sensible speed" of thirty miles per hour. The great advantages of that particular vehicle, as the prime minister wistfully reminded his colleagues, was that one could enter it without removing one's top hat. But though his manner might be that of an Edwardian proconsul, Harold Macmillan was a tough realist. Still savoring the allusion, he pointed out that many people now liked to travel at greater speed, and this being so, Britain ought to cater to this profitable modern eccentricity by building a supersonic airliner.

The general may not have shared Macmillan's indifference to the wonders of technology. He had after all been an early advocate of the tank and appreciated the value of technology in war. He saw that technological achievement brought prestige for France. Any considerations of modern airline economics or suggestions that the Anglo-French plane would have to be sold on commercial terms throughout the world, and that far-off nations did not want to subsidize French prestige, bored him. "Money was a matter for the quartermasters," he was heard to remark contemptuously.

The time of decision had arrived . . .

Speaking without notes, calmly and emphatically de Gaulle began to expound his thoughts with a magisterial emphasis.

England, it seemed, had asked to enter the Common Market on her own terms and this had posed "problems of a very great dimension." She could not yet bring herself to accept the European Economic Community "without restriction, without reserve."

This was the conclusion that the general had drawn from what he described, with carefully deliberate emphasis, as the "long, so long, so long" Brussels negotiations. It was just what Macmillan feared. France was diplomatically but deliberately slamming the door in Britain's face. But the general was statesman enough to know that even if he kept Britain out this time, he still had to allow for possible future involvement and good working relationships with her. The supersonic aircraft was an important part of his "technological Austerlitz," and Britain had to be held to the agreement. Carefully choosing his words, he suggested that "if the Brussels negotiations were not to succeed" (by this time, everyone in the room knew it was already decided), there was the alternative of "an accord of association." "Nothing," he added with deliberate emphasis, "would prevent the close relationship and direct cooperation, as these two countries have proved, *by deciding to build together the supersonic aircraft Concorde.*" At a stroke he had negated any plan Macmillan might have considered for withdrawing from the project. As the general went on to make crystal clear, if "Britain's own evolution of the universe" was to bring the English "little by little" toward the Continent, which "one day, perhaps, will lead it to be moored alongside," then part of this evolutionary process would be judged on British performance on the supersonic project.

Astute journalists noted that at the moment when the president's words had brought Concorde's raison d'être dangerously close to futility, they had witnessed the official christening of the project. To the amazement of the French officials, this was the first time that the name *Concorde* had been used publicly. Such an obvious and suitable name could only have been thought of by a child—and so it had been, by the ten-year-old son of a BAC official. It had passed up through the echelons of BAC and the Ministry of Aviation and had been greeted with approval by the minister, Julian Amery. When passed to the French it was greeted with disdain by government officials who believed it was "too static" and sounded like a Parisian landmark. On 13 January 1963 de Gaulle ignored his officials and performed an ironic christening.

It is interesting to speculate that had this fateful press conference taken place ten weeks earlier, before the signature of the agreement, there is little doubt that the Concorde project would have been stillborn. Had de Gaulle slammed the door before completion of the Anglo-French supersonic agreement, all the evidence suggests that the Ministry of Aviation and the treasury would have demanded a far more detailed analysis of design and costs. If the European pressure had not been so great, the British cabinet might not have rushed into supporting an open-ended commitment to what was little more than a sketch.

In the judgment of one former British minister, "If it is true that it was insisted on by Macmillan to get us into Europe, it was certainly the most expensive, noneffective ticket of entry ever."

THE MACH-2 ENTENTE

Julian Amery, Britain's minister of aviation, and Geoffroy de Courcel, French ambassador in London, concluding the Anglo-French Supersonic Aircraft Agreement, 29 November 1962.

AP

Aerospatiale

The French Caravelle, the world's first medium-range jet airliner, successfully penetrated the U.S. market. France hoped Concorde would follow suit.

"Nous ferons Concorde"—We will make Concorde. President de Gaulle inspects a model of France's new prestige project at the Paris Air Show, 1963.

AP

KEEPING AHEAD

Juan Trippe, president of Pan American Airways. His spectacular gamble with the Boeing 707 kept the United States ahead. It was a lead he was determined to keep in the supersonic age.

The Boeing 707 prototype. When it entered service in 1958, piston-engined competition was eliminated on long-haul routes, and the U.S. aviation monopoly was secured.

The United States enters the contest. President Kennedy announces his determination that the United States should "maintain its national lead in long-range aircraft." U.S. Air Force Academy, Colorado Springs, 5 June 1963.

Punch

"Just think of it, comrade—Siberia in three minutes!"

7

The Paper Liars' Contest

The die was cast. Britain and France were committed to the vast enterprise of establishing supersonic commercial flight. The decision had miraculously survived the intricate and rancorous politics of the Common Market negotiations, and the two governments congratulated themselves on having stolen the initiative from their American rivals. As Julian Amery saw it, "A constant consideration was how far we were ahead of the Americans. By our reckoning we made it two years." If the British and French manufacturers thought they had a calm and unchallenged spell in which to perfect their plans, they were mistaken. Yet the first stirrings of competition came from the East, not America. Throughout 1962, meetings were taking place in Moscow between the government and the powerful technocrats of the Soviet aircraft industry to decide on a Russian supersonic airliner program. Much depended on the legendary minister of aircraft production, Pyotr Dementiev, who had been in the saddle since 1944. Dementiev had survived the tyranny of Stalin and the purges of Khrushchev. As minister of aircraft production he had built up the powerful Red Air Force, with front-line fighters and bombers capable of matching American power. Even more, Dementiev's ministry was responsible for the large civil air fleets operated by Aeroflot, the world's biggest airline.

The arguments for Soviet entry into the supersonic race were strong. The Russians undoubtedly possessed the technology to develop a faster-than-sound airliner. They had been building MIG fighters to match the performance of American aircraft and had learned the secrets of metallurgy, avionics, and airframe construction, which could be utilized for an advanced airliner. Their engine technology was also strong and owed much to Rolls-Royce, who had supplied them with the Nene jet engine under a wartime agreement. The Kuznetsov plant was now able to develop the massive jets needed by a supersonic airliner, or a jet bomber.

As for Macmillan and de Gaulle, so for the Kremlin; prestige was a vital consideration in technology. Communist prestige demanded that Soviet airliners should be no slower than those of the capitalist West. The Russians had a proud civil aviation record which had shaken the West in 1956 when the jet TU-104 had flown into London's Heathrow Airport to inaugurate the Moscow service. At the time, the Boeing 707 and the Comet 4 were still two years from airline service. It was important for the Communist leadership to keep up the image of Soviet planemakers, who could make their voice heard in the Kremlin. The Red Star had to be seen all round the world, from Prague to the Ivory Coast, from Havana to Hanoi. What could be better than for it to appear resplendent on the gleaming tail fin of a futuristic airliner that even the Americans did not have?

Prestige apart, Russia could also gain immense advantage from supersonic flight, perhaps more than any nation. Ever since the foundation of the Soviet Union, a high priority had been placed on air travel as a way of overcoming the desperate shortage of roads and railways. Now the opening of the virgin lands in Siberia and on the Pacific Coast placed an even greater importance on fast air links. In a huge country short of skilled personnel and management, valuable engineers and technicians could be lifted to the booming Siberian industrial areas of Khabarovsk and also to Vladivostok in a matter of hours. Indeed, one Soviet planning group had estimated that air travel, even at subsonic speeds, can save the Soviet Union 2,000 million man-hours a year.

In 1962 the Council of Ministers of the Supreme Soviet decreed that a supersonic airliner should be started at once. Work was farmed out to the doyen of the Soviet aircraft industry. Andrei Tupolev, the distinguished Soviet academician, had, like Dementiev, his contemporary, played a major role in building up Soviet aviation. He had received the Stalin prize for his TU-2 bomber, one of the warplanes which had enabled the Red Air Force to turn the tide against Hitler. Many successful civil-transport aircraft had come from Tupolev's drawing board, where he worked in close association with his son Alexei. These included the TU-104 twin-jet airliner and the TU-114 mammoth turboprop airliner—completed in 1957 to mark the anniversary of the Revolution—which carried Soviet leaders on their state visits around the world. The Tupolevs set to work on their most ambitious project of all. The Experimental Design Bureau (OKB) at Voronezh began to project the outlines of a slender delta-wing aircraft, which looked very much like Concorde. This did not surprise the engineers in the least, since both planes had to do the same job. It had a similar range of 4,000 miles, carried 140 passengers, and had a designed speed of 1,400 miles per hour.

The news from Russia, as well as reports from attachés in London and Paris, began to alarm the White House. President John F. Kennedy had come to power in 1960, pledged to get America moving. The political consequences of being beaten by the Russians, not to mention the British and French, in launching an SST would be an enormous dent in his New Frontier image. Privately, he let it be known that his attitude was not unfavorable to the idea of a purely civil project. The hopes of the American SST lobby rose at the end of 1962 when the President established a special cabinet-level committee headed by pro-SST Vice-President Lyndon Johnson. This followed a study which the president had commissioned from Najeeb Halaby at the FAA on the future of United States aviation, aptly named Project Horizon. The report called for the "earliest production" of a Mach-3 supersonic. If the aircraft corporations could not find the money for the inescapably high budget, Halaby saw an opportunity to invest public money in a big and exciting national enterprise. He advocated that "government funds should be utilized through the research and design development, prototype, and probably production stages." This was a revolutionary proposal for funding an American commercial plane, but as Halaby had reasoned if the government was giving NASA billions to get a man on the moon, then the FAA should have an equal opportunity to create a national SST program.

In the autumn of 1961 the FAA had begun to swing into gear for an anticipated supersonic program with $11 million granted as preliminary funding. The request went out to American industry for studies to be submitted within two years. The delay worried Halaby. In the summer of 1962 he had been to Europe to check up on British and French progress. Like Kennedy's other SST emissary that summer—Eugene Black, former president of the World Bank—Halaby was alarmed at British and French progress.

Halaby rushed home, and as reported in *Fortune*, "made a tardy appeal to the White House and the Defense Department for a quick step-up in the U.S. research effort." It fell on deaf ears. In October 1962 Congress showed that it did not share Halaby's view that Anglo-French plans posed any kind of threat and slashed 20 percent from Halaby's request for $25 million funding. It was going to take more than a paper airplane on the other side of the Atlantic to persuade the U.S. Congress to spend huge sums of taxpayers' money in a commercial aircraft project.

The task of straightening out the difficult congressmen fell to the Johnson committee. It was instructed to report to the president in five months on all the aspects of launching a prototype United States SST for operations in late 1967. Kennedy's hope was to have passengers flying the Atlantic in an American supersonic as the astronauts were landing on the moon.

For all the president's determination, the endless muddle and delay in Washington over the SST began to alarm the American airline bosses. They saw that time lost in political cavorting and arm-twisting on Capitol Hill would result in an unassailable lead for the British and the French. They also winced at the thought of Aeroflot flying slender supersonic airliners into New York while they lumbered along behind in slower planes. If there was no American supersonic airliner available, the United States airlines would be faced with the invidious choice of buying expensive foreign aircraft like Concorde, or becoming uncompetitive. If there had to be a supersonic they preferred their traditional suppliers, Boeing, Lockheed, and Douglas, to provide them, rather than embark upon a new and uncertain relationship with the Europeans. A supersonic had to be as American as apple pie. The airlines who were most concerned were the big international carriers, Pan Am and Trans World Airlines. They would be the first to feel the blast of competition from BOAC, Air France, and other North Atlantic carriers, once Concorde came into service.

Pan Am was then still the domain of one man, Juan Trippe, president since the airline's foundation. He was a quiet unassuming man, who was scarcely noticed when he attended aviation seminars and conventions. Courtly and elegant, Trippe dressed in a 1930s style that would have done credit to Adolphe Menjou. Yet this charming, well-dressed gentleman could be one of the most ruthless operators in a highly competitive business. Nothing frightened Trippe. He made decisions with staggeringly high stakes running into millions of dollars, involving the future of the airline itself. Above all he followed a simple code: Pan Am had to lead. America's most famous airline had to be in front. This meant buying the fastest, biggest, and most profitable aircraft, no matter who made them, and Pan Am had to fly them first.

Trippe's decisions had affected world airline history. In 1958 he brought the all-jet Boeing 707 onto the North Atlantic. Within two years, all of his competitors—both European and American —had to abandon their piston-engined and turboprop fleets or go bankrupt. What is less well known is that in 1951 he was preparing to bring the British Comet into service with the major United States flag carrier rather than lose his competitive lead. His executives used to be shown a shrouded stand on his desk. As though displaying a carefully guarded secret, he would unveil the model Comet on suitable occasions to spur the American manufacturers into producing their own jet. Trippe prepared to use the Concorde in the same way as he had the Comet, but his problem was credibility. He knew that in 1963 the Concorde was little more than a paper airplane. How could Pan Am sign a contract for a nonexistent airliner and get anyone to believe that it meant business?

To find the answer, Trippe sent a team led by his right-hand man, Frank Gledhill, to England in the early summer of 1963 to talk to Concorde's makers, under the guise of sorting out a deal with Hawker Siddeley on the HS-125 executive jet. Trippe knew that he had to put a credible front on any move that Pan Am would make, particularly as it was known that his rival, TWA, had already dismissed the paper Concorde by saying they "didn't believe in the airplane." At that stage both BOAC and Air France were equivocal since neither had placed any letter of intent, order, or firm option.

The British manufacturers were surprised by Gledhill's visit and delighted to hear of the Pan Am interest. A meeting was quickly set up at Claridge's with the Pan Am delegation. The formula that came out of the discussions neatly sidestepped the problem of Pan Am's having to make a decision to buy a "non-airplane." Instead, an option system was devised which gave the outward appearance of formality but in fact was really nothing more than an agreement to reserve a place on the Concorde assembly line in return for a modest deposit. It was an original and unique idea and could be used to drum up orders for the nonexistent, but hoped-for, United States SST as well. The option system gave Concorde a misleading sales credibility which was later to backfire cruelly.

On 4 June 1963, Juan Trippe made the dramatic announcement that he had decided to take options on no less than six Concordes. It was perfectly timed and coincided with the Johnson committee's favorable report on the SST, which the president now planned to put into action. Pan Am's announcement preempted the president's move, and as *Fortune* later revealed, "this suddenly galvanized the Kennedy Administration into nervous action." In fact, Trippe received a phone call from an irate Kennedy. What he said can only be guessed at. The White House aides had already tried to talk Trippe out of making an announcement until the government was in a position to tell the world that it, too, was proceeding with an SST. However, as *Fortune* added cryptically, Trippe, "knowing the true state of things," decided to "stand on his heels and order Concorde first." He wanted Pan Am to be at the head of the queue, particularly as the British had offered him a lower price than those who would follow.

Pan Am's gambit had the desired result. American public opinion realized that, for the first time since the war, the major U.S. airline was going to purchase foreign planes for its prestige service. A stir went through the Capitol as press and public suddenly realized that the United States was not even going to show in the race for the supersonic. Fortuitously, Kennedy had a chance to salvage the nation's self-esteem. The day after Trippe's announcement, he was scheduled to speak at the Air Force Academy at Colorado Springs. The president had always believed that the United States would have to accept the great challenge of building a bigger and better SST, and that government funding was inevitable, but he realized that the implications for the American brand of capitalism were immense. The day before, Kennedy had addressed the World Food Congress: "We have the ability, we have the means, and we have the capacity to eliminate hunger from the face of the earth." This had been the noble theme of his address. On June 5, as he flew in the presidential jet to Colorado Springs, he was about to commit the richest nation on earth to spending billions of dollars on a high-risk project to satisfy national pride.

The scene was appropriate for a national announcement. Forty thousand Air Force cadets filled the open-air Falcon Stadium. Shoulders slightly hunched, jaw thrust forward, Kennedy spoke in his flat Boston drawl: "If we can build the best operational airplane of this type," he said, "and I believe we can, then the Congress of this country should be prepared to invest the funds and the effort necessary to maintain the national lead in long-range aircraft—a lead which we have held since the end of the Second World War, a lead which we should make every responsible effort to maintain." Then perhaps allowing the real reason for his decision to emerge, he admitted that the United States had been "spurred on by the competition from across the Atlantic."

The Colorado Springs speech spelled out a change, and a very fundamental alteration in the American system. Now meeting competitive foreign commercial threats no longer depended entirely on the board-room decisions of the aircraft industry. The way was now open for their business judgment and technical assessments to be vetted by Washington. The United States was embarking on a civil aircraft project for prestige, rather than for straightforward business reasons. It was the European style, but without the well-tried political reasons and processes for carrying out such a scheme.

Kennedy knew that the SST program was going to be a heavy political and economic commitment for the federal government. The Johnson report, which had reached the White House desk just days before, warned that the costs would grow, maybe to gigantic proportions. In the eyes of more than one American aviation commentator, "It was a frightening dilemma—surrender our number-one position in the aviation marketplace and lose face all over the world, or gamble billions at home on the assumption that American know-how and daring could build a more stupendous mousetrap, of unknown size and shape, with a technology that did not even exist. And do it in fact."

Senator Fulbright voiced the concern that many were feeling; he criticized Kennedy's decision, because he did not believe "that this nation's prestige will in any way suffer if someone else this time builds a bigger and more expensive mousetrap."

But the great paper-plane race was on and America could not afford to be left out. It remained to be seen which, if any, would get into the air.

President Kennedy's decision galvanized airline managements into decision. Not only had Pan Am expressed its determination to go supersonic by placing options on Concorde, but the United States government had pledged itself to the construction of an American supersonic airliner to be the best operational plane of this type. There was a flurry of activity in the international board rooms, with an unseemly rush from all sides to place options on both the American and European aircraft, even though neither actually existed. Such was the reputation of the American industry that the world airlines were prepared to put down deposits even though the United States SST was still only a collection of files in Najeeb Halaby's outer office. No contracts had yet been placed and nobody even knew what the aircraft would look like. The Federal Aviation Administration became the unlikely center for all of this high-powered activity, and Halaby had "briskly drummed up bids for a nonexistent production line, dropping the admission price to $100,000." TWA beat its rivals into second place by a matter of hours in placing an option for the United States SST. Smarting from the humiliation of coming in second, Juan Trippe hurried Pan Am's down payment to the FAA with a note, "Our banker's check in the amount of $1,500,000 in favor of the U.S.A. is enclosed."

The critical race for the SST had started, and the Anglo-French Concorde builders were the last to underrate the American industry. To their fury, the British manufacturers saw their own national airline, BOAC, begin to play the balance between the rival SST projects. Chairman Sir Giles Guthrie was deeply distrusted by the British aircraft industry since, ostensibly for economy reasons, he had wanted to cancel a large order for British-built VC-10 airliners preferring instead a fleet of Boeing 707s. The VC-10 was a popular aircraft in Britain, and the manufacturers were pleased with its success; but Guthrie, an ex-financier, did not like its economics. Now it seemed as if he would pass a vote of "no confidence" on the Concorde.

This could be disastrous for the Concorde which had at last reached the drawing-board stage. Everybody accepted that Air France would order the Concorde if instructed by the French government, but the British airline, under the chairmanship of Sir Giles Guthrie, had deliberately staked out a position of semi-independence in aircraft purchase.

On 25 January 1964, the row broke out in public, when Guthrie announced that he was sending a sales team to Washington to negotiate with the FAA for six of the American planes to complement his six Concorde options. This smacked of "letting the side down." The unsporting move did not find favor with Aviation Minister Julian Amery, whose paternal relationship to the Concorde project had made him particularly sensitive to BOAC's maneuvering.

Wasting no time, Amery instructed the BOAC delegation to "take no immediate action" in Washington. Sir Giles angrily resented this challenge to BOAC's newly won commercial freedom. He took the unusual step of publishing his answer in the company's weekly newspaper *BOAC News*. In a strongly worded piece he pointed out that "the minister, backed by the cabinet, has written to me to make it clear that the choice of aircraft is a matter for BOAC's judgment." He added acidly that "if, in the national interest, the government requires the corporation to depart from commercial interests, the minister will give a written directive which in effect will absolve BOAC from the responsibility of any losses that might ensue."

Amery was unruffled; a week later, in the House of Commons, he chose to give his reply to the challenge: "It is important that on this project, as indeed on others, we should not go out of our way, as some critics do, to run down British projects which are doing very well." This admonishment was greeted with a patriotic outburst of cheering from the government benches as the minister continued, "The terms on which BOAC finally make up their minds must be a matter for their commercial judgment of course," but he added with finality, "in consultation with me." It would be the last time the state airline openly attempted to carve a path that conflicted with government policy over Concorde. As a result, Sir Giles remained markedly cool to the project during his whole term of office.

A week later, BOAC's commercial judgment received ministerial approval when the corporation announced options on six American SSTs, with the face-saving announcement that the two aircraft appeared to be "complementary to each other, rather than directly competitive."

The American plane was doing remarkably well even without BOAC's help. At the beginning of 1964, options stood at 2 to 1 in favor of the United States airliner, with 63 options placed against 37. Halaby began to arrange a contest among the United States competitors to get the best design capable of beating the Europeans. Boeing, Lockheed, Convair, and North American rushed to their drawing boards, initiating what one Boeing executive called "the paper liars' contest."

When President Kennedy had announced his original plan,

Congress had expressed doubts about the cost. Now the Senate was even more worried that the project would be uneconomic. The American manufacturers, knowing the costs of building a supersonic, had made it clear that they could not take on the project without federal assistance. Just how much help the Administration would give was argued intensely for months in Washington committee rooms. At first, the White House wanted the manufacturers to pay a third of the development costs, the airlines contributing another third in advance, and the government finding the rest. After skillful lobbying and intense argument, the manufacturers' proposed contribution slipped from a third to a ninth.

Realizing that a start had to be made somewhere, President Kennedy had asked Congress to vote $60 million to set up a team under FAA leadership to mastermind the basic design research. But there was immediate opposition from the senator from Wisconsin, William Proxmire. A Democrat and an astute politician, he fired the first shot in his long campaign against the United States SST by trying to strike out the $60 million, because it represented "subtle nationalization" of the Free World's greatest aircraft industry. "We don't want to move in the direction the British and French have moved" he said, striking at the deepest fears of capitalism. "We don't want to nationalize our corporations." This specter of insidious nationalization and creeping socialism began to undermine the American SST even before it was built. It provided Proxmire with a well-publicized platform, but his first attack failed.

Two days later, the president, who was the great advocate of the SST, was assassinated and a great shadow fell over his enterprise. But the SST program had already been launched.

When President Johnson inherited power it was becoming clear that the vision of the SST presented by Halaby and his public relations team at the FAA was failing to impress the more hard-headed members of Congress. They were going sour on the sales pitch that Halaby's copywriters had presented for them in glowing terms like "Here government and private industry have before them a great adventure, perhaps the greatest adventure civil aviation has known—the creative development and profitable operation of commercial supersonic transport aircraft."

One of the first documents the new president found on the "in" tray at the White House was a report on the SST project that Kennedy had commissioned from his economic advisors: Eugene Black, formerly of the World Bank, and Stanley J. Osborne, a leading industrialist from the chemical industry. They had taken a cold economist's view of the SST in a report that said many hard-headed things about costs, commercial operations, and markets. It was about as far removed from Halaby's purple phraseology about "great adventure" as Shakespeare is from a company report. The weighty analysis warned the new president about the colossal cost of the projected program: "Never before will such vast sums have been invested in capital facilities, development costs, and production financing just to produce a commercial aircraft. If our nation is not willing to face the issue financially, technologically, and managerially, we would strongly recommend dropping the program now." The report warned particularly of the dangers of tying the United States SST project too closely to the Concorde program, suggesting that the SST was a "financial and technical gamble of such proportions that we cannot possibly recommend it." It ended by advising the president to delay the SST for at least another decade.

Johnson was also made aware that it was already too late to launch a crash program to beat the Concorde. If the European plane worked it would cream the market, and the United States would suffer a painful loss of prestige. This was the critical "go" or "no go" point. But President Johnson was the man who had fought for the B-70 and the idea of an SST four years earlier. He chose to stay in the game, and American manufacturers were invited to press on with the "great adventure."

In Congress the doubters balked at the prospect of pouring millions of dollars into what critics were disposed to call "Halaby's thing at the FAA." The airlines, anxious to secure their positions in the production line, nervously poured dollars into Halaby's project, and the FAA chief appeared before the Senate Aviation Subcommittee to stiffen their nerves. "If for any reason the United States should not produce a sound commercial supersonic transport, we will have defaulted the leadership in commercial aviation to the British, French, or to the Russians."

Not all the airlines took advantage of Halaby's offer. The

chairman of United, one of America's biggest airlines, openly condemned his competitor's so-called SST orders as "publicity stunts" designed to encourage Congress to spend money to develop an SST.

Early in the new year the United States aircraft manufacturers lined up their SST sketches for public approval—each one bigger and faster than Concorde. They were all predictably vague and in the "artist's impression" stage. North American had sketched windows in what looked remarkably like a larger version of their Valkyrie bomber. Lockheed produced a delta that seemed to be a big brother of Concorde, and Boeing had got hooked onto the "swing wing" idea outlined in the Project Horizon report, and which their executives knew was dear to the heart of Secretary of Defense Robert McNamara. In the first round of the "paper liars' contest," none of the entries satisfied the FAA. McNamara's committee vetted the plans and selected the most feasible-looking combination of airframes and engines—including Boeing—and sent the winners of the first round back to their drawing boards. Everyone had conveniently forgotten a warning in the Black-Osborne report, particularly since it appeared at the time to be one of the least important. It warned that unless the government gave the manufacturers a free hand in the design, construction, and testing of the SST "we can foresee a colossal failure, leading to a potential national scandal."

THE PAPER PLANES

The Boeing 733. A Mach-1.8 air-liner, carrying 227 passengers.

Keystone

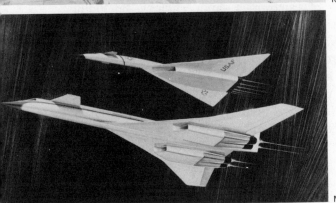

The North American Mach-3 NAC 60 showing its derivation from the triple supersonic B-70 strategic bomber, the Valkyrie.

Lockheed's Mach-3 supersonic delta, carrying 218 passengers.

N. American

Lockheed

THE MEN BEHIND THE CONCORDE

General André Puget. This former commander of the Free French bombers in Britain was popular with his Anglo-Saxon colleagues.

Sir George Edwards with an early model of Concorde. He said of Puget, "We were both determined to make things work."

George Héreil, known as "Monsieur Caravelle" for his leadership of France's subsonic project, did not become "Monsieur Concorde."

Le Canard Enchaîné
"*Sacrebleu!*"

8

Lorryloads of Francs

In the euphoric atmosphere at Lancaster House, the Anglo-French Supersonic Aircraft Agreement was sealed. The press did not forget to inquire how much Concorde would cost the taxpayer. Julian Amery had his answer ready. The total bill would be somewhere between £150 million and £170 million. Britain's half share would therefore be around £75 million, spread over eight years. This made a modest annual figure of £9 million which could be recouped on the sales of the aircraft. It seemed too good to be true. The *Sunday Times* at least was skeptical, believing that "some say that it is just a confidence trick; that the Anglo-French faster-than-sound airliner, Concorde, is a method of extracting £80 million of government money to bolster the aircraft industry. Others are kinder and think of it as a gamble." To the Macmillan government, however, now firmly committed to its "alliance of European technology," it was a necessary investment in the future. In spite of de Gaulle's refusal to grant Britain full membership in his European club, the Concorde symbolized a face-saving associate membership. The door was kept permanently ajar; if Britain fulfilled her obligation, she might be permitted to enter.

The House of Commons backed the Anglo-French agreement. Compared to some of the staggering defense bills that Parliament had been asked to meet, it appeared a bargain. The figures which were so confidently predicted seemed reasonable and added up so neatly that there was no real questioning of how they had been arrived at. So the first step was taken on the ladder of escalation which reached a staggering £1,000 million bill a decade later. Concorde's costs rapidly became a hunting ground for investigative journalists, M.P.s of the Parliamentary Committee of Public Accounts, and cartoonists. In two years, the total estimate rose to £275 million; by 1966 it had gone up to £450 million and leaped to £730 million in 1969. This sum was held for eighteen months before it surged upward to £825 million in 1970 and finally by 1972 to £1,070 million. These costs have been shared equally between Britain and France. Some of these increases have been clearly outside the control of the manufacturers. Both Britain and France devalued their currencies in the span of Concorde development, and Britain has floated the pound. The rate of inflation has also been rapid, with big wage increases taking up a large and important proportion of the Concorde bill. When all these factors are taken into account, the first Concorde estimate was laughably optimistic. One minister in Macmillan's cabinet, looking back, wryly commented, "Well, we all thought it would cost more than the original estimate, but I don't suppose anybody would have imagined it would have cost as much as it has."

Her Majesty's Treasury certainly believed the initial costs were in the realms of fantasy. They could not make public their fears, but at the time, were privately known to be at least "multiplying the estimate by pi." They could hardly be blamed; too many aircraft projects had been initiated on politically acceptable guesstimates, only to rocket to dizzy heights. A trebling, at least, of the published costs would be a realistic estimate.

A peculiarly surrealistic game seemed to be played inside the British government and civil service whenever aircraft costs were estimated and approved; all the normal rules of management and accountancy were seemingly suspended. Her Majesty's Treasury was experienced enough to know that the same game would be played on Concorde, but on a much larger scale and embracing two national economies rather than one. But they were powerless to stop it from happening. The traditional detachment of the Treasury officials led to a situation on the Concorde estimates that was little short of farce. This was revealed later when a House of Commons select committee probed the matter. In the face of hard direct questioning by M.P.s, the embarrassed Treasury officials were forced to admit that they could do little better than play the role of intelligent laymen. They excused themselves from seeking outside expert advice by pointing out that this was not Treasury practice. Incredibly, they admitted having no knowledge of how the French might have arrived at their costings, and suggested that, at the time, they had felt the Concorde estimates "might be on the low side."

The government's action could be seen in another light. They were milking the taxpayers of millions of pounds on the basis of a false prospectus. This would have brought severe legal penalties if carried out in the City of London. In defense, however, it could be said that it was not just the British Ministry of Aviation and the Treasury who had a particularly dismal record in estimating aircraft costs. Worldwide evidence suggested that escalation in budgets was almost an endemic disease with airplane manufacturing. Successive ministers of aviation might take refuge in the comment of one senior aircraft manufacturer, "No aircraft in my experience, in Britain, or in France, the U.S.A.—or for that matter probably even in the Soviet Union—has come out at what it was estimated on paper. If you are making a chair or a telephone it is possible to know that it might cost 10 percent more than the original estimate, but it is problematical in the case of aircraft which often need substantial redesigning during their development. It is impossible to foresee these problems."

Concorde presented many unknowns. Nobody could tell how much it would cost to develop a large supersonic airframe—and everybody was ignorant of the true cost of up-rating the Olympus engine to the power required for the airliner. The inescapable fact remains, however, that the first cost estimates were drawn up on the basis of a sketch and a six-page treaty with a partner who had markedly different views about the direction development should take. As one BAC engineer who had been deeply involved in the sketch recalls, "The amount of information available at that time was scanty to say the least, hardly enough to do a real estimate. The chaps who were involved in the negotiations knew in their own minds that the figures originally written in at the meeting stages, around £150 million, were as phony as hell." It became like so many aircraft projects, simply "a hard-arsed judgment."

What the specifications really represented, according to one of the team who drew them up, was that "both sides had agreed on a shape, where the engines were to go, and roughly what the plane would look like. The silhouette was the same, but there was no agreement then as to whether it was to be a medium- or a long-range plane; in that respect it was a stupid agreement." Faced with such uncertainty over even the basic design, it was little wonder that the Ministry of Aviation had to tax its considerable political skills to the limits.

Former civil servant turned aviation consultant Richard Worcester recorded the process graphically: "An entire ministry folklore exists on the technique adopted by the ministry when preparing a report. These are familiar to anyone working in Whitehall. Arguments, discussions, and proposed methods are outlined, and the text, when completed, is afterward given to statistics branch to lard with suitable figures and the appropriate annotations. The hope here is that these may clothe the skeleton with a thin skin of respectability."

If the costs of building a supersonic airliner were one thing, its importance as an instrument of British foreign policy outweighed any doubts. Britain happily accepted the proposal to build Concorde with few—if any—reservations. Even so, allowing for the rise in costs due to inflation, it is very unlikely that the Macmillan cabinet would have signed "an unstoppable blank check" had they known that over ten years the total bill would rise to well over a billion pounds.

At the time, however, the government believed that £75 million—plus whatever ministers privately guessed for escalation—was not an unreasonable price for achieving a special relationship with France at the height of the Common Market negotiations and securing the future of the British aircraft industry.

Gaullist ministers in Paris believed Concorde to be a bargain in raising France's aircraft industry to world status. Their civil servants, notably those at the Ministry of Finance, must have expressed apprehension at the magnitude of the commitment. After all, they were not as skilled as Her Majesty's Treasury in the game of aircraft-project cost control. The financial system worked differently in France, and plans for national economic growth could be adjusted successively to cope with the escalating price of the project. In the centralized system of the Fifth Republic, it was the head of state who could choose to direct the national destiny and General de Gaulle regarded the civil servants of the Ministry of Finance as mere "quartermasters." He was the "chief" and he wanted Concorde. Even so he called in the French planemakers, led by the president of Sud Aviation, and conducted a searching interview to satisfy himself on the facts. When they had finished putting their case, the General reportedly rapped his desk and pronounced, "Nom de Dieu nous ferons Concorde!"

By the middle of 1964 the complex industrial infrastructure stretching across two nations began to take shape. Not only were new research facilities established to develop the technology of supersonic flight, but massive new machine tools were installed to mill the prototype aluminum airframe. A complex bureaucracy also grew up to manage the project involving two national civil-service structures and two industries. The Concorde bureaucracy has been an achievement almost as great as Concorde itself. It has been a delight for the Whitehall civil servants and French "fonctionnaires," but a nightmare for the planemakers and a mine field for the politicians. There are no fewer than six main committees.

Overall control at the top of the project is exercised through the Concorde Directing Committee—a joint Anglo-French group which controls the funds and supervises the project. It is chaired by a senior civil servant from the appropriate British or French ministry; and in the interests of international fairness, chairmanship passes between Britain and France every two years.

This "equality of chairmanship" applies to the next committee, the Concorde Management Board, which exercises control through the Aircraft Committee of Directors, which controls the airframe, and the Engine Committee of Directors, which is responsible for the power plant. These committees, in turn, spawn more committees to cover sales, support, and the organization of the eight hundred or so subcontracting firms in two countries. The main Concorde contractors are named in the treaty and reflect the "equal shares to Britain and France" principle that dominates the project: Sud Aviation was given 60 percent of the airframe and design leadership against BAC's 40 percent, in order to balance Rolls-Royce's 60 percent share of engine development against SNECMA's* 40 percent. Civil servants spent considerable effort juggling the subcontractors to balance the national prides involved, rather than allocating contracts to those best qualified for the job. It led to some bitter and protracted arguments.

The cost of this bureaucracy and its actual contribution to the project is often questioned, particularly by those who are building the plane. As one designer exclaimed, "It's a bloody miracle that the plane escaped without any humps."

The French, in particular, have never been happy with the Concorde organization. It is too indecisive for them. They prefer a more centralized system, with the instructions coming down from on high to be unquestionably obeyed. As Sir George Edwards put it, "Over there an order is an order, not a subject for immediate debate as it is over here."

French unhappiness with the Concorde organization has been expressed by Louis Giusta, then managing director of Sud

* Société Nationale d'Étude et de Construction de Moteurs d'Aviation.

Aviation, in his Bleriot Memorial Lecture: "Within the manufacturers' Committee of Directors, organization has, in fact, become collegial, and this has resulted in difficult oppositions, leading to delays in making decisions. Only the goodwill of individuals has made it possible to live with such an organization."

This view is shared by Sir George Edwards of BAC, who believes that the way in which the Concorde program has been organized has meant that costs are up to a third higher than they need have been. Characteristically he suggested that "anyone who can get an unchallenged shilling or franc out of the joint government committees has earned it." One benefit it is impossible to quantify is that the endless checking and cross-checking of details in committees and study groups has led to a first-rate engineering product being built with few setbacks. The continuous process of checking can be said to have eliminated errors that might otherwise have gone unchallenged.

Feeding the enormous bureaucratic machine with vast quantities of paper and arguing for hours in committee in a mixture of French and English has been as much a part of the price paid for the supersonic leadership as the cost of research and development. "The documentation we had to prepare was a public scandal," commented one of the BAC team on the paper mountain that Concorde has created. "To protect the ministers against charges by the Parliamentary committee, each quarter we had to submit a pile of reports which were over one and a half feet thick."

The ramifications of the system were a recipe for conflict and cost escalation. Trouble started at the very outset. The key job in the organization was chairman of the Concorde Management Board. At the beginning of the project the then president of Sud, Georges Héreil, "Monsieur Caravelle," was very disappointed with the proposed committee structure. He believed that it should have been organized in a less cumbersome way, and could not understand why the job of the chairman of the Management Board had to rotate between Britain and France. Before the treaty was completed, he resigned the presidency of Sud Aviation. Some people commented that it was because he could not be "Monsieur Concorde" as he had been "Monsieur Caravelle." He became, instead, boss of Simca, the subsidiary of the American Chrysler Corporation.

It was a move which was popular with the British, who had never got on particularly well with this most French of Frenchmen. His place was taken by a figure who became very popular with the British and instrumental in pulling the project together: General André Puget, an anglophile and former commander of the Free-French bomber squadrons flying from England during the war. The combination of General André Puget at the head of Sud Aviation and Sir George Edwards as managing director of BAC made the Anglo-French partnership work.

At the beginning Sir George had a natural Anglo-Saxon doubt. "The first time that he and I met there was this little chap with twinkling blue eyes with an absolutely effervescent fist-clenched approach to the problem. It seemed as though his hair was standing on end exuding sparks all over him. But he and I clicked and the chaps saw that we clicked. We were both determined to make the thing work."

The Concorde organization was soon to be tested in a very severe manner. The temperamental and national differences between Britain and France made the solution of complex technological problems even more difficult. Of all countries likely to find difficulty in cooperating Britain and France were the most likely. Of all industries, it was the aircraft industry that was the most nationalistic. Aircraft men tend to be born flag-wavers; so much of their work is connected with achieving military supremacy or competing eyeball-to-eyeball in the cutthroat business of commercial aviation. It is an industry that produces more than its fair share of extroverts—robust and confident men dedicated to "defeating Isaac Newton" in their chosen way. Naturally they resent interference more than most, and those at the top have had a long experience of speaking their own minds, disapproving of the diffident and introspective approach of politicians and civil servants. In such an immensely political project as the Concorde, it is not surprising that major rows soon broke out.

The dispute which strained the new technological entente to its limits was over the exact size and range of the new aircraft. The Anglo-French agreement had not been helpful, leaving the door open for both a medium- and long-range airliner. France wanted to follow the tradition of the medium-range Caravelle, but the British industry opted heavily for the long-range plane, and there were insufficient resources for two Concordes.

Both countries had carried out only rudimentary market calculations. When France signed the treaty she believed she could sell at least 80 of the medium-range versions; Britain thought there was an equal market for the long-range Concorde. These were the days before the later, sophisticated, in-depth market studies; and even the American assessment made by the FAA showed a potential market for 500 SSTs. If Europe could capture just half that number, then the project would apparently not only pay for itself, but also return a large profit. Two important points were overlooked in the early calculations: first, the sonic boom was discounted, therefore there appeared to be a viable market for a medium-range transcontinental supersonic; second, the airlines became indifferent about the SST, following the Montreal IATA conference, where a general policy of "wait and see" was agreed upon. British and French manufacturers were therefore faced with a dilemma over which aircraft to build—the long- or medium-range version.

This first difference of opinion was extremely difficult to solve. The British stuck to their requirements for a long-range model for BOAC's North Atlantic and world routes. The French wanted a medium-range version to fly on Air France's routes on which the Caravelle was doing so well. The original plan had envisaged the French assembling the medium-range airliner and the British the long-range. Any shortfall in one or the other was to be made up by the joint production-sharing policy. The medium-range plane presented fewer problems to build, and the French argued strongly for going ahead with it first and sorting out the other version "as they went along."

The early meetings between the two sides were uncomfortable, with a complete contrast in style between the British and French. They were drawn from very different backgrounds and training. The French technocrats running the project were a remarkable elite, trained in the academic disciplines of the Ecole Polytechnique. On the other hand, the British had had a long and often rough apprenticeship on the shop floor, with its emphasis on practical training. According to George Gedge, then Bristol's production director and bluff West Countryman, "We started off by being British chaps and not thumping the table hard enough." Somehow agreement was painfully won. As George Gedge believes, what really paid off was the patience of the Bristol contingent, "the great British capacity to compromise and give ten times more thought to understanding people. Teaching them to share each other's language is a very small part of working together. Sitting round a table we learned to judge the mood of the meeting by the expressions on their faces, by the way they said things, the intonations of their voices." George Gedge characteristically summarized it: "Judging the right time to thump the table is what it's really all about."

The British could not "thump the table hard" until after the rush for Concorde options had been started by Pan Am in the summer of 1963. After this it was clear that no airline was interested in the French medium-range version. The BAC team was now adamant that all effort should go into improving the performance of the Atlantic-range plane. Behind the scenes the design teams in Bristol and Toulouse quietly concentrated all their efforts into improving the plane's tight economics. The table-thumping phase was over for the time being, but both sides knew that the newly up-rated Concorde was going to mean a dramatic increase in the budget.

The French had no problems. General Puget was a confidant of the president and knew that de Gaulle could handle the "quarter-masters" at the Ministry of Finance. He did not hesitate to make full use of his "special relationship" with the Elysée. This gave him an enormous advantage over his British colleagues when it came to turning the blueprints into metal. In the words of an envious BAC executive, "He merely picked up the ivory-handled telephone and asked for another lorryload of francs."

Across the Channel it was very different; Sir George Edwards had no ivory-handled telephone to Whitehall. He appreciated the tough struggle that lay ahead now that the real costs of the project were about to be appreciated by the treasury.

In London the "ominous silence," which the press pointed out had descended on the Concorde since the euphoria of the summer, was rudely shattered by the loud criticisms from the

House of Commons' watchdog, the Committee of Public Accounts. This committee of M.P.s scrutinized public spending and had examined the Concorde estimates and treaty with a fine-tooth comb. Their outspoken criticisms were painful for the government and embarrassing for the Treasury.

The estimates of £150 million to produce Concorde prototypes were revealed as completely speculative and what particularly worried the M.P.s was that "treasury witnesses admitted that government is now so fully committed that the authorization of the project is to some extent a formality." The Treasury also had apparently been failing its statutory duty. As the committee pointedly noted, "The Treasury played no part in preparation of or signing of the agreement and are not represented on the committee of officials set up by the agreement to supervise the progress of the project, although their French counterparts are." A Treasury witness said, "We have contented ourselves with receiving papers and minutes."

The committee was aghast to hear that when they asked for an economic justification for the project they were told that if the aircraft cost £3–£4 million each "we might be able to recover a good deal of the money over sales of say 150 to 200 aircraft." It was just not good enough. There appeared to be no hard, market analysis to back up this prediction. Fortunately for Concorde the committee could only voice its strong disapproval of the government for the way it had entered a project: "an example of executive action which commits Parliament to an unspecified heavy expenditure on a project on which the returns must be problematical." Most disturbing of all, they revealed publicly for the first time that the treaty was open-ended. Once again the exasperated committee could only deplore "the wisdom of entering into such an agreement . . . with another nation—no matter how friendly and esteemed—in which no provision whatever was made for the possibility of the project being abandoned."

The "no-break" treaty had been the brainchild of Julian Amery. The French had argued in favor of an escape clause, but Amery resisted. There was always the fear that France might turn out to be more perfidious than Albion. In the view of one of Macmillan's cabinet ministers, "I don't think anybody would have gone into a project like that, at that time, if the other party could have got out of it." They were determined to "see the thing through" because, at the time, they believed that Britain's ultimate admission to Europe was at stake.

The outspoken criticisms emerging from Parliament suggested that the project already amounted to a national scandal. The storm clouds were gathering over the Conservative administration too. It faced an election year in the wake of the ugly Profumo scandal and Macmillan had been suddenly swept from office by illness. The project on which he had staked so much began to run into trouble as news of a radical redesign leaked out.

At the end of January stories were suddenly splashed about that "Concorde faces a complete reappraisal." A major row was now brewing up over costs. Yet Julian Amery assured everybody that financial control was being exercised. "I do not think the budget has been exceeded so far," he told the House of Commons in January 1964. Dealing with the press stories about the redesign, he admitted that "the only question is whether the modifications to the engine and the wing structure may put something on to the estimate."

This bland statement concealed the months of arguments between BAC and Sud Aviation which had finally produced an agreement on what was virtually a redesigned aircraft. The pressure from the airlines and thousands of hours of wind tunnel tests had finally persuaded the French to change their minds about the medium-range aircraft and to agree to a general up-rating of the long-range version as well. Nineteen months after the treaty was signed, a workable Concorde design had at last been agreed upon. It is relevant to add the first-hand comment of one of the BAC team who sweated through those painful shakedown months: "On a big issue it takes a Frenchman about three years to admit that he has got it wrong."

The combined efforts of BAC and Sud were now at last directed toward proving to the politicians, airlines, and a skeptical press that they were making a plane that the market really wanted. Full of confidence, the Anglo-French team launched a major sales pitch at the 1964 IATA Technical Committee in Beirut. They went armed with the new mass of computerized data charts and artists' impressions of the "new improved" Concorde.

Although allies on the Concorde project, the old Anglo-French rivalry was just below the surface. BAC and Sud were earnest competitors when it came to selling their own separate national products. BAC were pushing their "111" medium-range airliner against the Caravelle. After making their joint sales pitch on Concorde, the British delegation spent the warm Mediterranean evenings infiltrating the plush corridors of Beirut's luxury hotels armed with BAC-111 books and brochures which they smuggled into bedside tables, "in case the airline bosses were short of bedtime reading."

In the conference hall, the BAC team pulled together with their French colleagues in presenting details of the new Concorde. It was to be a bigger plane: 14 feet longer in the body, with 15 percent larger wings; it would weigh 40,000 pounds more and have bigger engines. Most important, it was going to carry more passengers—a maximum of 118 over a range of nearly 4,000 miles. Concorde was planned to be in service by 1971 and to make its first flight in 1967. Confidently the two companies projected their plane as a "sensible and practical extension of present day knowledge." In a clear attack on the problems faced by the Americans in building a larger, faster SST in titanium and steel, they said, "We are using materials and methods which have been proven. . . . We are not going beyond the state of the art, and for those reasons, both our airplane and our timetable are realistic."

In order to get the prototype into the air, the two governments would have to agree to "something on the estimates." Money would have to be found for the major redesign on the Olympus-593 engines as well as the modifications on the airframe. The year lost in argument would have to be paid for. Everyone knew that Amery's original figure of £150–£170 million would now hardly cover all these changes.

On 9 July 1964, Amery faced a battery of questions in the House of Commons. He had just returned from Paris and a meeting with the French minister of transport where the new estimates for the redesigned Concorde had been agreed. Members found the minister's bland replies to questions on the progress of the project highly suspicious, since the matter of costs was studiously avoided. Scenting a hare of considerable size, the hounds of the opposition Labour party leaped to the chase.

"Would the minister give the latest estimates?" asked an opposition back-bencher. At bay, the minister replied in a low and seemingly disinterested voice that Britain's share would be "something like £140 million," clearly trusting arithmetical confusion to give him a chance to escape. A gasp of astonishment swept across the benches opposite. Even members of the government swallowed hard. The total bill had doubled to nearly £300 million. In the words of the *Times*, "Mr. Amery had caught them utterly off their guard, and before the questions on every lip could be framed, the House had passed on to the next business. Only the Labour spokesman on aviation was quick enough to get in one small query: "How long had the minister known that the cost would be almost double the original estimates?" "Since last weekend," Mr. Amery replied suavely.

Daily Express

"Voila! I said you can't trust the Anglo-Saxons!"

9

Slaying the Monster

On 16 October 1964, almost two years after the Anglo-French treaty, Britain's Conservative government was ejected from office. A heavy shadow fell over Concorde. The Labour party had won power after thirteen years in the wilderness, and Harold Wilson took over No. 10 Downing Street from Sir Alec Douglas-Home on a slender majority. Wilson, who had fought the election in the Kennedy-style theme of "Getting Britain Moving," pledged quick and abrasive decisions in the first hundred dynamic days of government. There was good reason to believe the new administration would favor an energetic technological policy. Wilson had spoken eloquently of remolding British society in "the white heat of technological revolution" at the 1963 Labour party conference.

Before the assembled delegates from the constituencies and the trade unions, he had fired the opening salvos of the election campaign aimed at making the Tories seem hopelessly outdated with their grouse-moor tweed suits. Labour intended that the social and economic scars of the industrial revolution would be healed by the white-coated scientist and technologist taking over from the coal miner and foundryman.

These were laudable sentiments, but the aircraft industry was deeply suspicious. No love was lost between the big aerospace companies and the Labour party. Wilson regarded the industry as "Whitehall's Monster," devouring more than its fair share of national resources. Labour party leaders remembered the long history of unsuccessful prototypes—from the Brabazon and Princess Flying Boat to the Swift transsonic fighter that had been initiated when they were last in power. In recent years they had seen the Conservatives hand out millions for the development of new aircraft like the TSR-2 supersonic bomber for the R.A.F., the P1154 vertical-takeoff fighter and HS-681 short-takeoff freighter. Added to this was Concorde. Anxious to emulate the example of Kennedy, the Labour party had employed a number of "think tanks" before coming to power, so that they would know exactly what to do in the first hundred dynamic days.

One person who had an influence on policy-making was the independent aviation consultant Richard Worcester. For many years he had been an outspoken critic of British aviation and its practices. In the spring of 1964 he circulated an aviation report which in his own words "contained the reluctant conclusion that the major aircraft planned would not suit the country." This far-reaching condemnation of the British aircraft industry so impressed George Wigg, friend and confidant of Harold Wilson, that "this shy retiring man with a brilliant insight into aviation problems" was encouraged to elaborate his policies further. The resulting document, "A British Aerospace Policy," was "examined by the Labour leadership." A series of meetings followed which gave Worcester "the impression that the leadership agreed with the reasoning, and the policy that they would fashion would be close to the policy I was urging them to adopt." The report was very equivocal on Concorde, since Worcester had long believed that it could be outstripped by a bigger and better

American SST; and it could hardly survive as a commercial proposition. Worcester advocated that British military projects should be dropped, and that American aircraft should be purchased instead.

It is hardly surprising that Worcester and his reports, modeled on the influential American *Aviation Daily,* were viewed with a certain amount of suspicion in the board rooms of British industry. His outspoken championship of all projects American made some suspect his objectivity. As one BAC executive put it, "We read his reports when we wanted to balance our own more enthusiastic predictions." But if Worcester's views were regarded with skepticism by the bosses of the industry, he found a ready ear in the inner circle of Harold Wilson's team.

The Labour government was determined to fashion an entirely new and certainly far smaller British aircraft industry. Its knife was well and truly sharpened, and many of the workers wondered where the first blow would fall. There was every reason why the prime minister had to act fast. Waiting on Harold Wilson's desk as he closed the door on the crowds in Downing Street cheering his election victory was what he called a "formidable memorandum" which stated that "Britain was facing a deficit of £800 million on her overseas payments for the year 1964, and a scarcely less daunting prospect for 1965." In his own view "it was this inheritance which was to dominate every action of the government for five years." There was a serious run on the pound almost before Wilson moved his furniture into Downing Street, and the prime minister was under considerable pressure to cut back government spending. Night after night he had to listen to pleas from the governor of the Bank of England for immediate cuts in government expenditure, and particularly the social services. According to Harold Wilson, this would have meant "half-finished roads left as an eyesore on the countryside, schools left without a roof." It would mean sacrificing welfare policies to "satisfy a foreign financial fetishism."

Harold Wilson had been returned as a socialist prime minister, and faced with the choice, his intention had to be to defend the nation's social priorities rather than continue with expensive aviation projects that were subject to runaway cost inflation. He knew too that the majority of Labour members at Westminster had no love for the Concorde, which many regarded as a Tory prestige project. The part that Duncan Sandys and Julian Amery had played in starting the whole scheme had earned it the tag of "A Macmillan Family Affair."

So it was that Harold Wilson's 1964 Labour government blithely approached the cancellation of the two-year-old £250 million Anglo-French Concorde project as if it were striking out a Class-B road scheme in rural England. But the project had already developed a life of its own. The timetable of action rapidly passed outside the control of the British government, turning what should have been a dynamic decision into a long, drawn-out, embarrassing bungle. It can be reconstructed as follows.

Monday October 19—Downing Street
The first meeting of Harold Wilson's Cabinet assembled round the famous table in Downing Street. One of their first decisions was to scrap Concorde, and only a handful of the new ministers appeared to have any regret. Ironically, the aircraft which was pushing the know-how of British and French designers to their absolute limits and which could open a new era of commercial flight was not considered a sufficiently important part of the technological revolution to deserve support. The immense spinoff from such an advanced project, together with the possibility that it could one day contribute millions to the balance of payments, was considered doubtful. Concorde was an expensive luxury to be axed without delay. The supersonic treaty with France was passed over lightly. As one member recalls, "At the time we were in the middle of an appalling economic crisis; we had discovered the £800 million deficit. Ministers were constantly being summoned to cabinet meetings and everybody in the whole government machine was at something like panic stations." On the table for its first meeting were the hurriedly formulated proposals for its statement on the economic situation. Since the new Parliament had not yet assembled, the traditional White Paper could not be used for the government's statement of policy. Instead, the proposals were known as "The Brown Paper" after the minister of economic affairs, the ebullient trade unionist George Brown,*

* Later foreign secretary and now Lord George Brown.

who was responsible for carrying it through.

Clause 13, subsection 6, of the "Brown Paper" was Concorde's death warrant. It promised a strict review of government expenditure "to relieve the strain on the balance of payments and release funds for more productive purposes by cutting out expenditure on items of low economic priority, such as 'prestige projects.' " Everybody knew what was meant by the euphemism of *prestige projects;* George Brown left no doubt. In the words of one minister, "It was a mistake to think that the government was specifically anti-Concorde. It was George Brown's rhetoric, illuminating a perfectly clear economic decision about priorities. When looking for something to describe as a prestige project, Concorde was the obvious choice. It was as simple as that."

Tuesday October 20—London
Faced with a day-to-day financial crisis, with pressure mounting on sterling, the British government turned to Washington for vital backing.

George Brown later admitted, "It looked as if with American help we could build up the economy within a reasonably short period of time." So a draft of the cabinet's decisions and the proposed "Brown Paper" was soon on its way to Sir Eric Roll, the economic advisor at the British embassy in Washington. Not only was he the key link between the British and American governments in the matter of financial matters, but he had just been appointed the head civil servant in the Department of Economic Affairs.

Wednesday October 21—Washington
The "Brown Paper" reached Washington. Once again the Americans saw that they were being asked for largess to bail Britain out of her crisis, and an opportunity to influence the fate of the rival European supersonic airliner (at that time three or four years ahead of its United States rival) presented itself. For President Johnson, who had piloted the American SST program through a recalcitrant Senate, any suggestion of American dollars being used to fund foreign projects which could take work away from Seattle, Santa Monica, and Burbank would not please the electorate who were about to cast their vote in the presiden-

tial election. In the subsequent high-level discussion on the "Brown Paper," the United States Treasury left no shadow of doubt that "prestige projects," ripe for the axe, should include Concorde.

Friday October 23—London
Prime Minister Harold Wilson now knew the terms of the American backing and took steps to spell out Concorde's cancellation in the "Brown Paper" to be published the following Monday. It was now becoming very late for the careful diplomatic moves that had to be conducted with Britain's other ally, France. Until he learned the American views, the prime minister might have hoped that a gradual withdrawal from the French commitment would be possible. Events were moving faster than planned, and the French government had to be alerted officially about Monday's publication of the government's proposals. The weakness of the British position now began to become apparent. In its enthusiasm to axe Concorde it had overlooked one simple fact—there was no break clause in the Anglo-French supersonic agreement. De Gaulle would have to be persuaded to abandon his cherished plan to end "American colonization of the skies," if the treaty were to be abandoned.

Saturday October 24—Weybridge, England
A brief was prepared by the Foreign Office for Sir Pierson Dixon, British ambassador in Paris.

Concorde's manufacturers were also informed. They were the last people to hear about the intended cancellation and they discovered in the time-honored way. Fleet Street was buzzing with rumors about the contents of the "Brown Paper," and by the afternoon, BAC headquarters had been telephoned by a journalist from a reputable Sunday paper. The rumors were substantial enough for worried BAC executives to take them seriously. Sir George Edwards shrewdly guessed what was up and lost no time in summoning senior executives. His key men were 4,000 miles away on a BAC-111 sales mission in the United States.

A transatlantic telephone call to a Dallas motel brought them the stunning news. "Once the Labour government was returned we knew the TSR-2 was a dead duck," admitted one of the BAC men, "but we just didn't see Concorde coming." If Concorde were to be canceled, as well as its advanced military project, TSR-2, BAC's management knew that it would be a massive blow to the company. It would mean the closure of the Filton plant, putting thousands of workers out of a job. But as the team set off immediately for London, trying to snatch British Sunday papers en route in unlikely places like Chicago, Sir George Edwards was assembling more information and preparing to dig in. Thirty-six hours later, when his executives arrived back in his office, he waved the "Brown Paper" at them. His first words, according to one of the team, were "There you are, we've had the Concorde."

Sunday October 25—Paris
Less than twenty-four hours were left before the British government's announcement. The instructions for the British ambassador in Paris had arrived at the embassy. Sir Pierson Dixon was not at his residence in the Rue Faubourg St.-Honoré, next door to the Elysée Palace, but away shooting on the country estate of Maurice Heutreaux, chairman of Hispano-Suiza, a major French aero-engineering contractor. His distinguished English companion on the afternoon shoot was none other than the former minister of aviation, Julian Amery, who was staying at the ambassador's residence for a long weekend.

Suddenly in the middle of a drive, a harassed official of the British embassy roared up in a cloud of dust with an urgent summons for the ambassador to return to the embassy. When Dixon reached Paris, he was astonished to find blunt instructions from London that Concorde was to be killed, and "would he please inform the French government." Since it was now late on Sunday afternoon, all attempts to track down French Foreign Minister Couve de Murville failed. Although by the time Julian Amery found his way back to the residence at midnight, the Quai d'Orsay knew what was in the offing, Amery did not, and retired in ignorance of what was going on since he had not seen Dixon that night. At 8:15 A.M. the following morning Amery was surprised to be awakened personally by the ambassador with the dramatic news that he was on his way to meet de Murville in one hour's time to inform him that the British government wanted to cancel Concorde. Amery was astonished and dismayed. But both realized that there was a potentially embarrassing situation, if Amery were to be at the residence once the news had broken to the press. So the former Conservative aviation minister reluctantly cut short his visit. As he flew back to London, the man who had nurtured the initiation of Concorde was doubtless wondering if the absence of a break clause in the treaty would really save the project.

Tuesday October 27—Paris
The French did not understand the British position at all. The news had been broken ominously during a meeting of the Conseil des Ministères that the British were pressing for cancellation. Monsieur Peyrefitte, the minister of information, was dispatched to announce, "It's a matter of a greatly increased burden which will be discussed between the two countries." The French clearly intended that the burden should be placed squarely on the new British prime minister. To make matters worse they had received very little warning. As the story of the Brown Paper broke in the press, its one specific proposal for government economy, the axing of Concorde, breezily implied that the negotiations with the French were well under way. "The government have already communicated with the French government their wish to reexamine urgently the Concorde project." In fact discussions were not due to begin until the minister of aviation visited Paris the following day to open discussions.

The French, however, were incensed. They scented United States collusion in the scheme to cancel and decided to be very tight-lipped about the news of Harold Wilson's decision. French newspapers were soon suggesting that Federal Germany was ready to take over responsibility in the event of British defection. De Gaulle was enraged by this latest example of Anglo-Saxon perfidy and instructed his ministers to leave the British in no doubt about France's absolute intention of holding Britain to her contract.

Wednesday October 28—Paris
Surrounded by reporters and news cameras, Roy Jenkins, minister of aviation, a confirmed supporter of the Common Market, flew to Paris with the unenviable task of killing Con-

corde. Not yet a member of the cabinet, he had been kept totally in the dark about the maneuverings to kill his department's biggest project. The news had come to him in traditional Westminster style, from Sir Richard Way, permanent secretary of his ministry, during lunch at Brook's Club in St. James. Jenkins now had to carry out the cabinet's instructions, which were "to get out of Concorde fast," although government sources officially indicated that the forthcoming meeting with French aviation minister Jacquet were really about a "reappraisal." The "negotiations" amounted to little more than thirty-four minutes of embarrassingly pointed discussion in which Jacquet reflected the adamant attitude of his government. According to well-placed leaks in the French press, Jenkins reacted to the blank French refusal to cancel by proposing a number of alternatives. These were to test the French resolve, and ranged from restricting the program to prototypes only, to sharing the burden with other European nations or even the United States. Top of the list was the suggestion that France alone should finance construction.

The French were totally uncompromising, and in a final flourish, Jacquet produced the treaty. According to one strategically placed member of BAC's board, who "happened to be in Paris at the time" and close to French sources, Jenkins "got a pretty boot-faced reception from the French, who referred him to the terms of the agreement signed in November 1962 and showed not the slightest inclination to be helpful."

A "saturnine" Roy Jenkins returned to London. Now it was his turn to be "boot-faced" as he faced the inevitable airport press conference. The French, he explained, had listened "carefully and sympathetically. . . . I did not expect them to commit themselves and they did not do so." He elaborated that the British government had wanted an urgent review because of "the economic situation at home" and because of "grave doubts about the economic viability of the plane." Then hinting at the option of a possible climb-down, "If we are convinced that the investment in the Concorde, from our point of view and from the French point of view, would help us to pay our way in the world, consistent with the amount of money spent on it, then, of course, we would have to go ahead; but at the moment, we have our doubts." But the French had been left in no doubt that the British government, if it had its way, would cancel the aircraft immediately. But the treaty prevented unilateral cancellation. So the French calmly decided to sit tight and let Mr. Wilson do the sweating.

Crisis and Denouement—November–January

The "angry silence" in Paris contrasted with the storm of public indignation that burst in London. On November 6 Her Majesty's Opposition called for a full-fledged public inquiry. Letters poured into the *Times* expressing deep concern for "the youth of this country and the young technologists" who would regard "the cancellation of the Concorde as a sign that there is little future for advanced technology in this country." Another correspondent asked, "Is it not worthwhile subsidizing the Concorde venture (which may, after all, turn out to be a money-making success) and thus ensure us remaining a leading aviation nation?"

Others urged the government to be firm. "We'll lose a plane nobody wants and gain a new world," expounded the left-wing weekly *New Statesman*, conjuring up glamorous visions of automatic cars, high-speed mono-rails, and "social automation," rather than military or aircraft "gadgetry." Even the staidly respectable *Financial Times* suggested that there "was a good case that the aircraft should be scrapped." This was heresy, indeed, but it concluded with a warning to Mr. Wilson: "If the money released from the Concorde goes straight into consumption or old-age pensions, the growth prospects of the economy cannot fail to be impaired."

The debate was reaching a hysterical level, but behind the scenes, the leaders of the aircraft industry were using every method to remind the ministers of the realities of cancellation. They knew that they were not just fighting for Concorde but for their very survival. Sir George Edwards left Roy Jenkins in no doubt that BAC would be forced to close its Filton plant, with a damaging effect on Bristol and the Southwest, traditionally an area of strong Labour support. A significant leader in the socialist *New Statesman* reflected the backtracking that had started in Downing Street: "Mr. Jenkins broods on international cooperation in advanced technology, and his advisors are considering whether an economic return can be expected from a project which costs so much. Allied to the problems of economics and technology is the less calculable one of diplomacy, and on that hinges the kind of relations Mr. Wilson's government wants with de Gaulle. . . . Should Concorde be scrapped, the diplomatic consequences would be considerable and these are being taken seriously by the government."

Mr. Wilson's team had been trapped by their diplomatic blunders. Charles de Gaulle left no move untried to prevent them from wriggling out of their treaty obligations. Determined to save France's technological "gloire," he formulated a "European Plan"; Sweden, Germany, Holland, and Belgium were approached to see whether they would help finance the project if Britain withdrew. All these moves were studiously leaked to the world's press. So, too, was the story of an approach to the Russians to supply replacement engines when the Soviet foreign trade minister, Patolichev, conveniently appeared in Paris to sign a trade agreement. The only solitary note of support for Harold Wilson came from de Gaulle's old rival, Gaston Deferre, mayor of Marseilles, who in a letter to Le Provençal asked if it was "unreasonable to complain that the British are thinking of abandoning the project when General de Gaulle slammed the door on them in January 1963."

Even the radical Jean-Jacques Servan-Schreiber, normally sympathetic to British problems with de Gaulle, turned on Mr. Wilson, saying, "However good the British arguments may be for suppressing Concorde, it is unacceptable that a unilateral decision should be taken without consulting the partners. . . . The consequences, in every respect, of the behavior will cost them, and even in purely financial terms, much more than the saving on Concorde. That is the Gaullist method. We have denounced it too often in France to be indulgent with British socialists."

Events were reaching a climax. On November 19 at the Conseil des Ministres at the Elysée, President de Gaulle called for a résumé on "le machine." Jacquet gave his progress report. After discussion the French government delivered its ultimatum to London. This clearly laid out three points: First, the treaty did not allow for any revision. Second, any delay in producing the aircraft would allow the Americans to catch up. Third, Concorde must be built as planned.

To back up his government's firmness de Gaulle turned the screw. He issued a directive that until the British government came to its senses, there was to be no further contact with the British Concorde team. Vital communication between the top executives came to a halt, although ingenious channels of communication were opened up through the public-relations offices of the British and French companies. The company executives "climbed down into the slit trenches" and waited for the governments to fight it out.

Harold Wilson was now on the hook. He either accepted the French position and went ahead with the Concorde, or he ruptured the treaty and risked the humiliation of an international lawsuit over breach of the treaty with Gaullist France. Furthermore, if there was a public row with France, the chances of Common Market entry could disappear forever. Locked in the midst of a sterling crisis and having to lean heavily on the borrowings from international banks, Harold Wilson knew he could not risk such a blow to international business confidence.

The British cabinet had to know how much room was left for maneuvering. All now turned on an interpretation of the treaty: could they risk a breach? The advice of the attorney general, Sir Elwyn Jones, was crucial. His legal opinion was chastening; Concorde was the subject of an international treaty registered at the United Nations, and subject to the procedures of the International Court at The Hague. Harold Wilson's options were painfully limited. As the prime minister wrote later:

> Had we unilaterally denounced the treaty, we were told, we could have been taken to the International Court, where there would have been little doubt that it would have found against us. This would have meant that the French could then have gone ahead with the project no matter what the cost, giving us no benefit from the research or the ultimate product. But the court would almost certainly have ruled that we should be responsible for half the cost. At that time, half the cost was estimated—greatly underestimated as it turns out—at £190 million. This we should have had to pay with nothing to show for it, the result of what we considered a highly improvident treaty on the part of Julian Amery.

There was little doubt that de Gaulle would take a strong line of action if pressed. The cabinet's previously firm resolve crumbled. "Cabinets blanch a bit at legal opinions" was the reaction of a senior minister who argued for "cancel it and be damned." But according to Harold Wilson, the attorney general's interpretation was that the total bill would not just be £100 million, but that the French could actually go ahead and build Concorde charging Britain half the cost. This was a matter of some speculation, but as one minister later remarked, "With hindsight, of course, we can now see that even if the attorney general's legal opinion was correct, our maximum liability would have been trifling compared to the expenditure to which we are now committed." One senior civil servant believes that Britain could have won had she hung on three more weeks. But for Prime Minister Wilson, "faced with this situation, we had little alternative but to go on." Britain could not risk the further loss of confidence which would be caused by an international lawsuit. The attempted execution had failed, but shadowboxing was to continue between London and Paris until the end of the year in an attempt to save face.

The British government tried to seek a final compromise solution with the French, to persuade them to slow down the program. But having suffered one diplomatic reverse, the British were in a weak position and General de Gaulle knew it. The French refused to discuss Concorde at all, unless they first received a categorical guarantee that Britain would carry out the treaty and build the plane. The weeks passed in increasing frustration; in the factories, work was grinding to a halt. This was giving the Americans a chance of catching up on the vital four-year lead of the Europeans. The December meeting specially set up to discuss ways of controlling the investment on the project was called off under French pressure, but time still was on the side of the Concorde.

The Ministry of Aviation and BAC began to press compromise solutions on the government. A so-called "knife and fork" solution began to be discussed. This meant that the prototypes would be hand-built without the full production-assembly jigs. The BAC costs department produced six sets of figures for six sets of compromise solutions. All, in the long run, would drastically increase the cost of getting the aircraft into production, but to the Labour government it looked like "cancellation with honor." But the French would not even discuss them.

Then came an intervention from an unexpected direction. For weeks, as the crisis raged, work at Filton and Toulouse had dwindled to almost nothing, and the workers had become very anxious. With the senior executives and civil servants officially maintaining an unapproachable silence across the Channel, the union leaders stepped in to break the deadlock. In a series of moves, with important implications for trade-unionism, the British and French union chiefs acted internationally. An old socialist militant, Eugene Montel—who had been a colleague of Leon Blum and was a deputy for Toulouse—arrived in London to lobby the British Labour party on behalf of the unions. On the British side, Clive Jenkins of ASSET * intervened and flew to Paris to bring pressure to bear on the French government for a compromise. These dramatic excursions contributed to the easing of the situation. Although they were refusing to compromise, the French became as concerned about the standstill as the British.

By the end of December, Harold Wilson's government drifted into the uneasy acceptance that Concorde would continue, compromise or not. The newly created Ministry of Technology, and its ex-union chief, Frank Cousins, responsible for Concorde, had been steadily won over by the technological arguments and the damage that massive labor redundancies would do to the economy. The cabinet turned to find another target for producing the economies it badly needed. They found it in TSR-2, already damned by Worcester's report of the previous summer. Costing a million pounds a week and suffering from engine delays, it was unprotected by de Gaulle. It had made a dramatic series of maiden flights, with both manufacturers and test pilot taking risks to get it airborne by the autumn so that it could prove itself.

This time the aircraft industry reacted rapidly. According to Harold Wilson, "Our probable intentions—though no final decision had been taken—became the matter of press discussion and immediately the aircraft manufacturers were knocking at our door." It was not only the executives who put the pressure on the prime minister. Workers in the aircraft industry had already

* ASSET: Association of Supervisory Staffs, Executives, and Technicians. A strong white-collar union.

marched down Whitehall, their lost day's pay and rail fares, the press reported, being paid by their employers.

The prime minister decided to confront the industry leaders over dinner. On Friday, 15 January 1965, the party assembled at Chequers, the country residence of the British premier, arranged by Harold Wilson to be "without all the attendant publicity that surrounds the door of Number 10." The table talk was "utterly frank," as the industrialists painted a black picture of what would happen if the government carried its plans through. BAC, the prime minister was told, would "break up." In the face of this blunt warning, Wilson and Jenkins went some way to "encourage" their guests about the future of the Anglo-French projects, including Concorde, but remained adamant about not giving any commitment on the military projects. It looked as though Concorde would pull through the crisis.

Early in 1965 work began to pick up again as the government decided to play the situation empirically. Britain had not given up searching for a way to escape from the commitment, but, for the moment, the shooting had stopped, and workers and management "climbed out of their slit trenches and got on with the project." For the first time in the ten-week crisis, senior executives were allowed to make contact again directly.

If nothing else, it had welded the Concorde men on both sides of the Channel into a team, fighting on the same side and bloodied in battle. In Dr. Russell's view, "It was the time when we got really friendly, we rallied together and it helped relations enormously."

Perhaps Sir George Edwards was nearer the mark when he said, "You can't make decisions on this kind of thing on the basis of what happens in a fortnight."

ROWS AND RECONCILIATION

"A boot-faced reception." Roy Jenkins, Britain's minister of aviation, confronts Marc Jacquet, French minister of transport, in the Concorde crisis talks, Paris, 29 October 1964.

All smiles. Four months later the two ministers chat jovially with Najeeb Halaby, administrator of the FAA, visiting London to discuss supersonic airliners.

Aerospatiale

THE MEN WHO DESIGNED CONCORDE

The French team, Pierre Satre (extreme left), also designer of Caravelle, and (extreme right) Lucien Servanty, who was instrumental in designing Concorde.

On the other side of the Channel. Sir Archibald "Doc" Russell, leader of the British Concorde design team, with his colleague ...

...Dr. Gordon Strang, who hammered out the final Concorde configuration with Servanty in Paris.

BAC

BAC

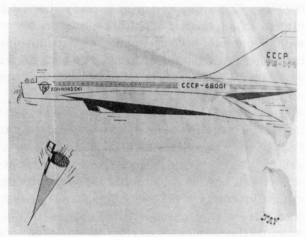

Evening Standard

"So much for that secret information from Concorde."

10

A Question of Confidence

While the British and French governments indulged in their unseemly public row about Concorde's future, the Belgian secret police had been keeping very close watch on a plump little professional man renting an expensive apartment in the fashionable Brussels suburb of Ixelles. His baggy suit and thick-rimmed glasses had led many people to wonder how he could afford to live in such a smart district. Jean Paul Soupert was a Swiss chemical engineer, but he soon began to reveal all the telltale signs of an international agent. He traveled extensively around Europe, staying in the best hotels and meeting a strange array of people. Two of these were ostensibly Roman Catholic priests, members of a teaching order called the Brothers of Christian

Schools, which was carrying out its mission in Toulouse, head-quarters of the French Concorde effort. The clerical brothers known as Stefan Krigovsky and Jean Sarrady showed an unexpected interest in supersonic flight. The two priests were not Soupert's only contacts. A German engineering consultant, Herbert Steinbrecher, also showed great keenness in talking to executives of the French Concorde manufacturer, and was also in touch with the Swiss spy.

The Belgians alerted the French antiespionage department, Surveillance du Territoire, who quickly moved to smash the Toulouse spy ring. The priests turned out to be two seasoned Czech agents; both they and Steinbrecher received heavy jail sentences. Soupert, however, had intrigued Western intelligence agents with the ingenuity of his operations. In a style reminiscent of a Graham Greene novel, Soupert had hidden rolls of 35 mm film, containing the Toulouse secrets, in tubes of toothpaste. These were regularly dispatched to East Berlin in the first-class lavatory of the Ostend–Warsaw Express. A telltale chocolate wrapper cast into a wastebasket told the East Germans when to make their collection from behind the toilet grille; any information was then forwarded to their Soviet allies. When Soupert's cover was blown, the amateur spy made the best of an embarrassing situation by offering to become a double agent for the British.

It is uncertain how far Soupert's information was of value to the Russian aircraft industry, but the discovery of such active espionage activities alerted the Anglo-French Concorde team to the fact that the supersonic race had started in earnest. Both superpowers were clearly determined to challenge the European lead. The Americans were still wallowing in a morass of competition committees and political inquiries; but the Russians were working stealthily ahead, shrouded in their traditional secrecy. In the opinion of Dr. Russell, "The Russians like to follow rather than lead." Put another way, it could be said that the Russians tend to copy Western designs, and they may well have gained some gratuitous research and information through their espionage net. The first model of the TU-144, sporting Aeroflot colors, which went on view at the 1963 Paris Air Show, certainly bore an uncanny resemblance to Concorde and quickly gained the title

"Concordski" in the Western press. The French and British designers magnanimously discounted the help any stolen information may have given Andrei Tupolev. They believed that the shrewd academician had decided to stay within the state of the art, and had produced the same design to cope with similar aerodynamic problems. Nevertheless the TU-144 did reveal some divergence in attitude to the slender delta design; the four big Kuznetsov engines were grouped under the fuselage of the Soviet SST, rather than beneath the wings, as in the case of Concorde. This was thought to be a risky alteration by Concorde's designers, who believed this could create stability problems. The Russian power plants were also different from the Olympus. They had a high bypass ratio on the turbofan principle which, unlike the Rolls-Royce turbojet, produced less airport noise but at the cost of some efficiency at higher speeds.

Concorde's manufacturers did not consider the TU-144 a serious rival on world markets. Although the socialist bloc could be expected to support its own product, and some third-world nations, like India, might be attracted to Concordski by Russia's traditional giveaway prices, the Western airlines would not "buy Russian." The political consequences of any potential Western purchase would be immense, and it would also pose embarrassing problems for the Soviet government, which would have to open up its aircraft factories to inspections for Certificates of Air Worthiness.

The "Russians were coming" and the vast Anglo-French organization now hummed into action in an attempt to capitalize on the lead time over its formidable transatlantic competitors. Computer lines were set up between British and French research centers, a plane shuttled between Toulouse and Filton ferrying executives to intense conferences in "franglais," and committees spawned more committees. In the BAC and Sud Aviation hangars, Concorde physically began to take shape. Like a mammoth Meccano kit the large sub assemblies started to cross the Channel to be set up on the assembly jigs in Bristol and Toulouse. By the spring of 1965 Concorde was no longer a paper plane like its American rival, but an aircraft, milled from aluminium and moving steadily toward its first flight.

American industry began to become alarmed by what was

happening on the other side of the Atlantic. Their own efforts seemed to be bogged down in a sea of paper. John Hoving of the FAA reported, "I am struck, as a matter of fact, by the anomaly that seems to run through the whole supersonic program: committees, groups, flip charts, artists, all going on and on, assembling an immense amount of paper. What I am assuming is that they will fly a paper airplane off the FAA roof one day, with or without the sonic boom."

Hurried changes were made in administration to try and inject greater urgency into the program. To get America's SST moving, the Pentagon advised the president to recruit a military man to run the FAA in succession to Najeeb Halaby. Juan Trippe was finally retiring from Pan Am, and Halaby had been appointed his successor. General McKee was nominated for the job, but Congress objected. It wanted a civilian, and what was more irksome, with his retirement pension and the FAA salary, McKee would be earning more than anyone else in state service, apart from the president and the vice-president of the United States. Their objections were dismissed, and the general was installed in June. He promptly confirmed Congress's worst fears by demanding a further $180 million for the project. *Aviation Daily* blamed the secretary of defense: "In essence there has been nothing going for the program, as far as the industry and the public have been concerned, but press releases—and they have been few and far between since the program was dropped into Secretary of State McNamara's lap."

The military seemed to be completing their takeover of the United States' supersonic when General Maxwell moved into the FAA as McKee's deputy. To calculating critics it looked as though this was a plan to get a supersonic bomber by the "back door." This was apparently confirmed when Maxwell publicly announced, "Anybody can use it. If I can haul garbage supersonically, then the garbage people will buy it. If the airplane is as good as we're saying it is, it will have an application on *their* missions." Exactly what interpretation people read into "garbage contractor" was left in doubt, but even the Americans were still a long way from a supersonic dust-cart.

Across the Atlantic, French industry was brimming over with confidence, but the British companies were still convalescing after the traumatic experience of Harold Wilson's first year of power. They bitterly counted their losses. Three advanced military projects had been scrapped. The HS-681 short-takeoff freighter, the P-1154 vertical-takeoff supersonic fighter, and the TSR-2 bomber were casualties. Many experts considered the TSR-2 the finest achievement of the British aircraft industry, with its terrain-following capability and Mach-2 attack speed. This high-powered replacement for the R.A.F. Canberra, to the fury of its designers, had been carted off to the bleak Foulness sands to be used for gunnery practice. In what many interpreted as a sellout to the United States, the American industry had benefited substantially from British cancellations. Although men had been thrown out of work in British factories, American workers were amazed and delighted as new orders came from Britain to fill the gap left in the R.A.F.'s equipment program. The Americans publicly welcomed the "brave political decision" of the Wilson government, especially as the orders boosted not only the Phantom, but McNamara's projected F-111 swing-wing fighter. The one major hope for the future of the British civil aircraft industry was Concorde, and the manufacturers knew that the Wilson government viewed this project with as much enthusiasm as the Ancient Mariner considered his albatross.

Ironically, however, the Labour government had begun to see a new significance in Concorde which brought some faint encouragement to the aircraft industry. In 1965, the Plowden committee had been set up by the government because "doubt has been cast on the future of the industry both within the industry itself and in the minds of those who wonder whether its value to the community justifies its cost." Although this committee was made up of people who had little knowledge of the aviation industry and was resented by the aircraft companies, it clearly spelled out the conclusion that "the major effort of the future should therefore be toward an association between the British and other European industries in a European aircraft industry."

The Plowden report was strongly opposed by the British industry, but it did provide an official gospel for Concorde to which all supporters of the project inside the Labour government could appeal. Now precisely because Concorde was the most ambitious European aircraft venture, it had to survive. Soon the

British minister of aviation, Roy Jenkins, was publicly sounding very enthusiastic about Concorde's chances. "We are anxious to get the market and therefore an important factor is how close the Americans are behind us. Compatible with getting a market, we don't want to rush into a decision without due consideration." The "due consideration" that the minister guardedly mentioned turned out to be yet another redesign of the aircraft. This would bring yet another escalation in costs.

Survival meant more than wishful thinking about the future of European industry. The success of Concorde would be judged on its acceptability to the world's airlines. They could be expected to play a ruthless game, balancing the American plane against Concorde. Every effort was now made to make Concorde more attractive to the airline bosses, who were demanding more seats and improved economics. The plane then being assembled was the aircraft that emerged from the Beirut IATA summit, with 118 seats, scheduled for service in 1971. But now that the Americans were flagging, the BAC team saw an opportunity to boost Concorde's customer appeal. It was decided to build the proto-types according to the design frozen at Beirut, and fly them as part of the test program. Then changes would be made in the next pre-production aircraft. The technical director at Filton, Dr. Strang, initiated the changes as a result of airline intervention. "It was really spearheaded by Pan American representatives who pressed for and got adopted a further lengthening of the fuselage and a rearrangement of access doors. They wanted an increase in volumetric capacity, and we gave them another seven feet and up to one hundred and forty seats."

It was a measure of the ingenuity of the BAC-Sud design teams and the flexibility of the slender delta that they achieved this extra load by exploiting the aerodynamics of the wing, once again vindicating its choice. By subtly changing the wing camber and tip configuration, lift was increased without increasing the span. The changes became the subject of a major squabble between the British and French sides; the dispute went right up to government level, and eventually the Concorde Directing Committee had to step in to order the new alterations.

Concorde might now have more airline appeal, but the real proof would be firm orders. For these everyone knew they would have to wait. In the interim it fell to Roy Jenkins, the man who had once been told to "kill" the project, to announce to the House of Commons that the new design would demand more money. The Jenkins announcement gave new ammunition to Concorde's critics. The war against the project hotted up, led by *The Economist*. Its aviation correspondent, the hard-hitting Mary Goldring, was not taken in. Angrily she protested, "Someone must call the bluff; the Concorde supersonic airliner will not be built." Hinting at confidential leaks from the top she announced, "This is no sourpuss guess; it is the concensus of opinion among the men most closely connected with the project."

A scathing editorial in *The Economist*'s 31 July 1965 edition attacked the Jenkins announcement of rising costs: "And yet the charade goes on; another round of sour critics, another week of cuts in government spending and Concorde—officially—still survives. Unofficially, most people have written it off as dead." Describing Concorde as a "bad aircraft," Mary Goldring pointed out that "extreme American caution, despite huge resources, despite careful research, should be a warning that supersonic airliners that can pay their way are not things to be designed on the back of an envelope." She ended almost in exasperation by demanding, "Has everyone, every political party lost his tongue? . . . Have they all got constituents in Bristol?"

What she failed to ask was whether they all had to cope with General de Gaulle in the Elysée. Relations with France were hardly good, as de Gaulle continued with his lofty condescension toward Britain's attempt to join the EEC, which, in spite of the General's 1963 veto, was renewed by Harold Wilson. There were those in the British cabinet who wanted nothing to do with Europe, and if Wilson had shared their view, it would certainly have spelled the end of the Concorde project, since it was the one vital link with France.

Even so, as the BAC teams worked strenuously to overcome the technical problems on the prototype before the Americans appeared on the scene, often wondering whether the Concorde they were putting together would ever take to the air. There were members of the Labour government who regarded the project as a millstone, which, but for the unfortunate Anglo-French Supersonic Aircraft Agreement, could have been shed from Britain's neck. The enemies of Concorde in the cabinet lived in hopes that some technical problem would suddenly appear which would throw the whole notion of supersonic travel into grave doubt. The Anglo-French treaty would then be unable to save "de Gaulle's folly."

In the spring of 1966, Concorde costs were clearly on the rise again. The House of Commons Committee of Public Accounts once again drew attention to the uncontrolled nature of its funding. They were particularly anxious about the way in which BAC could profit from the development money. As a private company, BAC took its normal profit margin for the work undertaken, although the company decided how, when, and where to spend the government's money. It was not only a question of profits, but also a matter of risk. BAC would not lose a penny if the Concorde never won an order; the British taxpayer would lose hundreds of millions.

Concorde was not a military project, but the committee was unhappy about the financial arrangements of the colossal undertaking. They urged "a more detailed program, with dates for different stages and the progress to be expected by specific dates." As well as casting doubts on the way in which the contracts were being organized between the two countries, the Committee of Public Accounts firmly said, "We note the ministry's explanation of the considerable increase in the estimates of costs, but we doubt the value of estimates which are so conjectural as to be almost worthless as an indication of the ultimate costs."

They had hardly spoken too soon. In April 1966 the government had to face the full costs of redesigning Concorde to meet the new airline requirements. The Anglo-French Concorde Directing Committee began to draw up new figures. The bill rose to almost double the existing £250 million estimate. In this atmosphere of spiraling costs and Britain's increasing economic difficulties, the French prime minister, Georges Pompidou, visited London. Concorde was on the agenda, with rumors that even General de Gaulle was becoming apprehensive about the escalating bill. Yet Harold Wilson was in no mind to express doubts about the Anglo-French project, since renewed efforts were being made to try and engineer British entry into the Common Market. Also, at the ministry, George Thomson had just been given specific responsibility as chancellor of the Duchy of Lancaster to "probe in a very positive sense the terms on which we would be able to enter the European Economic Community." The British government had gone even further to cement the Anglo-French entente. Following the principles enunciated by Plowden, it had set up a swing-fighter project with France.

The French mission which arrived in London on July 6 was not a happy affair. It paid little attention to grandiose technological ventures, but expressed an irritating concern about sterling. As the *Financial Times* put it, quoting a "high French source," "One could no longer expect there to be a sterling crisis every few months," if Britain was to enter Europe. Wilson was furious, and the leak began a new wave of speculation on the pound.

The French had begun to soften a little on the Common Market application, and when Pompidou stepped aboard his plane to return to Paris, a suitably ambiguous statement partly repaired the damage. He was "glad to see that on the British side, the possibility of joining the Common Market seemed closer than a few years ago." It was noncomittal but at least something. A joint communiqué also dealt with the vexing question of the Concorde project, with the two governments claiming that they were "confident in their intention of proceeding and that they were satisfied with the financial aspects."

The public French doubts about sterling, however, had their effect. There was a heavy run on the pound, and on 20 July 1966, Harold Wilson tried the Labour party's long-suffering patience to the absolute limit by introducing stringent new economic methods. Monetary controls were brutally tightened. There was a petrol-tax increase, surtax was raised. But the cut that really hurt the Labour party was an axing of £150 million in public investment. Cuts were also made in overseas expenditure, and most humiliating of all for British people, the overseas travel allowance was limited to £50 per person. The days of the impoverished British tourist, so reminiscent of post-war years, had returned. Yet astonishingly Concorde was not even mentioned. It had become a centerpiece of Anglo-French relations. As Wilson quietly said, "I then faced, as was to be expected, the roughest House any prime minster had faced for a very long time." But Concorde had once again escaped cancellation.

The enormous rise in Concorde's costs, as a result of the redesign, which made a total bill of £500 million according to 1966 estimates, shook Parliament. M.P.s rose to their responsibilities. In a major debate on November 28 several Labour M.P.s called for the whole scheme to be canceled. "The Concorde, at least in its early stages, is not for the ordinary man in the street. It will be for the international jet set, people playing the power game on other people's money—politicians, businessmen, and diplomats," charged one Labour M.P. The Conservative chairman of the Committee of Public Accounts, John Boyd Carpenter, a stickler for controlling state spending, weighed into the attack and went as far as to confess that none of his colleagues on the committee believed that "the figure would necessarily be as low as £500 million." He went on, "It is an unsatisfactory state of affairs when the decisions of one government to initiate and another to continue development of an aircraft are taken on figures which turn out to be so seriously underestimated."

The government blamed the original treaty. "The Concorde project is without parallel both in scale and complexity," claimed Niall MacDermott, financial secretary to the Treasury. As a sop to the Committee of Public Accounts he then assured the House that "the cost plus financing of contracts would be replaced by an incentive contract system which the ministry is evaluating." To many members this smacked of bolting the hangar doors after the £500 million plane had got its wings.

Concern over costs was not confined to the English side of the Channel. The French may have been more concerned with prestige in the early days of the project, but the latest round of cost increases frightened the French Ministry of Finance. The "quartermasters" went to work and persuaded de Gaulle to sack the anglophile General Puget. He had given his word to the cabinet to control spending, but still the "lorryloads of francs" were called for by Toulouse. In spite of Puget's connections, it was enough for de Gaulle. After Christmas, the general who had done so much to get the project going was informed that he was being fired. Stunned, the ex-NATO air commander discovered that his successor was to be Maurice Papon, the outgoing prefect of the Paris police. Papon was a strange choice and knew nothing about the aircraft industry. As France's most powerful gendarme he had acquired a dubious reputation for the methods used in maintaining law and order in the capital during the OAS terrorist offensive. There were rumors of de Gaulle paying him a political debt. The prospect of the replacement of General Puget as president of Sud Aviation by the ex-chief of the Paris police met with less than whole-hearted approval from the industry on both sides of the Channel. There was immediate dissatisfaction at Toulouse, where a communiqué from Sud Aviation was published, complaining that Puget had been given no notice of dismissal and darkly hinting that this might mean the end of "certain projects." The technocrats of Toulouse, who knew their previous master to be a champion of Concorde, would not find Papon such a sympathetic figure. His very first visit to the factory had provoked a walkout. A joint works committee on January 2 announced that the unions would "take all appropriate measures to get rid of him."

For a time even BAC executives planned intervention with an unprecedented personal appeal to the French government, but nothing came of it except rows behind the scenes that were carefully hushed up. Nevertheless, the British press was full of reports that France was about to cancel Concorde, but this did not materialize. The project was vital to de Gaulle's plans, and with a change of controller, there was a chance that these might be achieved, without the soaring costs that had upset the Ministry of Finance. Puget was consoled by de Gaulle and rapidly dispatched as French ambassador to Sweden. It was a sad blow against the Anglo-French team, which was now beginning to work effectively. The Concorde team could be forgiven for thinking success now lay within their grasp, if only the politicians could keep their nerve.

Transportation News
Digest Star

Fueling the white elephant

11

The Hot-Air Machine

On Thursday afternoon, 29 September 1966, the world's press, airline representatives, and local bigwigs gathered at the giant Boeing Development Center in Seattle and groped their way to places on the balcony in semi-darkness. Then, with a theatricality that was later criticized as "un-Boeing like" and more appropriate to Hollywood, the lights slowly went up to reveal the "beautifully ugly" white and gold monster. A disembodied voice announced, "This is THE BOEING SST," and the audience was sufficiently caught up in the emotion to applaud spontaneously. As the slender golden wings swung open on the $2 million mock-up, the applause grew. The droop snoot nodded up and down and a mysterious voice crooned, "Thank you. And welcome aboard the Boeing SST." As the hi-fi music beckoned, awed watchers moved reverently across the bridge into the mock-up where leggy "hostesses" explained the intricacies of the individual color-TV screens in the seatbacks, the "anthropometrically designed" seats, and the phono-vision system for calling the office or home at Mach 3. In the "mood"-colored interior of "loganberry," "regal purple," "orange strata," and "cerise," reality was a long way away. Some journalists wondered whether this was public relations gone mad, but it was a spectacular opening to the $4.5 billion United States SST program. What the brochures did not tell the journalists, but as one who was present later worked out, was that "to coin $1 billion you'd need 31,250 tons of silver, to be carried to the mint on a 14-mile-long freight train. If everybody in the whole world chipped in a buck apiece they couldn't begin to finance the SST prototype program!"

"The biggest and most expensive race in U.S. corporate and technological history" was heading into the homestretch. There were only two runners now left, and since each represented the biggest civil and military aviation contractors in the world, the finish promised to be truly spectacular. Almost neck-and-neck, the giant Boeing and Lockheed corporations strained every inch of their corporate muscle to win the biggest and richest prize in aviation history—the multibillion-dollar government contract to build the United States SST.

An impressive lineup of judges had been assembled to do justice to the occasion. A panel of no fewer than 235 top experts were assembled by the FAA to evaluate the complex design proposals submitted by the contenders. Sifting through the proposals and hearing the views of airlines who had put their money down on options for whichever emerged the winner was a long process. It was not made any easier by the intense lobbying of the two rival corporations, backed up by a massive paper offensive by their public-relations departments. What one Boeing man had called the "paper liars' contest" was threatening to get out of hand when the FAA called for a stop to all "press-agentry" intended to "influence anyone's judgment."

It was like Hollywood, but the unveiling of the Boeing 2707-100 mock-up was a gambit carefully timed to steal the thunder in the last critical weeks of the competition. Everyone was impressed by the revolutionary "swing wings," as they waggled in time to the music. This was something that their rivals were not offering. In June, when Lockheed's mock-up had been revealed to the world in similar Hollywood style at Burbank, Lockheed's engineers had often joked about Boeing's failure to show. Now they hinted at the problems Boeing was encountering about where to hang the large General Electric engines. A last-minute design change at Seattle had shifted the engine pods to the tailplane, to give more room for the wings to sweep and, said the Lockheed engineers uncharitably, to "keep them from burning the tail off." Now the paper liars' contest had taken on a new dimension: a struggle between the two largest model airplanes in the world— one made by Boeing, the other by Lockheed—a flyoff between $2 million plywood behemoths that would never leave the ground. Both would end their brief lives on an exclusive multimillion-dollar junk lot.

Lockheed had staked everything on the simpler delta-wing concept. Lockheed's Mr. SST, former test pilot Bill Magruder, had traveled to Europe to discover why the Europeans had put their faith in the delta wing. He talked to everyone he could about Concorde, and they made no secret of the advantages it gave for subsonic and supersonic flight. He personally flew the SAAB Draken fighter built by Sweden to test the delta configuration. When Magruder reported to his bosses, Lockheed decided to go for a modified "double-delta" wing. Burbank knew that the delta had certain disadvantages over a swing wing. It required far more engine power for takeoff and landing, and this meant greater noise. But it offered the simplest and most easily engineered answer to building a large supersonic plane. Also, there were nasty rumors that troubles had started to plague the swing-wing fighter, the F-111. What they were able to glean from Seattle suggested that the Boeing engineers might well be running into the same kind of problems. Lockheed engineers also guessed that their rivals had been overly optimistic about the weight-saving of their swing-wing design. "In the summer of 1966 they went to the same wing area and the same engines," recalled Magruder. "It took them three years to discover that you can't get away with it." At the last minute, Boeing was faced with a "fix job" before the FAA deadline. Lockheed entered the homestretch, odds-on favorite to win the SST competition, promising the same simple, safe, and economic design that the Europeans were already working on.

Whichever design was chosen, everybody knew that it would cost a "hell of a lot" and trouble was already brewing in Washington. Many congressmen and senators now felt that the whole SST affair had gotten completely out of hand. When the Senate Appropriations Committee met to consider the president's request for more funding, it ran into a barrage of criticism.

Ignoring the barrage of glossy literature and copywriter's phrases about the plane that "will mean the end of the mysterious East" and "reshape geography," the Senate committee concentrated on the cost of the SST. Estimates had risen from $1 billion, announced by President Kennedy, to nearer $4.5 billion, and the industry's designs were at drawing-board stage. Since the initial research into supersonic transportation began, Congress had voted nearly $511 million. Already more money had been poured into the SST than into Concorde, but the designs were still on paper. It was going to be the most expensive race in history—and it looked as though the American taxpayer would have to collect the bill.

In spite of the confident public assurances that came at regular intervals from President Johnson, it looked increasingly doubtful if even the dynamic McNamara could control the burgeoning SST complex. Cynics dubbed it "the hot-air machine," since final designs had still to emerge. The hours of talking and mountains of paperwork had produced nothing except requests for more federal funding. Three presidential committees and thirteen federal agencies had been involved. There had also been two high-level studies by independent analysts resulting in grave doubts and warnings about the magnitude of the scheme. Even the reputable *Wall Street Journal*, in a solemn editorial, warned of "Washington's sublime self-confidence in its ability to accomplish anything right now, if not sooner, even if it is impractical, immoderately expensive, or inadequately planned. It would be a fine thing if the government not only in the field of supersonic transports but in other areas, would now stop and ask itself: Is all of this urgency really sensible?"

The SST program was assuming breathtaking proportions—even for the United States. Distinguished senators became alarmed that for the first time the government was given the power to award the powerful military-industrial complex a contract to build an immensely expensive prestige product. Since the aircraft would be operated by private industry, it was becoming hard for congressmen to understand the equity of this large government subsidy in the land of free-enterprise capitalism. The press played up these fears. *The New York Times* blasted LBJ's "lack of candor" for pushing the SST program with "virtually the same priority on men and materials as that enjoyed by key war and space programs"—without telling the public.

The Vietnam war also began to emerge as an important consideration. As the American involvement increased, critics of the SST program could claim that the military-industrial complex was a beneficiary of both, that they were pushing for a multi-billion-dollar federal commitment to build a plane whose economics were dubious.

In the Appropriations Committee that September, Senator Fulbright was not alone in feeling that the Senate was being "pressurized" into "an utterly ridiculous project." He was correct about the pressure being applied by the Administration and the aviation lobby. Even in Washington, where thousands of dollars were spent on lobbying campaigns, all the stops had been pulled out. Airlines, planemakers, and subcontractors all kept the telephone lines busy with arguments to back the SST. Huge quantities of literature were produced and circulated to the press, TV, and congressmen to counter Fulbright's criticism.

The Johnson Administration, adept at skillful back-door politicking, had a persuasive argument to help steer the SST through increasingly troubled waters. An election was approaching and no politician liked to be blamed for killing an important American project which would keep United States technology ahead of all comers. Congress voted $142 million for the FAA, but the enemies of the SST bided their time, ready for a bigger and better attack next time around.

The announcement of the winner of the SST stakes was due on 31 December 1966. In the final weeks, as the FAA adjudicators canvassed the airlines and did their final sums, the two contenders became increasingly edgy. The public embargo that the FAA had clamped on the contenders began to wear thin. In Seattle, Boeing was openly calling its design "more difficult but more rewarding." In Burbank, Lockheed retorted, "Boeing doesn't know what it's going in for! We know."

Everyone expected that the president himself would make the announcement at his end-of-the-year press conference. It was an anticlimax. After talking about Vietnam and the need for peace, he ended by saying that the SST decision would be made public shortly. Was there to be yet another delay? More committees? Had the opponents of the SST in the Senate cast doubt on the president's determination to go ahead? Would the Europeans have it all their own way after all?

Lockheed knew the result within hours of the president's broadcast. General Maxwell of the FAA had been trying to reach President Daniel J. Haughton all day, but Haughton was out of town. Then the news came over the press wires from Washington. Boeing had won. Angry reporters at the Johnson press conference accused the president of "widening the credibility gap." Lockheed took the news stoically. In Seattle they celebrated a great victory somewhat apprehensively because, in the words of one Boeing engineer, "Now we had to get all serious."

"The designs had nothing to do with the decision" was the way a senior Boeing executive summed up their competition victory. To him the "airlines had confidence in Boeing" and that was what mattered. Certainly Lockheed could not match Boeing's track record in commercial aircraft, but nevertheless they were the largest military contractors in the United States. Naturally, there was a general feeling among the airlines that if anyone could make an SST work profitably, it was Boeing. It was a matter of confidence, and everyone believed that Boeing could deliver the goods.

The airlines were by no means unanimous in backing Boeing. There was a discordant voice from Australia's Qantas, where down-to-earth good sense suggested that the swing wing was just a bit too complicated for ordinary pilots. In a revealing article in *Aircraft Magazine* in December 1966, Captain Ritchie, then deputy chief executive and deputy general manager of Australia's flag carrier, launched a curiously bitter attack on the FAA's handling of the SST: "There was obviously an incentive to design an airplane to win a competition, not one oriented wholly toward airline requirements." What worried him was the complexity of the plane with "fifty-nine moving control surfaces, from retractable canards to triple slotted flaps. These depend on eight complex inter-linkages. By way of comparison, the Lockheed SST had only sixteen surfaces and three simple lockout devices. . . ." Voicing a lone critique of the Boeing design, he added that "eleventh-hour redesign" raised new problems, but he ended optimistically, "Boeing can be depended on to make its ideas work." That is what everyone from the president of the United States to the Seattle factory-hand was counting on as well. Failure at that stage was unthinkable.

The man picked by the corporation to run the SST show was a soft-spoken engineer named Holden W. Withington. He started with Boeing as an apprentice in 1941 after gaining a master's degree at M.I.T. Withington had worked on every major Boeing project since the Flying Fortress. In 1958, after Boeing had lost out to North American on the B-70 bomber, he headed a small team working on the original ideas for an SST. He was noted at the time for having one of the last authentic slate blackboards at the Seattle plant, still regarded in the age of the computer as the traditional and indispensable aid for all engineers. Although Boeing had won the competition with the swing-wing plane, it was caution and common sense to keep a back-up design in reserve, and a small team continued work on a delta design. It was this kind of thinking that had saved Boeing in tricky situations before, giving it a reputation for being able to "deliver the goods."

The variable-sweep concept fascinated Withington for a long time. It appeared to offer the answer to the conflicting demands for supersonic and subsonic flight within the same airframe. For takeoff and landing, the wings would swing out, giving the performance of a conventional plane; at high supersonic speeds they would be swept back to give the arrowlike configuration needed for aerodynamic efficiency at high speeds. It was a simple, elegant concept that appealed not only to aero-engineers but also to politicians. Secretary of Defense Robert McNamara had seen it as the solution to providing America's armed services with a standard supersonic fighter at minimum cost. This concept emerged as the F-111, and the "swing wing" had become an "in" thing at the White House and the Pentagon.

McNamara, who had made his reputation as boss of the Ford Motor Company, wanted to introduce the idea of commonality which existed in the motor industry into the air defense program. A swing-wing fighter could serve a whole range of purposes for the Air Force, Army, and Navy. Boeing tendered for the military swing-wing project, but failed to get the contract. In some ways this was lucky for the Seattle corporation, because the TFX turned into a fiasco, attracting the tag of "McNamara's flying Edsel."

The problems of the TFX project, combined with McNamara's habit of "imposing personal judgments," was going to be significant for the future of the SST project. A blunt view was expressed by Concorde's designer, Dr. Russell: "Anybody who thinks of a swing wing is crazy, except for a specifically few military reasons. A swing-wing commercial plane is a bloody stupid idea, but the United States industry got overconfident and it took them years to discover they were wrong."

Withington, however, had collected his team about him and had the massive reserve of Boeing at his disposal. With its banks of computers and squads of Ph.D.s, it had above all the experience of being the world's No. 1 planemaker. The aviation industry was spellbound by the magnitude of the challenge. If Concorde had been a leap forward, the Boeing swing wing was in the realm of "things to come." Withington, however, a wise and unemotive personality who might well pass for a midwestern farmer, was the last man to be bowled over by the excitement of his own ideas. He kept one eye on the progress of the back-room design team working on the delta configuration—just in case.

AP

THE WINNERS AND THE LOSERS

The winners. Lowell P. Micklewait, of Boeing, shows a model of the successful swing-wing 2707 to Major General J. C. Maxwell and General William McKee of the FAA. George McTigue of General Electric, winner of the engine contract, looks on happily.

The losers. The Lockheed delta wing model standing forlornly in a Hollywood setting at Burbank, California, before being consigned to the scrap heap.

Lockheed

Keystone

CRUSADERS AGAINST THE SST

Richard Wiggs, leader of Britain's Anti-Concorde Project, at a national press conference to attack the Anglo-French project.

William Shurcliff, Harvard scientist and founder of the Citizen's League Against the Sonic Boom.

William Proxmire, senator from Wisconsin, political leader of the battle against the American SST in Washington.

Paul Koby

The Guardian
The gentle sound of thunder

12

The Frankenstein Syndrome

At the time of Prime Minister Wilson's démarche with the French, Richard Wiggs, a thirty-five-year-old teacher of handicapped children, was recovering from a severe attack of pneumonia in Letchworth, England. Lying in an oxygen tent, he could do little physically, but he had been following with great interest the arguments and discussions about Concorde on the radio and in the press. Soon he was avidly reading everything he could on the subject and had become deeply alarmed at the notion that Concorde would soon be making a thunderous sonic boom every time it flew above the speed of sound. Wiggs was a born protester, and the idea for a nationally organized campaign to stop Concorde began to form in his active mind. On each side of the Atlantic, government and industry had taken the sonic boom for granted. Yet the existing subsonic fleets had already made life miserable for millions unlucky enough to live near an airport. Now, as one housewife feared, "with supersonic flight you will not be able to take yourself away."

Richard Wiggs was just the sort of man to channel these fears into some form of action. He believed in the use of well-researched information and carefully judged publicity, rather than the empty gesture of street demonstration. Industrious and meticulous, Wiggs knew he would have to supply regular streams of pamphlets and newsletters to supporters actively interested. With his shaggy beard and bright piercing eyes, Wiggs had more than the touch of the puritan about him. It comes as no surprise to learn that a forebear had been a recalcitrant seventeenth-century Quaker, Joseph Wiggs. In 1639 he had appeared before an ecclesiastical court and refused to remove his hat, addressing the judge with many "irreverent speeches, not without sordid and rude gestures." Everything undertaken by the twentieth-century Wiggs is pursued with equal relentlessness. There are no half measures. A vegetarian, he does not even touch dairy products, since this would be a concession to eating animal products. This critic of technology now turned his mind to Concorde, which he saw as a "symbol of the Frankenstein syndrome" and a "further phase in the destruction and despoliation of the environment and of the invasion of private life, by basically purposeless and misguided technological innovation."

The chance to launch his ideas for a public campaign against Concorde soon came. In the summer of 1966 a series of articles appeared, written by Bo Lundberg, in *The Observer*, a liberal British Sunday newspaper. Lundberg reiterated the charges against supersonic flight that he had made at Montreal in 1961, and which had been pointedly ignored by the aviation industry. In his Nordic vision, supersonic flight would be appallingly dangerous. Not only would there be dangers from weather and clear-air turbulence, but totally new menaces would emerge to threaten the lives of passengers and crew. Cosmic rays and solar flares could cause changes in the metabolism affecting the fetus in the mother's womb, and the fertility of pilot and crew could be threatened. If a hailstone punctured the skin of a supersonic transport, the results would be horrific, with everybody's blood boiling in a few seconds after the loss of pressurization. *The Observer* readers were shaken by this "doomsday" view of the new Anglo-French Concorde project. They were even angrier when they read what could happen on the ground. In Lundberg's opinion the sonic boom would create hell on earth if the airliners were allowed to fly over populated areas.

Letters poured in to the editor attacking the supersonic program. One from D. W. Rowell of Blackpool called for action rather than high-minded protest. Wiggs seized his chance and immediately replied, offering to set up an organization to fight supersonic airliners. To his surprise 200 letters arrived at his home in Letchworth, some containing donations. More significantly, they were mostly from academic and professional people. Soon he was employing the techniques he had successfully developed in a local campaign against Letchworth Council over leasehold reform. This was to buy advertising space in the press to be paid for by anybody wanting to associate themselves with the opposition action. A door-to-door collection had provided some highly effective hostile publicity which had discomfited the Letchworth Council and preserved leaseholders' rights.

Now Wiggs raised enough money to buy advertising space in the British journals *New Society, New Scientist,* and *New Statesman.* Each was read by a highly educated and informed public, well able to digest all the complex economic and technological arguments associated with the supersonic project. He knew that these persons would be the most effective campaigners in his attempt to kill the Concorde, constituting as they did a highly articulate middle-class elite. For a man who had left school at sixteen, without the benefits of higher education, he began to show a remarkable gift for organizing academics with very distinguished qualifications. Soon he had an advisory panel which read like a miniature *Who's Who* of Britain's university establishment. Two of its most energetic members were the American Dr. Jerry Ravetz, senior lecturer in the history and philosophy of science at the University of Leeds, and Professor Cedric Smith, professor of biometry at London University. With his flair for publicity, Wiggs named his organization "The Anti-Concorde Project," to be the diametric opposite of the official Concorde project.

The avowed aim of the Anti-Concorde Project, according to Wiggs' letter in the *Times* of 13 July 1967, was "to help create in Britain a climate of public opinion in which it will be possible for the government to terminate work upon Concorde, and to press the government to make this decision. Our further aim (in cooperation with similar movements in other countries) is to help to bring about the banning of supersonic transports internationally."

When Wiggs' advertisement appeared in the three magazines, he wrote in *New Scientist* on 17 August 1967 that the Anti-Concorde Project was not "anti-science, anti-progress or anti-technology. It is not anti-aviation." He warned that "the development of supersonic aviation is a disaster for the public and for aviation. It is evident that this development was undertaken without sufficient consideration, that it is enormously costly, and that if they are used, supersonic aircraft will, as a result of the sonic boom (produced throughout the entire flight at supersonic speeds), cause intolerable disturbance and damage."

The Anti-Concorde Project was, however, very small and insignificant, with just 160 members, until the government played into its hands in the summer of 1967. Anthony Wedgwood Benn, then new minister of technology, decided, as one of his first actions in his new department, to launch a series of sonic-boom tests over British cities. Benn's qualifications for the post of minister of technology were very good. He was youthful and technocratic, far removed from the "sons of toil" image cherished in a wide section of the Labour party. He was one of the party's whiz kids, married to an American wife and brimming with ideas, from the detailed organization of his famous homemade card index to the modernization of Britain's antiquated telecommunications. Benn was also a believer in participatory democracy, maintaining that British society was far too closed and secretive. He wanted the people to take a much greater part in decision-making. In the opinion of the Labour party's apparachniks, however, by far the most important qualification Wedgwood Benn possessed was his representation of the Bristol South East constituency, the home of many Concorde workers. Anti-Concorde ministers wasted no time in pointing out that the Bristol electors were the most expensive in the country, and that it might have been better to scrap Concorde and retire all the BAC workers on full pay. It is not surprising that in view of the press hostility to Concorde and the trouble with France, the new minister was heard to mutter on taking office, "If only Concorde would crash on the QE-2, all my problems would be solved."

Wedgwood Benn was determined to close the dangerous gap which stretched between the assumptions of the planemakers and those of the public on the sonic boom. The manufacturers plainly hoped to fly supersonically overland, but the politicians in Britain and the United States were anxious about public opinion. Already there was a chorus of complaint about the noise of conventional jets as they roared in over the cities, without having the whole country up in arms about supersonic airliners trailing a boom carpet fifty miles wide across the heart of the nation. In the early years, manufacturers had shied away from these problems. A joint declaration by Pierre Satre of Sud Aviation and Dr. Russell of BAC had stated that nine miles up "the calculated pressure rise will, in all normal conditions, be less than that found to give rise to complaint. It may be that, in unusual atmospheric conditions, and with peculiar topography, a noise resembling thunder will be heard. But this will not be an inevitable and regular occurrence." The British government was now determined to find out exactly what happened under practical conditions.

Most of the early experience of sonic booms came from relatively small fighter planes. It was first heard in 1947 when Captain Charles Elwood Yeager crashed the Bell X-1 through the sound barrier over the Mojave Desert. The boom is a shock wave caused by the hurtling mass of an aircraft cleaving a way through the atmosphere. The aircraft trails a cone of shock waves resembling the bow wave of a ship. The boom's intensity depends on the speed and weight of the aircraft and its overall effect is unpredictable, because atmospheric conditions can dampen or intensify the pressure waves. The sonic boom heard on the ground is, in fact, caused by the sudden change in pressure associated with the shock waves trailed by the plane; it is a characteristic sound, which in a large aircraft amounts to a perceivable double boom from the nose and tail shock waves.

The public reacted vigorously against the sudden unexplained and unexpected bang from the sky. In the United States, citizens disturbed by the sudden explosions were told by U.S.A.F. public relations men to accept them as the "price of liberty." One senator, incensed by unpatriotic complaints, warned the faint-hearted citizens, "It is far better to listen to the sonic booms than listen to the shrill, deathly screech of falling bombs." As the Pentagon ordered bigger and faster military aircraft, the bangs became worse, and the public relations department of the Strategic Air Command distinguished itself by reaching new heights of rhetoric. "Many of the window-rattling booms which resemble the loud sound of nearby thunderclaps are caused by the B-58 bombers of Strategic Air Command, the only Free-World bomber capable of flying at twice the speed of sound."

The most spectacular incident occurred on a humid, hot afternoon, 5 August 1959, in the midst of a dedication ceremony at the new Ottawa air terminal. In the course of a military flypast, the pilot of an F-104 Starfighter streaked in on a low-level pass over the heads of the crowd. Five hundred feet up, with full afterburners blazing, he made a climbing turn, bursting through the sound barrier, and the sudden acceleration created the most powerful of all sonic booms. The result was like an earthquake. The control tower literally exploded. The roof of the terminal was torn open, the curtain walls were twisted and the exterior cladding crashed to the ground. Astonishingly nobody was hurt, but the super-boom of 38-pounds-per-foot over-pressure produced a damage bill of $300,000. There was a large backlog of research on the sonic boom. In 1961 the city of St. Louis, Missouri, had been boomed night and day in a joint FAA/NASA experiment tactlessly named "Operation Boom." The citizens firmly believed that they were cooperating in vital national defense studies. There were few complaints from people putting up nobly with "the sound of freedom," until the mask fell and opinion pollsters revealed that the tests were for civil aviation research. There was a public outcry at being treated like guinea pigs. This boded ill for supersonic airliners. "Operation Heatrise" was an even bigger public relations failure. Trying to persuade the nation to love the sound of freedom, the United States Air Force had flown a B-58 Hustler bomber across America from Los Angeles to New York in just over two hours. Flying at Mach 2, it was the first plane to cross the continent in so short a time, but U.S.A.F. headquarters "just knew where Hustler was by following the complaints board."

The next set of guinea pigs had been observed by a British minister of aviation, Julian Amery, anxious to find out how the sonic boom might affect the Anglo-French Concorde. On 3 February 1964, "Operation Bongo Mark 2" got under way over Oklahoma City, and Amery became a guinea pig himself for part of the tests. Engineers had wired up recording machines in houses and offices throughout the city to find out how buildings would react. Scores of pollsters were on the street ready to sample opinion. Day after day at regular intervals the booms rolled over the town. In the first fourteen weeks 147 windows were broken in the city's two tallest buildings. Opposition grew slowly after the first jokes wore off. There were attempts to get the tests called off. Federal judges heard injunctions, but incredibly, the government wheeled in two psychiatrists to testify that outside stresses "such as the booms of the London blitz" reduce suicide rates and admissions to mental hospitals. The injunctions were refused. One thousand two hundred fifty-three booms later it was all over. The results were inconclusive, but Najeeb Halaby had told the London Daily Mail, "As a result of these trials I am seriously worried about the effect of supersonic airliners shattering plate-glass windows or even damaging the structure of buildings. We have to face the fact that supersonic planes may have to be restricted to flights over the sea. This, of course, would have a drastic effect on sales, bringing the total world market down to 500 airliners from the optimistic industry forecasts of 1,200."

Julian Amery returned to London in a sanguine mood. He had inspected the complaints book and was impressed by some of the patriotic statements made by the citizens of Oklahoma City. The British Parliament was skeptical. One member expressed his concern that "hundreds of thousands of people might be seriously inconvenienced for an increase in speed of travel for a mere dozen."

This was good egalitarian socialist stuff, mixed with a criticism of advanced technology. The hardy Parliamentary secretary to the Ministry of Aviation, Neil Marten, would have none of this feeble talk. He assured the House that a vast amount of research work had been done on the supersonic boom by his department. Perhaps he was remembering the time when he had been locked up in an open-topped box "like a privy" at Aberporth in South Wales and subjected to a battering by R.A.F. Lightning fighters targeting on his ears. "This is something people will learn to live with, just as they learned to live with railways, motorcars, and jet aircraft," he told his fellow M.P.s. The *Times* did not agree with the minister. Acidly, it commented, "The view of the Parliamentary secretary to the Ministry of Aviation that people learn to live with it is complacent to a degree. Why should they?"

The only serious public test held in Britain had been ordered by Wedgwood Benn's predecessor, Roy Jenkins. On a damp April morning in 1965 he had collected a crowd of journalists, M.P.s, aviation executives, and "men from the ministry" on the wind-swept flats of Huntingdonshire. Roy Jenkins himself attended, and a whole series of bangs were produced by R.A.F. Lightnings thundering overhead. The government hoped to simulate the Concorde-sized boom, inviting the audience to write down their reactions on the ministry's printed card. "Rather like a loud shotgun," wrote one journalist; another, "The booms were softer than the maroons used to call out the Padstow Lifeboat." In the deafening silence that followed, Roy Jenkins gave a press conference at which he was guardedly noncommittal over the precise nature of Concorde's boom but hoped that it would produce an over-pressure of about 21 pounds per square foot, less than many of the bangs which had cracked eardrums that morning. The journalists might have appreciated the show but the local population was not so happy. The R.A.F. received eight calls of complaint, but a scientist who had monitored the tests with instruments set among the tomato plants in a local green-house assured reporters that the over-pressure would need to be ten times greater for the glass to shatter. This was no comfort to the householder who rang the county architect to complain that his ceiling had just fallen in. The ministry pronounced the tests a resounding success; even the newspapers declared that the sonic boom was not all that it was cracked up to be. *The Guardian* noted, "The mild reaction to the government's demonstration of sonic booms has done more than calm the fears of officials responsible for the public relations of supersonic transport."

The manufacturers began to feel mildly hopeful that supersonic flight overland would be permitted after all. In January 1967 Pat Burgess, then Concorde's bluff sales manager, told a press conference that "BAC had studied a mass of evidence on public reactions to the U.S. boom tests and feels it will not be necessary to warrant a ban on overland flight." The manufacturers were backed up by the airlines. In April, Sir Giles Guthrie, chairman of BOAC, did not think that "supersonic overflying would be restricted." Wedgwood Benn, however, mindful of the views of the Anti-Concorde Project, believed, "It was quite wrong *not* to let people know what the sonic bang was like. There was at that time a great deal of ignorance about the sonic boom." The civil servants were lukewarm about Benn's idea for new tests, but when the proposals were put to the cabinet they got overwhelming support. "Many Labour ministers hoped that the public reaction would be so adverse that Concorde might at long last be canceled" was the opinion of one cabinet member.

The first tests took place over Bristol, where Concorde was being built. No warning was given, and when Lightnings from the secret test-base, Boscombe Down, thundered over the city, only twenty-six people complained. On the five following days the number of complaints dwindled to six, but the *Times* letters pages were full of demands for a complete ban. One writer claimed that "no part of our land will be safe from the cacophony of the Amsterdam to Acapulco, the Warsaw to Wichita and the Berlin to Boston flights." A man named Arthur Adams wrote to suggest that the acid test was to "repeatedly boom the prime minister while at his holiday resort in the Scilly Isles."

The first Lightning flight over London succeeded in jamming the ministry's switchboard. This was hardly surprising; there was only one line with three extensions available for complaints at the Concorde department in St. Giles Court. But the journalists enjoyed themselves with stories of men who almost fell off ladders and shopping housewives who heard all kinds of things, from a clap of thunder to a faint pop. One man congratulated the government; he was a seventy-three-year-old pensioner, David Jones, who had been gradually getting deaf over thirteen years. He claimed that his hearing was restored by the Monday flight over London. Commented medical opinion, "It is just possible that shock waves from the boom freed small bones in the ear which sometimes stick together and cause deafness." Several correspondents pointed out that the odd bang was hardly a fair test of the public reaction to what might be a day and night phenomenon. It was left to Philip Ehrmann, aged eight, to wind up the whole debate: "Dear Sir, While in the park yesterday I heard a big boom and all the pidgeons flu off in a terrible fright is it fair to the poor birds?" After just eleven sonic booms the minister of state for technology, John Stonehouse, was able to tell the press that he "was delighted with the way in which the public had responded to the invitation to give their reactions." Thanking the pilots who had conducted the tests, he added with a smile that everything had been "bang on." There had been more than six thousand comments on the test series and one hundred complaints of damage—mainly broken or cracked windows. Four thousand pounds were paid out afterward in compensation. Later the minister of technology, Anthony Wedgwood Benn, held the tests to be inconclusive and said that "no decision has been taken, at this stage, on what restrictions, if any, should be imposed on supersonic flight over land."

The minister, however, spoke too soon. A few weeks later, three French people died. In a farmhouse near Rennes, Brittany, a farmer named Prosper Meunier, his wife, and three neighbors were finishing lunch with coffee, when just before two o'clock a sonic bang from a fighter shook the old house and brought down the massive ceiling beams, burying them under eight tons of barley which had been stored in the granary above. The three deaths caused a wave of public indignation which swept France; this was made more serious after it was revealed that officially eight other deaths had been ascribed to sonic booms over the past four years, most of them from heart attacks at the moment of shock.

The farmhouse was not the first building in France to suffer; old towers had collapsed, and the Vézelay Church in Brittany had had to be shored up after persistent military flights. The principal inspector of ancient monuments, Monsieur Parent, was anxious about damage to the stained glass of the ancient cathedrals at Strasbourg and Le Mans. The French Ministry of Defense had set up an inquiry to study "appropriate measures for coming to terms with the problems posed by the effects of the sonic boom."

Richard Wiggs fell upon this information like a hawk, rapidly circulating it to the media and calling a press conference. His immediate target was not only the British ministry's blithe assurance that all was well, but also Sir George Edwards' statement, made just a few days previously, that Concorde's boom would be acceptable over populated areas. No fewer than ten people had apparently died in France as a result of sonic booms, he pointed out, emphasizing that many were a result of heart attacks. The ministry's Lightning flights had also apparently produced some serious and unpublicized results, "the crippled child who was caused days of terror; and an old woman thinking that the boom was her sick husband falling out of bed; a young woman spilling a cup of hot tea over a baby; a scientist having six weeks' work destroyed in an instant."

The boom tests provided Wiggs with a field day. Until the Lightnings flew over London, the movement had been muddling along. Now the torrent of letters in the press, the scare stories, and the minister's statements had enabled him to dash into action.

He appeared on BBC television to complain about the unfair way in which the ministry had "rigged" the tests, with only three telephone lines for public reaction. He drew attention to the organization's existence by letters in the heavyweight press. On July 13 he pointed out to author Pamela Hansford Johnson and actor Sir Alec Guinness that the Anti-Concorde Project was founded by "hundreds of people including scientists, artists, businessmen, civil servants, farmers, housewives, professors, M.P.s, etc., who are concerned and alarmed at the efforts being made to develop supersonic aircraft."

Soon Wiggs was receiving sackfuls of letters at his Letchworth home. Membership of the Anti-Concorde Project rose from a few hundred to over a thousand supporters. A regular flow of funds was organized with some people contributing up to £30 a month by bankers' order. Eventually the group's annual income was to reach about £5,000 a year. With new resources Wiggs was able to become the full-time organizer of the project, employing a secretary and an assistant. Like all good dissenters, he organized his communications thoroughly, sending round information sheets duplicated on a Gestetner machine so ancient that he admitted it should have been in the science museum. Some of his new funds were spent on a modern electronic copier, which dramatically improved the efficiency of the organization. The endless circulation of material to members of Parliament, opinion-formers, and committed journalists became one of the strongest weapons in Wiggs' armory.

In a clever approach Wiggs began to plan an advertisement campaign that would have done credit to Madison Avenue, and started to prepare a pamphlet on all aspects of the SST. His most significant move was to make contact with similar organizations abroad. By far the most important was the American "Citizens' League Against the Sonic Boom," set up by a concerned Harvard scientist, Dr. William Shurcliff, on 9 March 1967. This group was incensed at the attitude of the American aerospace industry toward the sonic boom. Unlike in Britain, the military-industrial complex in the United States was far more powerful and influential. Aided by his sister and Dr. John Edsall, professor of biochemistry at Harvard, Shurcliff recruited many members of the Harvard scientific community for his new Citizens' League. Their integrity was important in governing the initial approach to campaigning, which started with a $200 magazine advertisement. "From the start," recalled Shurcliff, "I and the other members made it clear that we must stick very close to the pedestrian truth. I was to indulge in no colorful writings, no rudeness, and I was to document all major statements." Very soon Shurcliff and his colleagues were face to face with the most powerful public relations organizations in the world, hired to protect the aerospace industry. From their own homes regular mailings to press, TV, and radio across the United States kept editors and broadcasters supplied with a constant stream of information, boom maps, and facts damaging to the SST. Shurcliff's league lobbied Congress, appeared on the media, and were primed with remarkably well-researched and detailed evidence to produce before congressional committees.

The link between Shurcliff and Wiggs meant that the super-sonic transport would be attacked globally. There was a continuous pooling of information between the two countries. It was realized by the astute academic thinkers that if either the Boeing or Concorde were canceled, there might be no supersonic civil operations. Would the Americans ever allow a European SST to fly into the United States if their own aircraft had been canceled for any good reason? Would the Europeans allow Boeing to succeed if their own Concorde were abandoned? The attack on the Boeing could be executed by an attack on Concorde, and vice-versa. The anti-SST groups saw it was essential to widen the attack to include the concept of an SST, wherever it existed. Since there were so many unknowns about supersonic aircraft flying so high and so fast, it would be possible to raise every new technical breakthrough as a frightening issue. What would happen to the rarified upper atmosphere once Concorde came into service? Would there be sufficient oil reserves to meet the apparently voracious demands of the supersonic? Could the boom kill people? The scientific supporters of Wiggs and Shur-cliff were ideally set up to circulate the smallest scrap of scientific information which could undermine the supersonic. Obscure reports and theses were scanned for any phenomena which could make a good press story.

One man who quickly perceived the political value of the environmental attack against the supersonic airliner was Senator William Proxmire. Representing the farming state of Wisconsin, Proxmire had always been convinced that the supersonic transport was a gigantic folly and waste of taxpayers' money. With his mania for the open-air life and physical fitness, Proxmire had been regarded as "some kind of nut" by the hard-drinking aerospace lobby. They were soon talking in different tones as the senator began to reveal himself to be a highly skilled politician. They began to wonder which supersonic transport would be hit, the one in Europe or the one taking shape in Seattle.

Daily Express

"You've got to admit, gentlemen, I've avenged Agincourt, Blenheim, Trafalgar and now Waterloo!"

13

Roll-out and Recrimination

It could have been a garden party except that the temperature was eight degrees below freezing, and a thin powdering of snow lay over Blagnac airfield. Chic air hostesses from customer airlines were trying to keep cheerful in front of a thousand guests, as an icy wind whipped over Toulouse, freezing their exposed legs. Ministers, top civil servants, and journalists from both sides of the Channel gathered to watch the ceremonial roll-out. The first airframe was complete and the aircraft could be moved from one hangar to another for completion. It was the very first prototype, smaller than the production aircraft, but it was a day to celebrate for the Republic of France and the Anglo-French design team. Jean Chamant, the French minister of transport, spared none of the Gaullist rhetoric; he spoke for over an hour, making his listeners feel that they had been dragged through an Arctic survival course. When Britain's turn came, Anthony Wedgwood Benn was mercifully short, and with typical English understatement he said, "Britain, like France, has a great stake in Concorde. Our years of cooperation have only been marred by one disagreement. Up till now we have never been able to agree as to how Concorde should be spelled. I have decided to resolve this myself. From now on the British Concorde will also be spelled with an *E*." It was a gesture calculated to delight the French and infuriate Whitehall civil servants, who for years had insisted on omitting the final *E* on all British memoranda. "The letter *E* symbolizes many things," Wedgwood Benn continued. "*E* stands for excellence, for England, for Europe and for the Entente Cordiale." As his words echoed over the frozen tarmac there were many Englishmen pleased to see their minister scoring a few points off the French. There were so many tricolors that anybody could be forgiven for thinking the whole thing a French occasion. Britain was represented by one solitary Union Jack that even looked homemade. The Royal Air Force band, flown over for the occasion, thumped out a rousing "Marseillaise" but "God Save the Queen," played by the French, was almost unrecognizable to British ears. The strange rendering was charitably attributed to the cold weather. After the national anthems, the two ministers cut the symbolic red, white, and blue tape. The long hangar doors slowly parted and the slender white form of 001 was towed across the apron like a moth emerging from a chrysalis. It was a moment of considerable emotion. After five years of argument, threats, and solid labor, the tangible symbol of the Anglo-French agreement was there for the world to see. For the French it was phoenix resurgent; for the British a visible return on their capital.

But would the production aircraft ever be rolled out to fanfares and champagne? Suddenly, at the end of the ceremony, as the guests drifted into the now empty hangar to thaw out on hard liquor, John Stonehouse, Wedgwood Benn's second in command, responsible for aviation, took a surprised Jean Chamant by the arm and whisked him into a small office for informal and desperately urgent discussions. Three weeks earlier, after a long and costly struggle, Britain had been forced to devalue the pound. The Wilson government had fought resolutely to maintain the value of sterling, borrowing vast sums from international banks. Economic expansion had been stifled, the loyalty of the Labour party stretched to its limit, but now the decks were to be ruthlessly cleared to take advantage of the pound's new value. Painful measures involving drastic cuts in public expenditure were under review by the chancellor, Roy Jenkins. A severe scrutiny of policy in all departments of state was under way so that resources could be shifted away from domestic consumption to exports. The remnants of the British Empire would now be wound up with troops coming home from bases east of Suez. Every penny spent by the government would be scrutinized, with Concorde inevitably attracting the maximum amount of attention. Once again there was speculation in the press that it would be axed.

The decision could go any way and it was important for the two ministers to discover the lengths to which France would go in defense of Concorde. Would it be 1964 all over again, if Britain sought to escape from the treaty? The meeting with Chamant was an embarrassing meeting. After the first difficult moments, to the surprise of the British, there was a thaw. Chamant admitted that he too was worried about the endlessly rising bill. The French ministère des finances actively disliked the supersonic project. Although Chamant was not specifically committed, Wedgwood Benn and Stonehouse came away with the strong belief that France would no longer regard the treaty as binding, once the research and development stage was complete. If Britain decided that prospects for Concorde were dim once the prototype was completed, then she could honorably withdraw. The meeting also paved the way for an agreement whereby both governments established objectives for the remainder of the development and production program. The manufacturers knew that they could no longer rely on unconditional French support. Sir George Edwards, managing director of BAC, had good reason to feel vulnerable and lonely. The Labour party had canceled TSR-2, and the scars had yet to heal. At least a Concorde prototype now existed, but putting the plane into production would require further major funding. Only the British and French governments could find this money, and their relations were hardly good after the collapse once again of British Common Market initiatives in the face of de Gaulle's uncompromising attitude. From now on, Sir George knew that the manufacturers would be working with "a loaded gun at their backs."

Everybody braced themselves for the chancellor's axe. On New Year's Eve 1967, the *Sunday Times* observed, "The general pall of doubt and uncertainty is by no means evenly spread. It hangs a good deal more thickly over the heads of some industries, companies, and individuals than others, as Sir George Edwards of the British Aircraft Corporation, Sir Giles Guthrie of BOAC, and other worried men of Britain's aircraft industry are no doubt aware." Even the Common Market case was fading as the British prime minister realized that too much effort was going into the delicate footwork "when the dance-hall proprietor had already made it clear that there was going to be no dance."

It was unlikely that the European cause would save Concorde this time. Relations with France had sunk to a depressingly low ebb in 1967, with de Gaulle's "velvet veto" of Wilson's attempt to enter the EEC. Wilson's visit to the European capitals of "the Six" had confirmed that the aging general still held the key to Europe. But his attempts to persuade de Gaulle to allow Britain entry on a proprietary right of technological cooperation, in which projects like Concorde would obviously play a key part, gained little success. In front of the Eurovision cameras at the Council for Europe Wilson had made a strong declaration of faith in Europe, rejecting "an industrial helotry under which we in Europe produce only the conventional apparatus of a modern economy while becoming increasingly dependent on American business for the sophisticated apparatus which will call the industrial tune in the '70s and '80s." De Gaulle approved these sentiments, but they did not budge him from his firmly held view that Britain, with her special relationship with the United States, would only act as the agent of America inside the Common Market. In spite of the British government's formal application to join the EEC under Article 237, it was still "Non."

For the British, the technological entente had begun to wear thin. The Anglo-French swing-wing fighter was canceled to the regret and suspicion of the British aircraft industry. The companies were convinced that this ambitious project had been canceled to please Marcel Dassault, de Gaulle's friend and France's leading planemaker, who had produced a rival all-French swing wing.

The Concorde itself did not escape the atmosphere of recrimination between the two nations.

While the press speculated about the chances of Concorde ever being allowed to continue, there were serious technical problems behind the scenes, with an impasse over the predictions of the airframe contractors. The problem was that the proposed design of the production airplanes had been due to be frozen into final form by the end of April 1967. A crucial report ordered on the express instructions of Prime Minister Wilson had forecast a massive weight problem for the aircraft. Concorde was expected to be more than five thousand pounds overweight. This was disastrous for its operational performance and some way had to be found of "sweating" this off. The designers were confident that they could master the problem by redesigning engine bays, door frames, and using lighter alloys on bulkheads. Pound by pound, the weight had to be saved. The civil servants were skeptical, and so, to the anger of the engineers, said one, "It was a question of our word against theirs. The airframe contractors reckoned everything would sort itself out. We didn't and we weren't prepared to argue." The civil servants threatened that unless immediate steps were taken to bring the weight down they would consider making recommendations to the government to abandon the whole project.

The designers went back to their slide rules and came up with a solution: a redesign of the entire rear end of the engines. In some ways the British team saw this as a victory over the French. They had always thought that the petal-shaped French nozzle was "the second most complicated orifice known to man." The redesign was perhaps the most crucial technical decision since the project was started. If the new nozzle did not work, Concorde would cease to be an economic proposition for any airline. Payload would be so reduced that the heavier plane would either have to sacrifice its Atlantic range or cut down on the number of passengers it carried. This would push up Concorde's fares to an unacceptable level. The pressure on Dr. Strang, Filton's technical director, was intense. "We had poor moments, but it was really a question of whether we could see the light at the end of the tunnel. Whether it was five feet or five inches wide." Fortunately for Concorde, the light got brighter.

The redesign was engineered with the help of a large United States company, Rohr Industries, which would make the new rear end, and the Concorde Directing Committee heaved a sigh of relief. Concorde was saved, but the development bill had risen once more. As the Concorde Directing Committee and the two government departments on each side of the Channel wrangled about spending, another problem appeared to sour relations between the British and French.

On January 19, the French manufacturers admitted to being unable to keep the original deadline for first flight. Jean Chamant leaked his excuse to the French press. The blame was laid fairly and squarely on Rolls-Royce, because, claimed Chamant, two of the four Olympus 593 engines had not been delivered. There was an immediate riposte from the British engine company, pointing out that the engines were already in Toulouse waiting to be installed in 001. Chamant humbly retracted his statement, but this time hit out at a long list of subcontractors who had not come up to scratch. By some remarkable coincidence, they all turned out to be British. Singled out for special condemnation was Boulton Paul, manufacturer of the power-control systems which operate the rudder- and wing-control surfaces.

The "Boulton Paul Affair" became an interminable dispute which still rankles. It was the best-known example of how collaboration does not work. The British company had been involved in an acrimonious dispute to win the contract for the important flying control equipment. The French dearly wanted this contract, and there were rumors that de Gaulle had personally promised it to Marcel Dassault. Britain, however, insisted on the contract, but the wrangle did not stop there. The French wanted minor, time-consuming modifications, and they even insisted on taking the equipment apart and putting it back together again before they agreed to use it.

The British company had warned the French that all these changes would delay the first flight fixed for the end of February 1968. But the French wanted to keep to schedule and refused to put the date back. Work on the American SST was proceeding apace in Seattle, and the British and French needed every minute of lead time. When the flight had to be pulled back, the recriminations were extremely bitter. Politically, the French also wanted to stop the British government levering themselves out of the undertaking by using technical failure as an excuse. Any faults had to be laid firmly at Britain's door.

The Boulton Paul argument revealed weaknesses in the Concorde subcontracting arrangements. Under the terms of the treaty, both sides were to be given an equal share of the work allocated by the Concorde Directing Committee on which both countries had representatives carefully balancing the interests of both industries. The main contractors, BAC and Sud Aviation, had to accept tenders from a pre-selected list and finally submit three alternatives to the joint technical committee. This committee of civil servants evaluated tenders and recommended a supplier. It was only natural that the need to divide the workload and use particular factories for political reasons meant that the final choice of suppliers did not always correspond with the wishes of the design team. This occurred in the case of the special glass for the aircraft's windows. Originally, British Pilkington purchased the rights to a new formula of toughened glass made by Corning Glass Corporation of America. Because of the French insistence on an equal division of work, the Concorde Directing Committee allocated the windows to France. The French Pilkington Company had to make a fresh purchase of the patent rights and start from scratch.

The pressure to axe Concorde rose rapidly in the post-devaluation crisis of 1968, but Concorde by now was a major industry, embracing four main contractors—BAC, Aerospatiale, SNECMA, and Rolls-Royce. A large number of factories, ranging from Preston in Lancashire to Marignane near Marseilles, were working nonstop on the project. The huge test facilities at Farnborough in Hampshire and Courbevoie, near Paris, were all committed to the enterprise. Eight hundred subcontractors were employed on avionics, undercarriage, hydraulics, radio, and air conditioning. Even American industry was involved with work subcontracted to companies like Stresskin. A huge mesh of computer links, communication lines, and transportation formed an infrastructure for the building of Concorde. The task of transporting thousands of pieces of airframe and equipment by road and air often exasperated the engineers. "It would have been difficult to contrive a more impractical way of building an airplane," said one. But it was an immense achievement.

It was also beginning to have an effect on British industry as a whole. In the early days, the production skills existing in the United States were simply not available in Europe. Gradually, however, the standards began to rise, until even the Americans began to seek information from British firms. "We know the quality of technology in the States," said George Gedge, then Filton's production director. "We used to go round companies and say to them, 'You are twenty years behind the time, mate. When you've pulled your socks up we'll come and talk to you.' As a result of this blunt treatment many did pull their socks up, and a number of shotgun marriages were arranged."

The cabinet discussions of Chancellor of the Exchequer Roy Jenkins' program of cuts on domestic and overseas expenditure took place during January 1968. It was a tense and long drawn-out affair with endless newspaper speculation on the likelihood of cabinet resignations. The decisions were bitterly fought. On Wilson's own admission, "The task of getting it through the cabinet without sensational resignations was the most formidable task I had attempted in over three years of government." On January 16 Britain was informed that there would be reductions of £300 million in the 1968–69 estimates and £416 million in those for 1969–70. Britain would pull back all her overseas forces by the end of 1971. There would be no bases outside Europe and the Mediterranean, apart from Hong Kong. The fifty F-111 aircraft on order from the United States would be canceled. In Social Security, there were to be charges for prescriptions—a deep affront to the Labour left wing, who believed in a free National Health Service. And, perhaps most agonizing of all for a Labour government, the school-leaving age would be kept to fifteen for another five years. Jenkins promised to follow these cuts with a severe budget reducing private spending. Labour members were up in arms. Why had so many sacrifices been made and yet Concorde remained untouched?

The reasons for Concorde's miraculous survival were threefold.

First, the aircraft was still a ticket of sorts to Europe. In spite of the hostility of de Gaulle, Britain could hardly renege on her promise that there should be a European technological community within months of proposing it. Concorde was a pacesetter for this and gave Britain the right to call on the others to join her in building an independent European economy. The argument had to be taken seriously, and it was one which might outflank the French. France could hardly claim that Britain was not a European power when she was investing so much in the biggest technological venture she had ever undertaken.

Second, Wedgwood Benn was able to argue in cabinet that Concorde was now in such an advanced stage, with so much invested, that the plane should be allowed to prove itself. As he said, "Very few people realize that in that period at about every six months we went over everything, particularly Concorde, but by this time it was becoming clear that the only sensible thing was to go forward and stay where you were." Prototype 001 was due to fly at almost any time, and because of the delays in Toulouse, the British prototype 002 was almost ready too. "Concorde survived," according to Wedgwood Benn, "not on the basis of emotional argument, but on the most elaborate calculations of money spent, investment to come, likely returns, likely sales, and the costs of bringing in foreign currency. Another important argument was what damage do you do, if you appear to be somebody who can never follow anything through."

Yet the overriding reason for the escape of Concorde, as admitted by even the most hostile ministers, was the effect of a cancellation on the country's morale. The country had endured a difficult and humiliating time, with recurrent economic crises, devaluation, and a drastic slide in British prestige. At least Concorde was a symbol of British resurgence. As one anti-Concorde minister said: "We could not pull out east of Suez *and* cancel Concorde. It would be too anti-British."

Anti-Concorde ministers could at least hold one grain of comfort. Concorde might kill itself. A series of exacting flight tests lay ahead of the prototypes, and if they proved that there were technical snags or any doubt about the safety or viability of supersonic flight, then the plane would be canceled. The anti-Concorde lobby prayed that the plane would fail to meet the exacting conditions agreed on at Toulouse on the day of the roll-out. They expected that the Concorde would, like the albatross of the Ancient Mariner, miraculously drop from the neck of the British taxpayer. In this the British were not alone.

Before the immense 4,000-hour test-flight schedule started, Concorde suffered a long and dramatic delay, this time because of the French. In early May 1968, the French students of the Sorbonne took to the streets in the opening stages of a near revolution which eventually led to the retirement of the general himself. Their rebellion against the stuffy Gaullist regime coincided with deep discontent in the French. A two-month strike, started ironically by Sud Aviation workers in Nantes, stopped France. Toulouse, always a center of strong socialistic groups, struck and progress on 001 halted. It seemed a slightly forlorn symbol of the ancient regime. It was not until the autumn that the plant was fully back at work, pushing to catch up on the long-delayed schedule for Concorde's first flight.

CONCORDE DIPLOMACY

Prime Minister Harold Wilson and Foreign Secretary George Brown visit de Gaulle in 1967, in a new attempt to break the French veto of Britain's Common Market entry. For the General, Concorde was a test of Britain's good faith.

The rollout of the first completed Concorde, prototype 001, at Toulouse to tunes of Anglo-French solidarity.

THE SWING-WING MONSTER

Holden W. Withington, project leader on the Boeing supersonic project. Finding the problems of the swing wing insurmountable, he resorted to the more familiar delta design.

The imaginative design of the Boeing 2707-200 swing wing proved too much even for Boeing's know-how.

Bill Magruder, former test pilot, head of the unsuccessful Lockheed SST project, and a firm believer in the delta wing concept, was to find himself in charge of the SST at the Department of Transportation under President Nixon.

Denver Post

"Perhaps if we widened the wings, lengthened the tail, shortened the nose . . ."

14

The Lady or the Tiger?

In January 1968, William Shurcliff opened fire on the Boeing SST as his Citizens' League Against the Sonic Boom began to step up its campaign. The Harvard scientist extrapolated the costs and disturbance from NASA information on the St. Louis Operation Bongo. The bangs over the midwestern city had resulted in 5,000 complaints and $58,648 had been paid in compensation for damage to property. If this experience were repeated all over the land of the Wright brothers, the Citizens' League maintained that life in America would be lived against an almost continuous background of distant thunder. The 150 supersonic airliners to be built by Boeing would create no less than 75 million square miles of boom carpet. Since the whole of the United States was only 3

143

million miles square, this meant everyplace would be boomed an average of 25 times a day with an estimated damage bill of a mere $3 million a day. In typical Shurcliff style, the report went on to add, "Obviously the total harassment would be far greater than this $3 million a day suggests. We have not considered here the time wasted by home owners in assessing damage, filling out claim forms, consulting with lawyers. Nor have we considered the horror and fear that many persons may experience; shattered windows can be replaced, shattered nerves cannot." Just to rub in these Malthusian predictions of doom, Shurcliff added that 1,200 SSTs were expected to be in service by 1990.

If Boeing was slow to refute Shurcliff's figures, it is not surprising. The chairman, William Allen, was beginning to doubt whether his famous company would ever be able to produce even one of the 1,200 predicted SSTs. As *Fortune* reported,

> Boeing Co.'s attempt to build a supersonic airliner has turned out to be the most bafflingly complicated job of research and development in the history of American industry—and it may end up the costliest. The undertaking has come to demand engineering resources, human and inanimate, second only to those going into the national effort to put a man on the moon. During the five years that Boeing has been engaged in this task on a significant scale—the last two at maximum effort—the company has run up 30,000 hours of research on eight different wind tunnels scattered across the nation, 80,000 hours of analysis on computers that include the largest in existence and a total of 8½ million engineering man-hours altogether—all this to the end of reducing the Boeing vision of the SST engineering drawings from which the shop can begin to fabricate a prototype.

In two years of desperate effort Boeing tried to make the concept of the swing wing work, against a background of political and governmental interference which was more characteristic of European than United States industry. In an increasingly difficult political situation over funding, the FAA was forced to adopt a firm line with Boeing for the fulfillment of their contract deadlines. The contract with the Federal Aviation Administration was extremely demanding. The United States government was determined that taxpayers' money would be carefully spent, and two hard-nosed generals—McKee and Maxwell Taylor—were sitting at the top of the FAA monitoring the

SST program. The generals stipulated that the American prototype, unlike the Concorde and TU-144 projects, should have the
performance of production machines. It was an unfortunate
measure of American over-confidence to try to get a revolutionary aircraft, the most ambitious ever built, *right*, the first time.

Under the FAA instructions, it would be impossible to "get a
machine flying," then take care of any snags before going into
production, although astronomic sums were at stake, and nobody
could afford to make expensive mistakes. Even with the billion
dollars of federal funding for prototype research and development, Boeing realized that they would need as much again to
fund final production, which would be more than the whole
corporation was worth.

The design for what was planned to be the largest, fastest, and
most impressive aircraft ever built demanded an immense engineering effort. The supersonic giant would carry almost as many
passengers as a jumbo jet. The FAA had also requested a higher
cruise speed than either the European or Russian plane which,
although good for America's image, meant that Withington's
team would be forced beyond the state of the art.

Apart from the swing wings, the projected cruise speed of
1,800 miles per hour would bring a skin temperature of more
than 500 degrees fahrenheit (260 degrees centigrade) and dynamic pressures of 1,300 pounds per square foot on wing surfaces.
These were already common on military aircraft, which had
already been built of steel and titanium to cope with such
stresses of temperature and pressure. These could wreck any
plane made of lighter aluminum alloys. Titanium had become the
glamor metal of the supersonic age, and Boeing was no stranger
to its use, but making a large airframe out of the metal presented
a challenge. Vast heat-treatment ovens would have to be built
since the tough metal had to be formed at a high temperature;
gold-plated cobalt drills had to be designed to mill out the
complex shapes; and new techniques of stainless-steel honey-
combing were required to provide both the stiffness and lightness
required for the airframe. All these problems, the corporation
knew from previous experience, could be tackled—given the
necessary resources.

The 1,800 mph airframe was only one breathtaking problem

which paled before the technical problems posed by the swing wing. The crucial pivots which supported the wing sections were to be mounted on titanium bearings a yard in diameter. The wings would be activated by giant screw-jacks hydraulically operated by three mechanisms. The weight of this gear alone was estimated at over 40,000 pounds. Theoretically this should have been compensated by higher efficiency in the variable wing.

There were predictions of trouble. Some perceptive engineers warned that the pivots could not carry the whole stress of the wings at supersonic speeds. The retort was that the whole stress of the Golden Gate Bridge was held at four points where the cables were anchored. In strictly engineering terms Boeing was right, but Withington found his team confronting a multiplying weight problem. It was not only that the wings were heavy but also they had to be structurally stiffened to support the swing-wing mechanism. Weight is a big headache for all aircraft designers, and supersonic aircraft are by their very nature far more susceptible.

In an SST, the weight problems are magnified, because for any given weight of airframe, the payload is only half that achieved in a subsonic. On the Concorde and Boeing SST, the payload was only 8–9 percent of the gross weight, compared to 15 percent on a 707 and 20 percent on a 747. The margin for error in weight on a supersonic is only half that of a subsonic. A 3 percent or more error in design will rob the final plane of more than 15 percent of its vital payload. Boeing's swing wing, now designated the 2707-100, had serious weight problems from the outset. In the spring of 1967, as Withington's designs were recycled through the wind tunnels and computers by his staff, new problems of stability and control were emerging daily. Not only had the critical hinge to be strengthened, but its hydraulics and associated gear had to also be reinforced. Once this had been achieved, tests showed that the wings had problems of flexibility; more weight had to be introduced to improve their structural integrity. To overcome the problems of control, small canard wings were added to the front of the fuselage. As *Fortune* later graphically put it, "The propensity of the design to put on weight, like a compulsive eater, was beginning to trouble him. The heavier the structure grew, the more fuel would have to be taken aboard for the engines to burn in order to lift the additional load, and this would give yet another upward twist to the spiral."

It had become clear to Boeing in 1967 that the engineering problems were so complex that the prototype's target flight date would have to be rescheduled. The date to which the company was committed by its FAA contract was "not later than 1970." Withington knew this was "clear out of sight." The White House saw it differently. President Johnson was determined to keep public confidence in the project. He threw his presidential weight behind the enterprise, arguing, "Although the promise of the supersonic transport is great, the program still carries high technical risk and financial costs. Industry's willingness to share those risks is a clear sign of its confidence in the program. . . . With a successful program, the government will recover its investment with interest. The taxpayers of this nation will benefit."

The Boeing team knew that they had only one chance of avoiding a painful public embarrassment. The aircraft weight limitations in the FAA contract would have to be eased. Otherwise, the project's risk to Boeing shareholders' money would become unacceptable, and the company's finances put at risk.

On 23 June 1967, Withington flew to Washington to put the problem to General Maxwell at the FAA. Although Maxwell's Tennessee "country boy" manner was never far from the surface, those in the industry knew that this concealed a tough mind, formed at Princeton and with long experience of command. Withington found that Maxwell was far from receptive to Boeing's request for a liberalization of the weight parameters. Withington's aircraft had to prove the reliability of the SST's economics, as well as its aerodynamics. Maxwell pointed out, "You can argue, as you have, that the safe way to play it out is to prove first of all that the design can operate safely and reliably at Mach 2.7 and count on fixing up the excess weight later, one way or another. But the prototype has the additional responsibility of proving the economics of the production plane, and a prototype too big to operate from existing terminals won't do anything for that half of the exercise." To the Boeing team, the implications were ominous. They had to get it right the first time; there was no opportunity for including improvements in later models, which is how the Concorde and most aircraft programs in history have worked. For a project as sophisticated as the SST, with its swing wings, high speed, and critical economic demands, it looked like a recipe for the impossible. Withington and his team flew back to Seattle, revised their designs to include the canard wings, and called the new version the Dash-200.

The bright new ideas were no solution. No sooner had the calculations of the Dash-200 design been put through the computer than the Seattle team found that the weight situation had actually deteriorated. The new prototype would be 25 percent overweight. It would be unable to carry passengers! In a last-minute attempt to salvage the design, Withington appealed for another six months to "sweat off" the excess weight and for another margin of increase on their contract figure. Maxwell came back with a deadline of 15 January 1968 for them to prove their case and gave them a target of 675,000 pounds. At that stage, Withington's calculations showed an all-up weight of 750,000 pounds.

Boeing was warned that the new contract conditions had to be complied with if the prototype was to be built. The logical answer was to construct a prototype to test the design and to sort out the aerodynamic problems before a production version was built. The reasons were largely political, as explained by Dr. Bisplinghoff, head of M.I.T. aeronautics department and key advisor to the FAA: "If the airlines are one day to operate an SST they and the manufacturers will have to raise a great deal of capital to build the plane. That kind of money will be forthcoming only if the capital market is persuaded on the basis of the prototype's performance that the production plane will carry a money-earning payload."

Thirty-seven and a half tons now stood between Withington and success. With an energy and determination described as "gut splitting," Boeing threw everything into the drive to sweat off the excess weight. Withington's staff went over the design, literally rivet by rivet in search of ways to save weight without prejudicing safety. At the end of the "sweatbox" operation, the Dash-200 design lost 23,000 pounds, but 52,000 surplus pounds still remained. Unfortunately, a good third of this was at the expense of passenger comfort with small seats, less galley space, smaller gangways—even the lavish TV sets disappeared. However good this was for the engineers, Boeing salesmen knew that the airlines would rebel. Just as Concorde had faced the same dilemma and the engineers had capitulated to the customers, so Boeing would be forced to do the same.

Withington now began to look for a technical miracle. In a sweeping decision—with three months to go to the deadline—Boeing committed a new team to rework the complete design, and a new top-level "think tank" to assess its chances. Through this unparalleled concentration of technological competence, the awful realization finally began to seep through: the design was an impossibility according to the parameters demanded by the FAA. One of the Boeing team recalled, "The more we came to know, the less well the things worked out for us. Instead of entering a situation where the problems began to offset one another, the problems were actually compounding. When they should have started to converge, they continued to diverge. They were beginning to point more and more in the same direction, to a conclusion that we had been trying to hold off—namely that achieving the payload range goals in the Dash-200 was unlikely unless the design moved up to a much higher loading than the contract contemplated, or unless some change in the configuration changes were made."

In December, with the deadline only weeks away, Bill Allen, chairman of Boeing, told Withington, "We've got to decide for the lady or the tiger." The corporation's pride was at stake and there were nasty rumors that the enemies of the SST had caught wind of the problems and would move to persuade Congress to kill the project.

For Withington it was grim. This proud and famous aero-engineer now "had to go and tell the world Boeing screwed it." Two years had been lost, but mighty Boeing was not prepared to confess its failure publicly without putting up an alternative. They requested Maxwell to grant a year for review of the situation and the submission of alternative designs. This painful decision had been reached after a grand meeting of all the technical executives who had been involved. It was a watershed at Boeing. "Several of these ordinarily reserved executives momentarily lost their calm," as *Fortune* reported. "Profound differences of technical opinion were argued out in detail, verbally and mathematically on the blackboard. It was an extraordinary exhibition of the freedom of expression that had given Boeing engineering its reputation." When that meeting broke up, "the hard facts were on the table." Boeing would opt for a new, fixed-wing design, just like the British, French, and Russians. It was time for the "boys in the back room" to make their appearance.

Seattle was apprehensive when General Maxwell arrived in February 1968 to hear the hard facts for himself. Boeing had passed the deadline, and the general warned them that they were now in danger of being charged with default. Yet with so much time lost there was little Washington could do. It would take too long to revive the Lockheed design, and resources had already been committed in Seattle. In April, Maxwell agreed to a new Boeing design. Fortunately, although time had been lost, no production work had been undertaken. The problems were still on the drawing board. A new and even tougher contract was drawn up in which Boeing would hazard $45 million of their own money if they failed.

Once the new chance had been bought, Withington ordered the team who had been working on the fixed-wing design to come up front. At the same time, he set up a final review of the swing-wing design—in the course of which Boeing would spend half as much again in engineering man-hours as it had on the original 707 design operation. Even at that stage, more than 4,000 engineers were searching for a viable solution to the SST.

For all their travails, Boeing suddenly received touching encouragement from an unexpected source. Jean-Jacques Servan-Schreiber, the French radical politician and editor of *L'Express*, rushed into print with a strong case for the Boeing swing wing and a condemnation of the Concorde. In his book, *Le Défi Américain*, Concorde was dismissed as the last of an old breed, doomed to obsolescence by the titanium and steel giant with swing wings. Servan-Schreiber claimed, "On two essential points—use of an entirely new metal to crack the heat barrier and the swing wing to change speed—the superiority of the conception is so dramatic that we have to ask why the Europeans never came to grips with it. We could have mastered both these problems. It was a question of vision, planning, decision making, and risk taking." He even quoted a French engineer as saying, "If they had told us to build a swing-wing plane, we could have done it. But we would have been scared to death all the time we were doing it. To be honest, we did everything we could to avoid it." He was wrong.

Lockheed, Satre, and Russell were right, in their engineering judgment, to stay within the "state of the art." Withington had certainly found the swing wing "more difficult" but hardly "more rewarding." As the swing wing was finally fluttering to the ground under computer analysis, against the fixed-wing alternatives, Boeing confessed: "We never succeeded in integrating the design. That is, we could never fit the engines, landing gear, and the wing pivots together and still make the weight requirements." To Withington, it is almost an article of faith that the swing-wing concept must work someday, when the right structural materials are available "to figure out how to make it work." Realizing that this day would be a long time off—probably in the 1980s—by the autumn of 1968 the Boeing team had concentrated its efforts on a design that they had originally debated in 1963. It was for a delta wing with a tail, which, claimed Boeing, would make it less noisy than the tail-less aircraft. Designated the Dash-300—the proposals were worked out in detail and shown to General Maxwell. Struck by its simplicity compared to the swing wing, he indicated his approval with "Why, it's pure vanilla."

On 8 December 1968 Boeing finally admitted publicly that its painful flirtation with the swing wing was over. Plans were announced for a new design, the Dash-300. Lockheed, Boeing's "friends down south," felt cheated; "it was just like our original design." It would carry 234 passengers, announced Withington, and was designed "with the pilot in mind." He later confessed that "the airlines were relieved, that they had always been concerned with the complexities of variable sweep." Indeed, some of the critics had been unkind enough to point out that the earlier version of the SST required a "test pilot with a doctorate" to fly it. Withington answered them that the new plane "had been subjected to Boeing tameness criteria."

"Pure vanilla" was the new catchword, but Boeing's admission of failure marked a significant defeat for American technology.

Overnight, public relations machinery was switched in favor of the fixed-wing design. The public and some congressmen became confused. The giant yellow plywood model that had been waggling its by now outmoded wings to the Muzak was towed out of the Seattle plant and deposited without ceremony on an exclusive $2 million West Coast junk pile. Altogether, "Boeing's Ordeal" had cost more than $200 million in research expenses, 80,000 hours on computers, and 8.5 million man-hours of design time. There was not a single piece of tangible airplane to show for it, and the taxpayer began to wonder what on earth this project was all about. The vultures began to gather over the corpse of the swing-wing Boeing 2707-200; the time was at hand to strike against the whole SST program.

If Christmas 1968 was a gloomy time in Seattle, celebrations were planned in the heart of Russia, on the other side of the world. The snow had been cleared from the runway at Zhukovsky airfield outside Moscow, and groups of fur-coated technicians, Aeroflot officials, government bureaucrats, and Red Air Force officers waited patiently as the test-pilot hero of the Soviet Union, Edward Vagonovich Elyan, came to the end of his long operational checks on the flight deck of the TU-144 prototype.

In the crowd, wearing a tall fur hat, was the still burly, but aged, figure of Andrei Tupolev. The cameramen focused on the great white bird swinging at the end of the runway in a shimmering haze, the heat from its jets momentarily thawing the frozen group. The Tupolev teams had worked fast and furiously. Since the Supreme Soviet had sanctioned entry into the supersonic race, Pyotr Dementiev, the minister of aircraft production, had made sure that there was no shortage of materials. Resources and manpower had been funneled into the project by GOSPLAN, the state planning committee. Much of the research and development had taken place in the Voronezh plant, located on the rich black plain southeast of Moscow.

The TU-144 had been kept a closely guarded secret. In the mind of the Kremlin, it was always possible for the aircraft to be used in a military role, and there should be no casual revelation of Soviet research and development in the Western press. There had been one or two exceptions to the rule. Sir George Edwards had been invited over to look at Tupolev's prototype in 1967, when it was under construction.

"I went pottering around the thing and talked at great length to the designers. They talked freely to me about what they had been doing, and I told them that in my view they were going to have to make two changes in the airplane. One was to shift the engines—which they later did—and the other was that they were going to have to produce more sophisticated aerodynamics on the wing." This advice was taken in good spirit by Tupolev; after all, as Sir George recalled, "I had known the old boy and his team for donkey's years. He once even offered me a job."

The workers, standing outside waiting to see the plane they had constructed take to the sky, had also been witnesses to a moving little ceremony by Britain's minister of aviation, John Stonehouse, when he had visited the Tupolev plant during a 1967 trip. After Toulouse and Filton, the minister was surprised to find the Russian factory primitive by comparison. There was the same unmistakable pterodactyl shape, but the Western observers could not escape the impression that the thick-set workers clambering all over the slender airframe were peasants straight from the steppes. The paradox was sharpened by the fact that the supersonic airliner was planned for the sophisticated jet-set market that the Russians wanted to break into. Moved by the occasion, the British minister seized the opportunity for an important address. Through an interpreter, Stonehouse made a brief speech about international friendship and cooperation, in the shadow of the TU-144. The Russians broke into spontaneous cheers. It was an intriguing incident which brought together in a few moments a British cabinet minister moved by a sense of history, Russian workers, and twentieth-century technology. Later when the Western press was trying to find out the details of his visit, Stonehouse, in a gentlemanly way, was careful not to offend his hosts by revealing any secrets about the plane.

The British and French had always been ready to return Soviet goodwill, and there had been many visits by Soviet delegations to Toulouse and Bristol. It is not surprising that the Russians were very well briefed on the Concorde's progress. They gave the impression of knowing its tiniest details of construction. On the occasional exchange visits they showed immense interest in Concorde. Once on an official trip to Toulouse, Tupolev's son, a rising star in the Soviet aircraft industry, noticed a change in Concorde. Immediately, he pulled out a tiny tape measure disguised as a key ring and, before anybody realized, he had measured one of the engine air-intakes. The director of the French plant, Bernard Dufour, was amazed. "He just pulled it out, reached up, and claque, claque . . . 'I have measured your engine air-intake. . . . I find you have increased it by nearly 8 percent,' he added with a knowing smile."

The idle gossip of the Moscow crowd was overwhelmed by the thunderous roar of the four Kuznetsov NK-144 turbofans. The needle-nose of the prototype began to move, the huge delta gathered speed, the droop of the nose rising as the air roared past. There was a glimpse of the helmeted crew on board, in full test-flight gear, as the nosewheel lifted from the runway. A second later, the undercarriage of the world's first supersonic airliner climbed into the frosty Russian sky. The sun picked out the blood-red flag on its elegant tail, and the world was left in no doubt, as the news was flashed in the press and on television, that the Soviet Union had pulled off another spectacular first.

FIRST FOR THE SOVIETS

The TU-144 on its first flight over Moscow, 31 December 1968.
After the flight, a jubilant welcome for test pilot Edward Elyan from veteran Soviet designer Andrei Tupolev.

AIRBORNE AT LAST

2 March 1969. The first Concorde flight, prototype 001, takes off from Toulouse, almost a year behind schedule.

Aerospatiale

Back on the ground, André Turcat, popular French hero and deputy mayor of Toulouse, with members of his flight crew.

Aerospatiale

"There she is!" Brian Trubshaw, chief of flight operations for BAC, who took the first British prototype 002 into the air with copilot John Cochrane.

Press Association

"You're right! It is eating ants!"

15

The Technological Austerlitz

Early-morning mist shrouded Blagnac airport on 2 March 1969. The pressmen who had arrived to report a headline story, Concorde's long-awaited first flight, settled down to hours of interminable waiting. For two frustrating days, the weather had capriciously delayed the big event, and now an east wind prevented the critical takeoff along the north-south runway, equipped with a giant nylon tennis net to catch the £12 million insurance risk, should anything go wrong. A crowd had already gathered on the roof of the air terminal. The citizens of Toulouse knew almost by telepathy when an aviation event would take place on the plateau above the city. Old men remembered how "la ville rose" had established its reputation as the most air-minded city in Europe. Just as Toulouse collected to watch the magnificent Anglo-French Concorde, one of the wonders of twentieth-century technology, prepare for flight, so people had gathered in the center of the city almost two hundred years before to watch the ascent of Montgolfier balloonists. The intrepid aviators in their cocked hats and silk stockings had sometimes provided a spectacular demonstration, especially when the gaily decorated balloon burst into flames and crashed to earth. The neat hairstyles of 1969 did not reflect the flamboyance of the eighteenth-century ladies about town who had worn the fashionable "en globe" hairstyles to remind everybody that their hearts were in the skies. Women had played an important part in fostering Toulousan interest in aeronautics. In 1805 one of the first women aviators, Madame Blanchard, rose from the city in her balloon. Moving across the roofs she was suddenly caught in a crosswind and dragged away into the countryside. Thinking quickly, she dumped her lunch of chicken and bread overboard to prevent a too rapid descent to earth. Saved by her presence of mind she drifted on and eventually landed in a small village. The inhabitants were terrified and advanced on her with muskets and staves. Suddenly, however, a cascade of silver coins fell from her skirt, and the peasants had different thoughts. The mayor arrived and sorted everything out, taking Madame Blanchard off to be "entertained with all the attention that one can expect from such a respectable man."

As the top executives of BAC and Sud Aviation waited near the same spot 150 years later, they must have hoped that no untoward incident would add to Toulouse's rich flying history.

It surprised everybody when, shortly after midday, word spread that André Turcat, Sud Aviation's test pilot, was going for the takeoff. Skeptics found it hard to believe. For months now, Concorde had been roaring up and down the Toulouse runways at full power on taxiing trials to check brakes, controls, and engines. Even as the Olympus turbojets burst into life, there were those who thought that the takeoff attempt could well end up as another routine exercise for hundreds of spectators who arrived daily at the airport. It was not until the gleaming white shape, belching black smoke, was racing across the airfield, accelerating by the second and shadowed by the photographic reconnaissance jets, that everyone sensed that the spectacular climax of seven years' work was approaching. Quite suddenly, twenty seconds after rolling, the nosewheel rose from the ground, and Concorde lifted into the air for the first time with a shattering roar. The spectators cheered over the crackling blast of the Olympus engines, blazing bright orange under full reheat.

From the moment it left the earth for a brief twenty-seven-minute flight over the spring fields of southern France, with nose and undercarriage locked down for safety, Concorde achieved a spectacular metamorphosis. It acquired a life of its own, with a popular mystique which impressed even its long-standing critics.

As André Turcat brought 001 in to land after a triumphant flight, he was feeling out the characteristics of the new plane with its thin delta and droop snoot. The people of Toulouse looked up as the elegant new shape came in over their heads to touch down with a roar. After she rolled to a halt, Henri Ziegler, president of Sud, and Sir George Edwards of BAC went forward with Brian Trubshaw to press their congratulations. It was a moving moment. They had successfully protected their dream plane against the tongues of critics and the knives of bureaucrats and had seen it fly. Now it would be that much harder to kill. Crossing the tarmac, the British team must have had some moments of regret that the "gloire" was not theirs.

For André Turcat it was a moment of exultation. He was the hero of France. The intellectual pilot—with the face of a medieval knight and the cool manner of a savant—was a native son of Marseilles. While he had flown France's most ambitious aircraft, some of the old Turcat cars built by the family firm were running the streets of "la ville rose." To the excited crowd gathered around him, Turcat said, "It flies pretty well. It was as perfect as we had expected." The press and television reaction was enormous. For the French it really was a "technological Austerlitz." The airlines were caught up in the publicity slipstream; full-page advertisements had already been booked by Pan Am to tell the world that "before long eight sleek Pan Am Concordes will be among the first to welcome you into the new age of flying."

France had shown her usual skill and panache in exploiting the publicity value of the striking new aircraft. In spite of near revolution and a devaluation of the franc, France was supporting

Concorde almost to a man. The vacillation of Britain's government, the coolness of BAC, the endless carping from the press and politicians had allowed France to take the lead, certainly in reaping the prestige and publicity value of the aircraft. Britain had agreed that France should be first to fly the first prototype, should be the first to fly through Mach 1. France would also by luck or design be the first to carry a head of state, Georges Pompidou, and also to carry journalists at twice the speed of sound. In addition, the French Concorde would be proudly shown as often as possible to the public, with a first presentation at the Paris Air Show that spring. The French prototype would be flown to South America the following year to boost French exports.

All over France there were Concorde cafés, Concorde supermarkets, and dozens of products launched with a Concorde association from shampoos to matches. Many people could be excused for thinking that Concorde was exclusively a French product, with a full-sized wooden mock-up parked at Orly, near the main terminal building, constantly reminding the world of French achievement. Such a display would embarrass the British. Even attempts to show the life-sized wooden model of Concorde in London had ended in failure. Britain had agreed to pay half the cost of the model so that it could be shipped to London after the Paris Air Show and displayed in Horse Guards Parade. Sud Aviation, in spite of previous agreements to have the wooden aircraft constructed in such a way that it could be easily dismantled and shipped to England, somehow forgot the agreement. When BAC officials hopefully looked it over they discovered that the only method of moving the wooden plane to England was by barge down the Seine, across the Channel, and up the Thames. Even if this spectacular feat had been accomplished, the Ministry of Works stood ready to deny permission to use Horse Guards Parade because it could not be used for "commercial purposes."

BAC looked forward to having their share of publicity and knew they were not far behind the French. The test team were confidently completing taxiing trials on 002 at Filton, ready for the day when it would fly and bring the whole project to the point when public approval could be rallied behind Concorde, persuading a doubtful government to persevere with the program.

It was Brian Trubshaw's job to take 002 into the air on 9 April 1969. The day started badly. Watching eagerly with the TV cameras were the British minister of technology, Wedgwood Benn, determined not to be left out of the show again, Sir George Edwards, and Henri Ziegler, together with André Turcat. At the end of the Filton runway that had been made by flattening two villages in 1949 for the ill-starred Brabazon, Trubshaw started the Olympus engines. The plane was to make a fast taxi-run and, if all went well, make the first flight. But there was a snag; the reheat system which sprays fuel into the jet pipe to give added thrust failed on No. 4 engine. The engine was shut down, and Trubshaw decided to try again. This time the reheat ignited and the plane approached lift-off speed as it raced over the dip of Filton runway. The watching crowds held their breath as at 120 mph the nosewheel lifted from the tarmac. "It looks good," Trubshaw told copilot John Cochrane, and instead of braking, as he had on every other occasion, he gently eased the stick back and took Concorde 002 effortlessly into a summer sky, leaving the assembly hangars vanishing in the distance. As Trubshaw pointed 002 east and inland toward the R.A.F. airfield at Fairford, Gloucestershire, VIPs dashed by helicopter across the fifty miles of open country in time to meet the new plane as she landed. Flying at 200 mph with the droop snoot lowered, Concorde was in the air over England. For Sir George Edwards it was a considerable achievement. "This sort of event is better to look back on than to look forward to." He told the press, "I do not know of any way in which you could have had this flight five weeks after the first one unless you had the resources of the two countries behind you. I hope my successors will sell hundreds of Concordes."

On its flight from Bristol, Concorde had passed over the ancient market town of Malmesbury, where in 1065, after intense ornithological observation, a Saxon cleric strapped on homemade wings and leaped from the parapet of the church tower. The birdman sadly broke a leg, but survived the crash landing to tell people how he had experienced the fifty-foot flight to the ground. Nine hundred and four years later, the first British supersonic airliner, 002, was approaching the runway when it too had its problems; Trubshaw discovered that both radio altimeters had failed. The ex-R.A.F. bomber captain had been test flying for almost twenty-five years and possessed more than enough judgment to bring the multimillion-pound prototype in to land safely. The failure of both altimeters on the first flight was nothing compared to problems he had coped with during years of testing all kinds of military and civil jets. "In a crisis," he had said, "one becomes quite cold-bloodedly involved in just trying to save people and the airplane." In the small control room of the Fairfield Flight Test Center, everyone held their breath in a moment of tension, before the wheels struck the runway with a screech and the drogue parachute flew out to brake the machine to a halt. Television cameras brought the scene to millions of viewers, unaware of the tense drama which had just ended behind the scenes. In a spectacular seizure of public attention, the BBC regular programs were broken into to show the takeoff. For the first time, 002 had its own small share of the glamor surrounding 001. "It was wizard—a cool, calm, collected operation," was the typical comment of Trubshaw to the press.

The watching minister of technology was quick to comment, suggesting that the dramatic flight had been handled "in such a relaxed British way—something like a British cricket match— but a lot of people, including myself, will sleep more soundly tonight than during the past few days." He had good reason to feel relieved since he had announced to his colleagues in the cabinet, Parliament, BAC, Sud Aviation, and the press: "Concorde is going to prove itself. Many members of the British cabinet expected Concorde to fail the rigorous examination." "The thought was that there would be so much drag at supersonic speed that it would not be able to carry any passengers at all between Paris and New York," said one minister. The hope was that the plane would prove itself a commercial flop. If this meant waiting for a few more months of flight testing, it would be worth it. One leading cabinet critic, however, felt that Concorde was buying itself more time: "With every year that went by it became more difficult to cancel. The right moment never presented itself. Wedgwood Benn would always make the most elaborate cases for postponing the decision." The minister of technology believed it was important for the government to keep its options open, although it was useless to maintain the program under false pretenses. In his view, "One of the arguments I got accepted by my colleagues was that while it went on we must work flat out for its success. It was no use doing it in a surly manner; spending £1 million a week, this would have been absurd."

The Anti-Concorde Project had decided to step up its activities, even though many people may have felt pride as Trubshaw took 002 into the air. In February, while André Turcat had been running his engines at Toulouse and testing instruments for the first flight, readers of *The Guardian* were surprised to open their paper on a full-page advertisement by the Anti-Concorde Project. "Should the Concorde be canceled?" it cried. It then went on to make sure that every known fact hostile to the aircraft was set out without any balancing reply. The language was calm and logical; it was an extremely effective piece of propaganda. The spiraling costs were neatly inset with a chart, and on the top of the page, Wiggs had included the distinguished names he had been able to attract to his scheme. Two formidable intellectual ladies, Baroness Wotton, formerly professor of social studies at London University, and Baroness Stocks, a highly articulate member of the House of Lords, headed the list. Others included Thurston Dart, professor of music at London University, and Dr. Neville Coghill, the Oxford Anglo-Saxon expert. Also on the list was Dr. William Shurcliffe of Harvard. The advertisement warned of the sonic boom and asked why Concorde had been started, suggesting that it had been intended to get Britain into Europe, but "as this has failed, it has been continued on in order to compensate for reduction in defense work and to support an ailing and unprofitable section of the aircraft industry."

In the "voice of sweet reason" the advertisement called for informed public debate along the themes set out by Wiggs, "looking into costs, the sonic boom, airport noise, and pollution." The Anti-Concorde Project claimed that "in cooperation with responsible journalism it had contributed greatly to the development of informed public opinion that supersonic civil aviation must be stopped." The advertisement quoted two of the responsible newspapers which had never missed a chance to attack the project, *The Economist*, which called Concorde "the biggest boob of its generation," and *The Observer*, which had embarked on an all-out crusade to stop the aircraft, calling it "a monster that is certain to rank as the world's biggest commercial fiasco."

It was small wonder that the tests and flight program to which Concorde was subjected became the most discussed and analyzed aircraft program in history. The BAC Flight Test Center at Fairford became a hive of activity, with the PR men in the ministry and the head office at Filton constantly on call for the slightest whiff of trouble. Brian Trubshaw, never a man to like publicity, found the attention distasteful and almost a hindrance to the flight test program. Teams in France and Britain settled down to the long task of proving the plane, knowing that the critics were waiting to pounce. From the BAC board room, running the difficult test program in a "goldfish bowl" was likely to provide plenty of opportunities for questioning their wisdom and efficiency.

In 1969 the men building Concorde felt that they might win the battle after all. "It had certainly been pretty tiresome from time to time to think that Concorde was about to have its bloody neck cut, but now it was up to us to make our contribution and to get on with the job of making people eat their words," said one of the test pilots. It was in this atmosphere of grim determination to make the scheme succeed that the flight test crews got down to the long and arduous job of proving that Concorde could do what its designers claimed in the biggest single test program ever undertaken for a commercial plane. Only after a flight program of more than forty-three hundred hours, and satisfying requirements of the Air Registration Board's inspectors, would the first fare-paying passenger be permitted to step into a Concorde for a scheduled flight.

As with space flight, the Anglo-French program is supported by colossal ground facilities. Every step has been taken to estimate the performance of the aircraft in the conditions of actual flight. The highly sophisticated "wave" wing shape has only been evolved after thousands of hours of testing on hundreds of precision models, costing more than £1,000 each. Some have been dropped from helicopters and others, complete with working undercarriages and droop noses, tested in wind tunnels to simulate landing and takeoff. After intense research, the safest and most efficient configuration of Concorde has been arrived at.

The heart of the SST is its engine, and the development of the Olympus has involved a massive program of research and testing, embracing the resources of both Rolls-Royce, who took over Bristol Siddeley, and the French company, SNECMA. Thousands of hours of static testing have been spent in the soundproofed test beds at Patchway, near Bristol, and at Ville-roche in France. At Pyestock in Hampshire the engine has been operated for hundreds of hours at sustained Mach-2 flight, giant heaters warming the air to 153 degrees centigrade before blowers force it into the intake. New solutions have been found to the problems created by the need to fly safely at supersonic speed. Turbojet engines need to scoop in air at subsonic speeds, and a highly sophisticated system of variable-geometry flaps has been devised to bounce the supersonic shock wave at the entrance of the air-intake, slowing down the air flow for the engine's acceptance. In one of the more unusual tests, frozen chickens have been fired into the engines running at full power, to simulate bird collision at takeoff.

The enormous fuel requirements of the four Olympus engines called for a major engineering innovation. A multimillion-pound 350-ton fuel-test rig was built to simulate all the conditions of supersonic flight. This system is absolutely crucial to Concorde because not only does it have to supply fuel at up to 100 tons a minute to the engines on takeoff and balance the changes that occur in the transition to supersonic flight, but it also does the vital job of keeping the plane cool in the searing heat of Mach-2 flight. This full-scale model has enabled the designers to incorporate vital modifications that could otherwise have brought actual flight operations dangerously near to disaster.

The airframe has received the most massive and prolonged testing. After the Comet experience of structural failures, no mistakes can be afforded with Concorde. It was essential to test both the method of construction and the aluminum alloys being used to see how they would stand up to the rigors of supersonic flight. At the British government test facilities at Farnborough, and the French equivalent at LeHers, huge sections of Concorde were sealed in special containers and subjected to alternate cycles of heating and cooling by rows of infrared heaters and liquid nitrogen. Row upon row of jerking machinery tested the metal alloys for fatigue and creep, subjecting them to the temperature differentials of flight conditions, and on a tiny island in the Atlantic off Saint-Nazaire, structural metal specimens have been lined up on the seashore for corrosion tests.

In the most spectacular test of all a complete Concorde airframe has been encased in a huge metallic glove at Farnborough so that fifteen years of operational life, with cycles of heating and cooling, can be duplicated, as scientists check every detail. After the aircraft has been in airline service for two years, it will be possible to predict, with absolute accuracy, how long a Concorde will last in the conditions of supersonic flight.

In the summer of 1969, with the flight test program just beginning, the end results of all this time and effort were two tangible airplanes, whose job was to justify the vast amount of research and development. Although the flight-testing schedule was pressing and any delay would cost hundreds of thousands of pounds, both governments felt it was time to show the taxpayers that they were getting something for their money. It was decided to fly both prototypes at the Paris Air Show that June. It was a calculated risk. "Frankly, if 001 and 002 collided over the Paris Air Show due to weather or both pilots having a heart attack," confessed Wedgwood Benn, who had to approve the idea, "the whole project would have been endangered." They made an impressive sight. George Gedge of BAC Filton, who remembered Le Bourget, said, "It turned my tummy over to see both of them flying at the air show." To another engineer it was like "hearing 'Rule Britannia,' 'Land of Hope and Glory,' and 'God Save the Queen,' all rolled into one."

In the favorable climate, Wedgwood Benn took advantage of the general surge of enthusiasm to announce yet another increase in costs. In May, just before the double flight at the Paris Air Show, he told the House of Commons that the new estimates were for £730 million, of which some £330 million had already been spent. The jump of nearly 50 percent over the previous estimates of £500 million had been caused in large part by the British devaluation, inflation, and the need for further design changes on the production aircraft, which included revised wing tips to increase range, a longer fuselage, and the advanced new one-piece engine nozzles which were going to save a vital 5,000 pounds on the payload. The minister and his civil servants had by now solved the difficult problem of how to finance production of Concorde. It was no good building a prototype without the facilities for production models, and to do this it was necessary to start laying down the basic assembly line, investing in machine tools and sophisticated jigs, and finding work to keep the plant going. However much the government and BAC wished otherwise, the capital required, estimated at £150 million in Britain alone, would have to come from the Treasury. BAC was entitled to borrow up to £125 million of government money on which interest would be paid at commercial rates, with the government carrying the risk; the company could borrow a further £25 million from the commercial banks with the Treasury as guarantor. It looked a neat solution, and short of the nationalization of BAC, which had been considered and rejected after deft maneuvering with the City, it solved the immediate problems of finance. But it tied commercial decisions again to political considerations, which would bind Concorde still tighter to the vagaries of Westminster politics.

The 1969 test program utilized both prototypes to gain the maximum amount of proving time; each flight by one aircraft was taken a stage further by the other.

Concorde began to show that it was a remarkably successful aircraft. The engineers, by their first-rate work in developing a revolutionary aircraft which performed in such a trouble-free way, had undoubtedly saved Concorde. As Sir George Edwards stated when Harold Wilson called a summer general election in June 1970, "It's been better than I expected." The flight tests were, however, only partly complete, but already encouraging information was beginning to flow which could lead airlines to start seriously considering adding supersonic aircraft to their fleets. As the country went to the polls in 1970, pessimistic workers at the Weybridge plant, who were already working on the first six aircraft, were taking bets that they would be on the scrap heap by September.

"And here's a late score just in, the American taxpayer 51, the SST 46."

16

She Went Negative

On the morning of 5 March 1970 readers of *The New York Times* opened their papers on a devastating full-page advertisement. The bold black type leaped at them.

**SST. AIRPLANE OF TOMORROW
BREAKS WINDOWS, CRACKS WALLS, STAMPEDES CATTLE,
AND WILL HASTEN THE END OF THE
AMERICAN WILDERNESS.**

In smaller letters, no fewer than thirteen grim consequences of supersonic flight were listed. In highly charged prose the startled readers were told that the sonic boom's vibrations would disperse the Newfoundland fisheries and affect the human nervous, endocrine, and reproductive systems, damaging the unborn child. The weather would be seriously affected and the world's fuel resources would be burned up at a colossal rate merely to provide "elitist" flights. The perplexed New Yorkers were urged to "write, telephone, and wire your congressman." The reader was warned that if he did nothing he would end up feeling impotent and damned, "locked in a small room and the walls and ceilings closing in on us," because the SST typified the "sort of thinking that will lead us into an unnecessarily short and miserable life." With a clever PR touch, "clip-out" mailing slips were provided, addressed to President Nixon, telling him that "growth for the sake of growth is the ideology of the cancer cell."

The advertisement was the opening shot in the final campaign to finish off the Boeing SST. Significantly, it had been placed in the press by the recently formed "Coalition Against the SST," which had brought together a number of highly articulate and dedicated environmental groups. In a concerted effort to persuade Congress to drop the SST, the formidable group had acquired backing from wealthy Baltimore English teacher Kenneth Grief. Grouped together under his environmental banner were the Friends of the Earth, the Sierra Club, the Wilderness Society, and a group with the unlikely name of the National Tax Action Inc. At the heart of the movement was William Shurcliff's Citizens' League Against the Sonic Boom, which had already proved highly effective with over 25,000 active supporters and a regular newsletter packed with anti-SST propaganda. The organizers knew they could count on the support of millions of environmentally conscious Americans of all persuasions who had begun to question the object of it all. The pollution of the environment had emerged as a cause to unite them. The physical as well as the social destruction of the great American Dream emerged as a growing factor in political life. Americans who would never dream of joining a demonstration on Vietnam and who deplored extremes of all kinds suddenly began to make their feelings known in protest about the despoliation of their continent.

In reality, the motor car was by far and away the biggest cause of environmental damage afflicting many parts of America, from the factories of Detroit, to the jammed highways and smog-ridden air of the West Coast. But the car represented the liberty of the individual to travel wherever and whenever he wanted. Although cars and the factories that produced them were prime destroyers of the environment, they were too involved with the spiritual freedom of Americans to become an immediate target. The airplane was an obvious target of earthbound observers over whom it flew, leaving them with a helpless feeling of frustration about being able to do anything to control it.

Aircraft noise was a scourge of urban life near busy airports, and the burgeoning environmentalist lobby singled out aviation for special treatment. They could do little to fight the large fleets of jets already flying, but they could be much more effective against those still on the drawing board. The SST, waggling its wings like a giant yellow insect three hundred feet long in Boeing's Seattle plant, had early become the hate symbol of the pollution campaign.

In spite of their clamor, the environmentalists were unable to bring about the destruction of the Boeing SST on their own. Tactical maneuvering by astute politicians on the floor of the Senate was needed to trap a wily Administration. The Coalition Against the SST received powerful practical support from the hard-nosed politicians in Congress seeking any opportunity to attack the Nixon Administration. President Nixon had adopted the SST program as one of the trappings of the presidency, just as surely as Kennedy and Johnson, but in the Senate, William Proxmire of Wisconsin bided his time to attack what he believed to be the lunatic SST project, now scheduled to cost a billion dollars. Armed with ammunition supplied by the Coalition Against the SST, who could readily lay on a list of top-rate academic speakers to criticize every aspect of the scheme, Proxmire could force the White House to defend its project publicly in the lion's den of a Senate inquiry.

Although President Nixon was determined to pursue the supersonic project, doubt was now clouding the SST plan. Boeing, the world's most renowned builder of airliners, had been unable to make its swing-wing design work and had revised plans to build a fixed-wing delta, just like Concorde and the TU-144, which were now flying. Public confidence was shaken and congressmen began to wonder whether more good taxpayers' money would follow the vast sums already spent in building a plywood mock-up. The FAA had little to justify four years' work, except glossy brochures, and it was not even in the advantageous position of the British and French governments who knew that it would be wasteful to turn back after so much money had been invested in an actual flying aircraft.

In 1969, after the inauguration of President Nixon, the SST became an urgent priority for the White House. The technical catastrophe at Boeing inevitably brought the new Administration face to face with the sort of decision alien to Nixon's Republican capitalist philosophy—to cancel a vital project or to pour millions more federal dollars into a plane that had hit serious difficulties and which was building up opposition in the vociferous pollution lobby. Nixon, who in his campaign had pledged "to arm the people with the truth," immediately set up a presidential "ad hoc" committee to review the status of the program. The committee's views, however, only strained the president's pledge of truthfulness, for when it reported, it presented a very different document from what the president had been hoping for.

The twelve-man team composed of leading officials from the Administration took the SST program apart. Their conclusions damned the whole project. They raised serious doubts whether the plane would ever be commercially attractive enough to sell in the large numbers required to repay the colossal government investment. They wondered whether airlines could afford both supersonic jets and the huge fleets of jumbos that they were planning to buy. The first models of the huge 747 were now rolling off the Boeing assembly lines, and the Ad Hoc Committee doubted if even the great Seattle company had sufficient resources to build both the jumbos and the SST without risking serious financial trouble. The president was reminded that "the government may be required to act as guarantor of, or to provide any additional funds needed by the airframe manufacturers." It seemed a dangerously open-ended commitment.

The sums, as the committee pointed out, were staggering—even by West Coast standards. Apart from the two prototypes, Boeing would need more than twice the company's net book value to get the SST into production. Even the consideration of employment, which would have received greater attention in any European economy, was dismissed as insignificant. Against such a big financial risk "employment should not be considered as a justification for proceeding with this program." On what might have been expected to be a favorable technological fallout from the project, the committee concluded, "The SST program cannot be considered as providing unique technological inputs to military programs."

If it did nothing else the committee put its finger on the key problem that bedeviled all attempts to achieve economic supersonic flight: "No doubt all of the technological problems are eventually solvable, but how soon and at what cost? The record for new aircraft being designed to make technological jumps of this magnitude is confined strictly to military production. The record in those cases is not good. Production costs have often been more than three times what they were predicted to be."

If the Ad Hoc Committee's report on SST economics was bad, then the section on the environmental pollution of the SST was devastating. Noise was the number-one problem. The SST would have to operate supersonically over water because "the effects of the sonic boom are such as to be considered intolerable by a very high percentage of the people affected." And with the boom outlawed, airport noise would become a significant factor likely to weigh heavily against SSTs, with their colossal engine power. The report made fearful reading. "Aside from hearing loss, noise may cause cardiovascular, glandular, respiratory, and neurologic changes," it pointed out. Dramatic though this statement was, the committee did not support its hypothesis with scientific data. It was merely a mild prologue to the rest of the section, which conjured up visions of turbulent flight that could cause fractures in unrestrained persons, warned of the toxicity of ozone in the cabin air, and cautioned that pregnant women "in the first trimester" should not be allowed to travel in SSTs. The environment section ended in a grand finale and warned of the global impact of water vapor in the upper atmosphere, which might cause catastrophic effects on the world's weather. Although unsupported by real scientific analysis, the report hinted that fleets of SSTs would turn the earth into a super-heated greenhouse in which the polar ice caps would melt and flood the continents.

President Nixon was appalled when the report was delivered to him confidentially in March 1969. He very shrewdly suppressed its findings, knowing full well that it could mean the end of the American project. This did not prevent a spirited debate inside the Administration which raged for seven months. Opposing the SST were the president's science aide and his economic advisors. Fighting for the Boeing's life were John Volpe, secretary of transportation, and the new administrator of the FAA, John Schaffer. Only the intervention of "a genuine American hero," Charles A. Lindbergh, kept the president in line behind the project.

An increasingly important fact in the argument over the SST, of significance both to the White House and the Coalition Against the SST, now emerged. The Ad Hoc Committee had been forced to consider the impact of Concorde on the American SST program. Any decision on the American supersonic would automatically involve the European aircraft industry. This could present a very sensitive international issue. If the Anglo-French plane were canceled, then it would be possible for the United States Administration to cast aside its own albatross-like SST, without losing face. But the chances of the United States Administration persuading France to abandon Concorde were slender when the prime minister, government, and much of the civil service of the United Kingdom had failed. The chances seemed remote to the political realists on the committee, but they reported optimistically, "Cables from our embassies in London and Paris indicate that some British and French officials close to the program are skeptical of Concorde's commercial viability." If the Anglo-French plane refused to die quietly, there were other ways in which America might determine the fate of the Concorde once she had abandoned the Boeing. The report hinted, "U.S. noise standards could conceivably bar Concorde from access to the principal U.S. airports, which would undoubtedly doom the Concorde program."

It was significant that the report, having given the "thumbs down" to the American scheme, openly suggested ways to kill the Concorde. With her grip on the civil aviation industry, the United States was in a strong position to influence the future of the European competitor, particularly by bringing pressure to bear on the question of aircraft noise. The SSTs were of necessity noisier than the coming generation of quieter turbofan jets. The turbojets which powered both the Boeing SST and Concorde were chosen because of their efficiency at supersonic speeds; they made the supersonic potentially noisier than even the current generation of subsonic jets then flying.

The aerospace industry sought to underline the stakes. In a neat booklet circulated to Congress and opinion formers in April 1969, Boeing warned the Americans of the danger of losing a $25 billion market, claiming that "the long-time American dominance of the world commercial airplane market stands in danger of being forfeited unless this country matches and exceeds the European effort."

In the summer of 1969 the United States Department of Transportation tried hard to persuade the Europeans to re-schedule their project, hoping that after the first flight of the Concorde prototypes Britain and France would be more willing to slow down spending and their program. The suggestion from the Department of Transportation was that "the British and French combine in building a slower supersonic plane and that the Europeans and the Americans might then agree to a de-escalation of their supersonic race." But "the builders of Concorde showed no interest." This was not surprising, since the Europeans had already been given notice of the decision of Congress, backed by the environmental lobby, to pass new legislation limiting aircraft noise. New regulations to be enforced in 1975 meant that a vast expenditure would have to be made in developing silencers for the Concorde's engines—as well as for nearly all the other jets then flying.

In September the storm broke. Nixon was forced to ask Congress for $96 million to keep the project under way. The issue was now in the open, and in the wrangling that followed, the differences of opinion inside the Administration were starkly revealed. The president was forced to publish the Ad Hoc Committee report, and there was fury in Washington. A key member of the Senate Appropriations Subcommittee, Congressman Sidney Yates of Illinois, was "amazed that President Nixon had approved the request for the SST. The committee, which consisted of many of the ablest people in his Administration, recommended overwhelmingly in favor of suspending work on this project." Pointing out that the $750 million limit imposed by President Kennedy had almost been reached, Yates warned Nixon, "This is the logical time to call a halt to the program and I shall try to strike out the appropriation."

The Administration's political managers, however, succeeded in pushing through the presidential request, although $11 million was chipped off. The vote was 58 to 22, but *Time* magazine pinpointed the American dilemma. Under an editorial entitled "Riding a Technological Tiger," the magazine analyzed the situation: "It is still debatable whether a supersonic transport is a better investment than, say, an aircraft that could take off and land downtown. . . . The government has spent $450 million so far on feasibility and design studies; Nixon's proposals would commit the government to invest $1.3 billion to build two prototypes. After that Boeing and its suppliers are expected to finance the early production costs, which will bring the overall total to $3 billion. Under a tough contract with Boeing, Washington will recover its investment when the 300th aircraft is sold. The government will turn a $1 billion profit if sales reach the FAA predicted minimum of 500 by 1990—a return that works out less than that from putting the money in the bank."

The Boeing reaction was hastily to set about recruiting more black engineers to counter the criticism voiced in Congress that the SST would create few jobs in the ghettos. But this was not the real issue at stake, as *Time* pointed out: "The still unresolved questions, which Congress must answer, are whether technology must move at a forced-march pace and whether the boom of supersonic flight in the 1970s is worth the prophesied investment of national talent and treasure." The press was voicing the mounting public concern that suspected that the manipulators of the military-industrial complex were at work behind the vast project. There were unfortunate links with the Vietnam conflict. The anti-SST lobby found supporters rushing to its cause. The Boeing 2707 was becoming a symbolic focus for national dissent, and if the American conscience was frustrated over doing anything about Vietnam, then there was an expiation that could be made at home.

The second round in the battle of the Boeing soon opened. Although Nixon had managed to press through the 1969 appropriation, the Coalition Against the SST was determined to kill the project next time the president asked for funding. Nixon himself took steps to protect the project, appointing test pilot and former head of the Lockheed supersonic William Magruder to organize the administration's SST program. He operated from a new Office of Supersonic Transport, set up specially inside the Department of Transportation, where it would be easier to shelter the SST's funds along with allocations for federal highways and other appropriations to "advance the transportation art." Bill Magruder, however, had the unenviable task of fighting the growing Coalition Against the SST. Already the Citizens' League Against the Sonic Boom had increased its membership from the nine founding fathers, who met under Shurcliff's presidency in 1967, to over 25,000 by 1970, with an income of $25,000 a year.

This had been built up by a combined team of Shurcliff, his colleagues, and his sister, who proved skillful at adapting their cottage industry to a "Madison Avenue" public relations campaign. Regular mailing to press, TV, and radio throughout America kept editors and broadcasters supplied with a constant stream of information, boom-maps, and damaging facts to the SST. They lobbied Congress, appeared on TV and radio across the country, and gave remarkably detailed evidence before congressional committees.

In the land that worshipped the entrepreneur, the tenacity and drive of Shurcliff's league attracted much press attention for its David and Goliath struggle with the mighty aviation lobby. The column inches and the air time that CLASB attracted left the aviation lobby wondering whether the editors of the media were paid-up members of the Citizens' League. The professional public relations effort had failed to take Shurcliff seriously, convinced that "in the land of the Wright Brothers" attacking airplanes would be a minority pastime reserved for cranks and lunatics. Now, with the nation's media paying serious attention to the Citizens' League, the PR men woke up. It was already too late. No matter how hard the paid lobbyists of Boeing and the FAA pressed their cases, reception in the editorial offices was frosty, and the media turned hostile to the SST.

A new edition of Shurcliff's *SST and Sonic Boom Handbook*, a gold mine of hard fact and opinion directed against supersonic flight, was reissued. Sandwiched between shocking-pink and black covers, the paperback became something of a bestseller at ninety-five cents a copy. Over 10,000 copies were distributed free to congressmen, Administration officials, newspapers, the aviation industry, and even to the president himself. Boeing executives and FAA officials were annoyed to find copies reaching their inner offices in alarming quantities. "I mailed them with plain brown wrappers," explained Shurcliff, "with no return address indicated to reduce the chance that the mailroom clerks would collect and burn them."

A regular newsletter "prepared informally for members" was also dispatched to thousands of paid-up CLASB members; containing caustic press cuttings, quotes from Congress, and alarming statistics on the sonic boom and supersonic flight, it triggered newspaper articles and congressional lobbying on a scale only matched by the previous year's "Peace in Vietnam" campaign. Members and press learned that prominent surgeons "drew sustained applause" when they complained, "We are spending twice on the SST what we are spending on medical research in one year, and . . . it's going to cause more disease, more noise, air pollution, and traffic congestion. And who the Hell wants to get to London a few hours earlier anyway."

Shurcliff's newsletter told how the boom from military jets had rocked the little country town of Alvarado, Texas ("It collapsed a portion of the post-office ceiling and broke J. C. Smith's leg"); it told how medical authorities in Ohio suggested that repeated loud noises such as sonic booms could affect pregnant women; and it told how British colleagues in the Anti-Concorde Project were taking steps to protest against the coming supersonic test of Concorde. To many readers it gave the comfortable feeling that thinking, decent people everywhere were uniting against these terrible machines.

This broadside by the CLASB was highly effective, and the average American might be forgiven for thinking that the SST was the first metallic outrider of the Apocalypse, trailing in its wake not just the "earth-shattering boom," but widespread skin cancer and the fourth ice age. Nor did the coalition lack eminent scientists who advanced to produce theories that the SST would trigger one global catastrophe after another. None of these theories could be lightly dismissed by the Administration, aware of the political importance that the environment had assumed. The government's scientific agencies found themselves saddled with the almost impossible task of allaying fears, given credibility by press support and wide coverage. To counter the simplistic and emotional manner in which the public was presented with the ozone skin-cancer theory and scores of others was extremely difficult; a complete rebuttal would depend on proving the impossible. If a hypothesis had been produced that the SST would radically upset the environment in some particular way, then, according to the critics, the implication was so serious that the SST supporter would have to prove absolutely—beyond any scientific doubt whatsoever—that this was not the case. It was clearly an impossible task with some of the wilder assumptions.

Early in 1970, the second chance to kill the Boeing presented itself when the president announced that the Administration needed a further $290 million to build the prototype. The Coalition Against the SST armed itself for the fight. Marshaling all the paraphernalia of American lobbying, the coalition targeted sixty key senators who they believed could be won over to the cause. Their most powerful ally was Senator William Proxmire from Wisconsin. Leading the opposition in the House of Representatives was Sidney Yates, a Democrat from Illinois who had already played on deep-seated resentment about the way federal funds were being used. "The SST will not belong to the United States," he was fond of pointing out. "The SST will belong to Boeing."

Proxmire was the most daunting opponent. He had always opposed the SST and the way it was funded. A tough operator who knew better than most how to use the smoke-filled committee rooms of Capitol Hill to his advantage, he had an impressive record of cutting unnecessary government spending. His stand was made easier because unlike some of his colleagues he knew that large plants of the military-industrial complex did not dominate his state's economy. Proxmire had made his reputation by uncovering a number of scandals in government spending, particularly in the aviation industry, where he had been ruthless with Lockheed over the C5A contract. In fact, he had become something of a Ralph Nader of the United States aviation industry, and although the industry did its best to "pin something on him," they could only discover that the senator was a "keep-fit" fanatic who ran miles around Washington's parks every morning. Like Nader, he had made many powerful enemies, but the worst that they had been able to produce in casting a doubt on his integrity was that "he had had his hair fixed"—a reference to the fact that the senator was keeping up his public appearance by having cosmetic attention paid to his receding hairline.

Senator Proxmire was vice-chairman of the influential Joint Economic Committee of Congress. This enabled him to set up and chair a series of subcommittee hearings on the economy in government. Unlike select committees of the House of Commons, the nearest English equivalent, Senate committees are far more under the control of their chairmen, less impartial, and an accepted way of political engineering. Moreover, they are backed up by teams of full-time professional researchers who ferret out facts. They can call witnesses and pay expenses for people to travel to give evidence. It is the chairman who invites witnesses to attend, and not unnaturally, Proxmire used the hearings on the Boeing program to build up a formidable body of expert opinion against the project.

If anyone in the White House or at Boeing doubted the object of the Proxmire hearings, their doubts were dispelled by the senator's opening remarks from the chair. Addressing the witnesses and committee assembled in Room 1202, New Senate Office Building, Proxmire said, "I remain mystified concerning the public benefits of the SST. I will turn to our witnesses today and next Monday for possible enlightenment." The fact that with the exception of the Department of Transportation, they were all likely to be handpicked, hostile witnesses was overlooked by the press, particularly in Britain. As Proxmire acidly pointed out, "We invited other witnesses to this hearing. Mr. H. W. Withington, vice-president of the Boeing Company, has unfortunately declined our invitation on the grounds that his 'personal presence' would 'add little to the already published documentation available.' Mr. Withington is too modest. His personal presence would have added a great deal of flavor to our proceedings."

Proxmire's first witness was outspokenly hostile. Congressman Henry Reuss was from the senator's home state of Wisconsin. For him, the SST was "an environmental outrage." He even went so far as to suggest that the knotty problem of Concorde should be dealt with by an outright ban "because it is an environmental outrage and just too noisy." Quoting opinion polls which showed that more than 80 percent of Americans were now against the SST he challenged the president to ask the voters what they thought of "the greatest con game in history." "Let the president submit his case for the SST to the people. Let him go on nationwide television and explain why this plane is worth billions of dollars of the hard-pressed taxpayer's money. I am sure that the letters to the White House would quickly reveal that there is no kind of majority, silent or otherwise, for the SST."

In this vein the hearing proceeded, eagerly written up in the press on both sides of the Atlantic, as one after another the supporters of the Coalition Against the SST made their case against the project. One of the stars was Mary Goldring, specially imported from her desk at *The Economist* in London to tell the Americans what the European challenge really amounted to. Not surprisingly, the well-known British opponent of Concorde did not give an impressive picture of sales or economics for the aircraft. In fact, some British executives in the aircraft industry suggested that she should be confined to the Tower on her return to London, to await a charge of high treason—a harsh proposal, since at one point in the proceedings, she patriotically rejected the idea that the United States would be able to kill the European plane by banning it from American airports.

Chairman Proxmire: "You feel that there will be retaliation, there will be diplomatic protest, there will be pressure, and you think that the likely result will be that the standard will be modified, or as you say, bent?"
Miss Goldring: "This is rather a cynical deduction, but this is what I think would happen."

SST ON THE SKIDS

John Volpe, secretary of transportation, testifies before the crucial Senate Committee on the SST in 1970.

Jubilant Proxmire. His long campaign ended in a decisive victory after the Senate's anti-SST vote of 24 March 1971.

THE PRICE OF FAILURE

Boeing workers gather before the 2707 mock-up to hear the grim news that cancellation would mean the loss of 7,000 jobs in Seattle alone.

President Nixon, defeated on the SST, consults with his advisors on the best ways to mitigate the effects of Congress' decision.

The hearings were filled with lively exchanges as the chairman vigorously pursued his cause. One significant piece of cross-examination that illustrates the kind of emotional level the debate was reaching came on the second day when the noted opponent, Congressman Yates, was being questioned.

Congressman Conable: "Are you serious about this greenhouse effect by Concorde trails? I have a feeling that we sometimes resort to unnecessarily esoteric arguments and somewhat improbable conclusions in our anxiety to turn back a proposal of this sort. If we are going to get a 'greenhouse' effect from the Concorde trails I would say that would indicate that there are going to be a lot of Concordes in the air, and that you would be unwilling to acknowledge that, on the basis of the testimony you have given about the tubular construction and discomfort?

Congressman Yates: "Mr. Conable, I was as incredulous as you were this morning when these physicists came to visit me. And I said, 'You cannot mean this about the Concorde trails having this greenhouse effect!' And they said, 'Yes we do mean it.' They talked about the ionosphere. And I have never felt the generation gap more fully than in my conversations with these Ph.D.s this morning. They talked about the ionosphere and the Concorde trails bounding up against some ceiling up there, just staying up there, the condensation staying in the nature of a cloud cover."

Congressman Conable: "In other words they were not talking about the volume of the pollution caused; they were talking about its location in the ionosphere?"

Congressman Yates: "That is right. They are flying so high, and the condensation stems from the exhaust. And the operation of the plane will leave this kind of an effect in the ionosphere. And in time they say . . ."

Congressman Conable: "It may very well raise the temperature of the world?"

Congressman Yates: "That is right."

Congressman Conable: "Melt the polar ice cap?"

Congressman Yates: "Yes."

Congressman Conable: "I would hope that we base our opposition to the SST on something more substantial than that, although I must acknowledge I am not part of this esoteric scientific fraternity."

The journalists on both sides of the Atlantic who printed scaring stories of what the SST was supposed to be doing to the environment were not scientists either. Headlines about boom damage and skin cancer made good copy—and they were given some kind of official credence by the Proxmire hearings. Good copy was also provided in the grilling of representatives of the Department of Transportation, who found themselves uncomfortably holding the SST baby. Beggs and Magruder faced some tough questioning:

Mr. Beggs: "I think the argument again has to go back to the question of leadership in civil aeronautics and the sales of transports abroad. And that certainly is beneficial to a large number of the American people."

Chairman Proxmire: "Of course the State Department, our experts in that area, disagree with you. We cannot find anybody except the people in your area and the people affected in Congress by aviation who will agree with it."

Mr. Beggs: "I think they will argue that the balance of payments will not be as we say."

Chairman Proxmire: "The State Department is talking about national prestige. They say it should not be undertaken for that reason."

Mr. Beggs: "O.K. But I am not arguing the national prestige so much here as I am arguing the question of our substantial lead in civil aeronautics and what this has meant to the nation. And I think it has meant a great deal. Think of the vast majority of people of the world who travel in American transports, the image that is created in their minds of the advanced technological position of the United States. I think that is a very important asset."

Chairman Proxmire: "Any nation that has gone to the moon, that has the terrific technology we demonstrated for that, certainly does not have to be in the front end of everything at all times at all points . . ."

[Magruder felt otherwise]

Mr. Magruder: "May I speak to that?"
Chairman Proxmire: "Yes."
Mr. Magruder: "Speaking as one who has been trying to get other countries to buy U.S. airplanes and maintain that leadership, I am concerned about the fact that there is a Concorde, and in addition, the fact that there are six airplanes authorized for production. . . . If this country defaults the SST to the foreigners who are also working very hard to penetrate the airbus market, with the A-300 and with other airplanes, and are joining together on both engine and avionic technology that is not behind ours in advancement, they may well have a much more attractive market than you can foresee at this moment in time. . . . If we begin to indicate that we are not going to keep this [SST] up, then we are going to tamper with the market, not just because of a single airplane, but because of the whole broad spectrum. And I submit that this has not been discussed in the past."
Chairman Proxmire: "Thank you, gentlemen, very very much. You have been two excellent witnesses. You have done a fine job, although it is obvious that I do not agree with you."

If anyone doubted Proxmire's word they had only to read the majority report published two months later. "It is our conclusion that few significant public benefits appear likely to result from the supersonic transport development program. On the other hand, very significant social costs are associated with this program. More productive uses of government resources are clearly available. No further federal financial support of the supersonic transport development program is justified at this time." And, as a rider to the main report, Proxmire dismissed the European project in a sentence: "The Concorde does not pose a competitive threat of sufficient magnitude to justify continued federal-government support of the U.S. SST."

The newspaper headlines in Britain and America treated Senator Proxmire's views as though they represented the conclusions of Congress. They neglected the closely reasoned report of a dissenting member of the committee, Congressman Clarence J. Brown of Ohio. It began by registering Proxmire's attitude: "If the Joint Economic Committee had been advising Queen Isabella we would still be in Barcelona waiting to prove the world was round before daring the Atlantic. The same kind of thinking displayed in this report would have kept the American government of the last century from developing transcontinental railroads—or President Kennedy ten years ago from undertaking a program to reach the moon." Dismissing the emotive environmental conclusions of the report, he pointed out acidly, "Claims of a new ice age, fundamental alterations in weather patterns, or the deterioration of marine life if SSTs take to the air fall more in the area of conjecture, not unlike the arguments against the use of aluminum pans in cooking. While they have not been disproven, they have certainly not been proven to any impressive extent. If all technological change must await proof of its safety, then technological change will be slow indeed. In the past, technological change had been successfully undertaken with a view that it would benefit mankind, and any harmful effects could be corrected—by technology. This approach brought man out of the cave." His summing up was directed at Proxmire: "The report sounds good but adds little in the way of hard facts or logic by which to measure transportation policy. It is a vehicle for flaying the supersonic transport program, but not a very convincing one because of its lack of logical conclusions drawn from any hard facts."

The minority report was left unread and largely ignored. The Proxmire hearings were an immense propaganda victory for the environmentalists and the Coalition Against the SST. The Boeing project was now in deadly peril as pressure mounted on members of Congress to scrap the whole enterprise. Throughout the summer of 1970 furious battle raged in the press, on radio, and television, as well as in the crowded rooms of the political managers on the "Hill." Inevitably the Concorde was affected, with the Europeans being involved on the fringe of the American argument.

The Nixon Administration fought skillfully. On 27 May 1970, the House of Representatives voted by 176 to 163 in favor of the total Department of Transportation appropriation, which included an allocation for the supersonic. To halt the plane on that vote would have meant stopping federal funding for the roads, railways, and airports of the United States. The environmentalists were stung into even greater activity, their attention concentrated on the Senate, which would now have to approve the bill. The forthcoming November elections were a factor to consider since a change in the composition of both congressional houses could result in an anti-SST vote. All the same, the Administration could not force a vote before the elections because many of the pro-SST senators seeking reelection did not want to commit themselves to a cause which might prove unpopular with their own local voters.

By now, the aerospace industry had become thoroughly alarmed. Faced by an increasingly hostile press, Boeing's top executives knew that the time had come to do something positive. "We were faced with what you could almost describe as a theology," one vice-president recalled. "We had to argue our case against a religion." The corporation decided on a series of top-level approaches to the media as the only way to cool the hostile climate. So it was that Holden Withington and his colleagues found themselves flying back and forth across the United States, knocking on the doors of newspaper editors and TV station managers trying to put the reasoned case for the SST. It turned out to be an unrewarding task. From *The New York Times*, which turned out to be the most anti-SST of all, right down to mid-state TV stations, the reaction was depressing. All that the Boeing executives found was how well the opposition was putting its case. They could not understand how amateurs could get their message across when highly skilled public relations agencies were failing. It was an odd experience for America's top engineers to find themselves waiting in empty reception rooms for audiences with editors who presented a cold and often impolite front. "In one of the big Chicago papers," recalled Withington, "I was kept waiting for over an hour; then at last, after a hell of a time, some girl came down to see me. It was obvious that she was a secretary, and she was clearly embarrassed. I talked with her for a bit, but it was obvious she couldn't stand it anymore. She told me, 'My boss told me to take care of you and not to waste his time.'

The credibility gap yawned between planemaker and public. Boeing executives were inundated with mail suggesting they were surviving on a public subsidy. "We never could get across to Proxmire or anyone else that the government was arranging a high-risk long-term loan," summed up the exasperation felt by Boeing management. The anti-SST lobby had skillfully homed in on the subsidy angle and the one indisputable irritant connected with the new era of commercial aviation—the sonic boom— called in a fatal PR slip in an industry handout, "the twentieth-century sound." Whatever assurances the FAA, Boeing, Magruder, or even the president himself gave, the suspicion was deeply laid that once the SST was off the ground it would boom from coast to coast. They had seen maps of the United States on TV and in the press criss-crossed with wide, blank "boom patterns." It was really a case of no money—no boom. The mail cards demanding an end to the SST filled the "In" trays of Congress, piling up like votes at an election count. The endless environmental row rolled on through the summer like a thunderstorm.

In a clever switch of tactics, the Coalition Against the SST opened up a new front and exploited the financial vulnerability of the SST. In a move to down the "billion-dollar buzzard" the coalition lobbied the nation's leading academic economists, changing the pitch of the campaign from the emotionalism of the environment to considerations of hard cash. This they calculated would impress the Senate subcommittees. Thirteen of the top economists in the United States were induced to issue a statement condemning the SST. In Olympian style, J. K. Galbraith of Harvard dismissed the balance of payments arguments, canvassed by Magruder, stating that "these calculations are strictly fraudulent and should detain no one." The prestige of Nobel Prize winner Professor Paul Samuelson of M.I.T. was added to the testimony. He believed that "even if the SST had no adverse effects upon the environment, in the form of sonic booms and contamination of the atmosphere, it would be an economic and political disaster. . . . Congress must act immediately to end what must be regarded as an economic fiasco."

In the Senate, the Boeing cause was vigorously defended by a group known as the "Senators from Boeing" led by Senator Jackson of Washington, the home of the Seattle plant. He was backed up by Senators Taft and Saxbe of Ohio, where the engines were being built by General Electric. Senator Magnuson, chairman of the Subcommittee on Aviation, was also a keen advocate of the project and was in a position to influence the subsidies of local airlines. He wrote to thirty senators reminding them about the subsidies for their local airlines, at the same time pointing out the importance of the SST and "hoping for your support on all the transportation needs of the United States." The letter soon found its way into the press, where it was used as ammunition in the storm brewing over the autumn appropriations. The arguments became tense and furious; nerves were beginning to fail, even in the aviation industry. Some major contractors like Avco, Aerojet, and General Corporation and Tool Research decided to pull out of the project before they were affected by cancellation. In Seattle, however, thousands of skilled workers raced against the clock to finish the giant Dash-300 mock-up, the new plywood plane with delta wings to replace the swing-wing model that was rotting on a junk pile. Behind the scenes all was not well with the engineering of the new design. It was, much to Withington's dismay, already running into the weight problems that had plagued its predecessor.

The problems of engineering a delicate honeycomb airframe from titanium still dogged the Boeing engineers. Stresskin and other expert companies still had no answer to the new problems. Enthusiasm for supersonic commercial flight began to cool at Boeing.

In Seattle, increasingly worried executives "kept hearing that Nixon was in favor of the program, but he never actually did anything." They still believe that if the president had "made two or three phone calls" in October 1970 he could have stopped what happened. Instead of the president making a direct appeal at a stage when he might have really halted the slide against the SST that was gaining momentum in Congress, his aides and department chiefs were left to do the lobbying. This did not produce the desired results. When the Department of Transportation sent around a brief showing what each state could expect to receive in subcontracts, the anti-SST lobby circulated similar maps showing what each state's taxpayers would have to contribute as their share of the $1.3 billion bill.

The last-minute efforts of the aerospace industry failed to save the SST. The transportation bill went through the rounds from subcommittee to full committee. As it progressed, the majority in favor of the SST became narrower and narrower. At last it reached the floor of the Senate in a motion to delete the SST appropriation on 3 December 1970. In three hours of speeches against the SST by Senators Proxmire, Nelson, Muskie, and Percy, countered by Magnuson, Murphy, and Goldwater, the issue was joined. As one Boeing executive put it, "When the votes were counted 52 senators called for a halt to the program, and 41 wanted it to continue." As one Boeing executive commented sadly on the occasion, "In the subcommittee vote it was 2:1 in favor of the SST. In the full committee it was cut down somewhat. When it came to the full Senate, she went negative!"

The press was delighted; huge headlines and glowing editorials celebrated the Coalition Against the SST's famous victory. In many people's eyes the Senate "had dared to weigh common sense and a livable environment against jobs and profits."

But the SST was still alive. The Administration could exploit the conflict that now existed between the House, which had passed the appropriation, and the Senate, which had rejected it. In the Senate-House conference that took place to resolve the situation on December 10, a compromise funding of $210 million was suggested. An enraged Senator Proxmire, who saw the manipulations of the Administration at work, started a filibuster and a deadlock ensued. The president now belatedly committed his own prestige in an attempt to salvage the SST finally. To him the blow was personal. At his news conference of December 10 he told the nation, "What is involved here is not just the 150,000 jobs which will be lost if we don't build it; but what is lost here is the fact that the United States of America, which has been first in the world of commercial aviation from the time of the Wright Brothers, decides not just to be second, but not even to show."

The White House had left it too late, but there was still a slender chance to save the Boeing in the spring of 1971. Congress ended its filibuster in an interim agreement for a ninety-day continuation of funding until the newly elected Congress could finally decide the issue. It was a nerve-wracking time for the men in Seattle who knew their livelihood was at stake. Alarmed, the Administration and the aerospace lobby set in motion a massive advertising campaign to turn the tide of public opinion and reverse the Senate vote. But their opponents had already scented a significant victory for citizen democracy. The coalition redoubled its efforts, throwing everything into the last round. It took a new tack; it was going to preserve the world from the SST. The coalition's supporters believed that U.S. rejection would automatically halt other SSTs, and so make the world safe from "the monsters."

The final stage of the long struggle to save the SST inevitably took place in the seemingly interminable Senate hearings. The man who had done so much to involve the United States in the supersonic power game, the former administrator of the FAA and now boss of Pan Am, Najeeb Halaby, made a last-minute plea: "Failure to support the supersonic transport program will ultimately mean that we run the risk of relinquishing world leadership in aviation as we already have in shipping." He warned Proxmire that "the whole anti-SST movement was not without its dangers. One of the terrifying things to one who is dependent on technology is that there seems to be abroad a feeling of anti-technology, technology is the devil that has caused every problem that we have in the United States today. But my only resource, the only resource for American industry in the future, is to improve technology without damaging the environment, so that we can meet the payrolls, can keep the ride going at a low price, can increase the size of the market." To keep the ride going—at any cost—the Russians were there to help. "That is the real threat we face, if there is no Concorde, if there is no U.S. supersonic, for which I think most of the world airlines would wait, then the Tupolev is the only SST."

The aerospace lobby pulled out all the stops. Full-page ads were appearing all over the country with toothsome all-American kids holding tiny models of the all-American SST. "Would the true American citizen want to see his son's inheritance snatched away by foreign competitors?" the headline asked. Such an approach made little impact on a public conditioned to believe that the SST meant skin cancer for millions, booms that stampeded cattle, and earth-shattering noise at airports. It backfired badly when the press asked where the $300,000 had come from to pay for the campaign. If the plane was such a good commercial proposition, should the aircraft industry not have financed it instead of asking for more taxpayers' money? The hastily recruited "Volunteers for the SST" was accused of being financed out of misappropriated public funding. This was brought to a head by a book of *Fairy Stories*, arguing the SST case. On publication it caused a furor. It was one of the more bizarre failures of the Nixon Administration. "Blatant propaganda" was how Proxmire described the story of "a big, friendly silver cat called Supersonic Pussycat" presented in the book as "a sweet chick with good looks," who with her mindless friend, Deci-bel, was all set to fly to Paris in two hours. "But along came a mean old senator who cast an evil spell and so poor old Supersonic Pussy was never allowed to take off. Miaow, Miaow, Miaow." The mean old senator would later uncover a misappropriation of $12,892 "and 40 cents" of taxpayers' money with which the Department of Transportation had gone into publishing. President Nixon had to get out of that fairy-tale business—and fast.

The fight on Capitol Hill reached a new intensity. The current slump in the airline business and the huge, red balance sheets of Pan Am and TWA now came into the reckoning. Doubts were cast on Concorde, because Proxmire knew that if his side could question its chances of success, many who would otherwise have their doubts would join the opposition to the SST. Sometimes this "Concorde-knocking on Capitol Hill" assumed humorous notes. Congressman Reuss, long-time opponent of SST, made a great play of the fact that the French ("of all people") wanted to cut the galleys: "Perhaps they'll announce next that they will cut out the lavatories and so operate on both ends of the alimentary canal at once."

On the eighty-ninth day the final defense of the SST rested with the president himself. Most senators were already overwhelmed and hoping, like the airline bosses, that the SST "would just go away." A significant factor for many was the pressure from their wives who were particularly attuned to the ecological issues.

The vote, when it came on March 24, was an unprecedented defeat for the industry and the president, a victory for the anti-SST campaign and Proxmire in particular. It was narrow: 51 for, 46 against. Asked why he had decided to change his previous stand and oppose the SST, Senator Clinton Anderson of New Mexico gave a typical answer: "I read my mail."

To the senators from Boeing it was a shattering defeat, and Henry Jackson announced that "the know-nothings have taken over." Senator Proxmire and the hard-working lobbyists of the environmental groups, led by Dr. Shurcliff's Citizens' League Against the Sonic Boom, had succeeded in stopping American technology. Snubbed and angry, President Nixon told the nation: "Today's action by the Senate in disapproving funds for continued development of the supersonic transport prototype is both distressing and disappointing. It represents a severe blow not only to the tens of thousands of workers affected, and to their families, but also to the United States' continued leadership position in the aerospace industries. More deeply it could be taken as a reversal of America's tradition of staying in the vanguard of scientific and technological advance. I am determined that this vote on the SST will not be a change in basic direction." Watergate was soon to close in on Nixon, preventing any such choice.

There was a last-ditch flurry of activity to save the Boeing on May 12 with a motion in the House of Representatives to continue the project at least until the end of June 1971. Commenting on the House action, William Allen, Boeing's chairman, said that although it was "tragedy for the United States not to have an SST" it could cost anything between $500 million and $1 billion to restart the project since subcontracts had already been terminated and would have to be renegotiated and the production team would have to be reassembled. By this time, however, Boeing had lost all heart for the contest. The Senate refused to go along with the House and the SST finally died on the night of 19–20 May 1971.

When the U.S. SST was killed, over $1 billion had been spent on its development, but the social cost was far higher. Seven thousand Boeing workers were laid off at once, together with 6,000 from General Electric. The city of Seattle, with 15 percent jobless, became a mini-disaster area.

Thousands of men began to look for new jobs and the Ph.D.s joined the dole queue. *Time* summed it up neatly as "a slowdown in the technology of haste," pointing out that "it was obvious to winners and losers alike that something new is afoot, a questioning of old values, old landmarks, old priorities."

The question now asked on both sides of the Atlantic was whether the death of the United States SST would be a mortal blow for Concorde. If the Americans had decided to opt out of the SST race, would they force others out too? The airport-noise issue was ominous. The British maintained a nervously respectful silence. The French reacted altogether differently. On March 25, Henri Ziegler, president of Aerospatiale, announced to the world that the future always disproved the beliefs of reactionaries. His statement ended on a resolutely confident note: "The Concorde program must be pursued with more energy and confidence than ever."

Evening Standard

"I don't care if it is a cardboard model—I'm flying in it to meet Pompidou!"

Concorde

HOPE IT'S NOT CATCHING

USA

Trog

The Observer

17

"Rotten Bad Luck"

In Europe, the British and French builders of Concorde watched with grim fascination as their mighty American competitor fought the combined forces of environmentalists and politicians. Now that two prototypes were flying from Fairford and Toulouse, the planemakers began to feel increasingly confident that the massive eight-year-old investment would pay off, even though the British press could not resist sniping at the project. A great deal of public skepticism had arisen since the dramatic takeoff of 001 and 002 had been flashed on Europe's television screens a year before. The British machine had spent months on the ground undergoing no less than 3,500 modifications, while the fatal English disease—industrial unrest—had affected the program.

The Concorde's Olympus engines had been delayed by an eleven-week strike at Rolls-Royce and technicians at Filton had exercised an overtime ban. Above all, there were nasty stories circulating in the press that Concorde might not be able to carry its projected 120-passenger payload across the Atlantic in the first few years of service.

The answers were soon to come. A major series of tests was planned for the summer of 1970, which would make or break Concorde. The flight program would determine the all-important drag characteristics of the airliner. Any miscalculation in Concorde's design would be identified, which could reveal the aircraft to be a hopelessly uneconomic proposition even for the most enthusiastic operator. On July 12, at the start of the vital drag tests, the *Sunday Times* commented that "Concorde's demonstration flight at Farnborough Air Show in September may well be its last."

Airlines as well as the governments watched the tests with immense care. The supersonic Concorde, which had no form of subsonic competition when it was launched in 1962, now had to compete with the Boeing 747, which offered airlines the welcome message of bigger seating capacity, lower overall operating costs, and higher profits. The new elephantine airliners cost at least £100 million each, and few world carriers could contemplate the purchase of both an expensive jumbo fleet and the even more costly Concorde. As a breakthrough aircraft carrying a heavy charge for research and development, Concorde was certain to have a high price tag. If the manufacturers now ran into serious technical trouble the airliner would price itself out of the market.

Throughout the summer months 001 and 002 flew regularly from their test bases, describing great arcs over the Mediterranean, Bay of Biscay, and North Sea. Each trip brought in more valuable data which was rushed through the computers and calculators. Then to the relief of the designers, management, and the whole Concorde operation on both sides of the Channel, the figures began to come out exactly as predicted, with only a tiny 1 percent margin of error.

Geoffrey Knight, the chairman of BAC's Commercial Airplane Aircraft Division, was elated. "On a project such as this, any experienced chap knows that there is at least a 50/50 chance that the numbers will come out wrong, and I think it is fair to say we have had our moments of anxiety about it going under. From the point of view of the chaps who want to cancel, it is rotten bad luck that the plane does all the things we said it would."

Now the airlines would have to face Concorde as a fact of life. The sales teams began to gird themselves for the rapidly approaching moment when the decision would move away from the technologists to the accountants and marketing men.

The confidence of Concorde's builders began to soar, and prospects seemed even better with the return of the British Conservative government in June 1970. A sigh of relief swept through the board rooms of the aircraft companies. After the turbulent years with Labour, the British planemakers had already begun to count their blessings, heralded by a Conservative administration. The industry's thoughts were well expressed by its arch enemy, Richard Wiggs, who believed that "the Labour government was basically against the Concorde project and would have canceled it if it could; the Conservatives [successors to the Conservative government which signed the Concorde agreement of 1962] basically support the Concorde and will allow the project to continue if it can."

Premier Heath had always been friendly toward Concorde and had been heard to say at Farnborough in 1966 that "one could not expect to bring Britain back to the forefront of the world without being prepared to spend a lot of money." Even more important, the new prime minister was positively pro-Europe and determined to reverse the humiliation he had suffered in 1963 when de Gaulle vetoed Britain's Common Market application after weeks of toil by him in his role as chief negotiator. The aerospace business looked forward to a bright future with the new government, but they soon began to wonder. Geoffrey Rippon, the new minister of technology, although on record as saying that Britain could not survive "flogging hand-knitted union jacks to tourists," began to speak ominously of a thoroughgoing review of the project. From other parts of the government there was talk of abrasive action to improve the performance of the British economy with "lame ducks" being left to fend for themselves and a painfully detailed scrutiny of public expenditure. It began to feel like 1964 all over again.

The new British government immediately went into a curious state of purdah about Concorde. In contrast to France—where the plane had become a national symbol used in cafés, supermarkets, and on branded products—scant attention was given to the aircraft in Britain. There was a minimum of publicity, and the new aviation minister, Frederick Corfield, a pipe-smoking West Country solicitor, seemed to be selected for his taciturnity. The press soon nicknamed him "Fearless Fred," whose belief in the supersonic revolution was so tempered with caution that he never made an unguarded statement. Even his office contained no model of Europe's most impressive aviation achievement.

Anxious about public opinion, and wondering whether to permit supersonic overflights, he planned elaborate operations for boom tests, in an 800-mile supersonic corridor down the west coast from Oban, in Scotland, to Cornwall in the south. It was the only route over which Concorde could gain a clear run without interfering with Britain's heavy commercial air traffic. Radar stations were placed on alert, and weather ships monitored the western approaches with special attention.

Flight operations were rudimentary compared with the enormous activity on the ground, some of which resembled a comedy film. All along the boom route, sample buildings had been wired by ministry scientists. Tests had been conducted in the magnificent medieval splendor of Salisbury Cathedral—with perhaps the most elegant and famous spire in England—called "Operation Underlord" (Understanding Loads on Religious Dwellings). A bang "no bigger than an eightpenny firework" had been set off outside. At the same time, bells were rung, and the effects were measured on delicate instruments. To the relief of the dean and chapter, the elegant spire appeared to be unaffected. "There is very little cause for concern about the primary structure of a cathedral judged by our experiments," the Farnborough scientists declared. Summing up, D. R. R. Webb claimed that "when Concorde flies supersonically it will cause a cathedral to vibrate in much the same way as it vibrates when anybody talks." To ensure that all would be well in the practical circumstances of a Concorde-sized boom, the ancient cathedrals of St. David's, in South Wales, and Truro, in Cornwall, were carefully wired and transducers installed. Other buildings, like blocks of flats and ordinary dwellings, buildings with big plate-glass windows and two doors, were also made ready. The press and television were also prepared for tests which were fixed for September 1. European and American TV crews poured into the area; reporters gathered in the West Country towns and villages. The locals gazed in wonderment at the weird microphones and electronic gear unloaded from the TV trucks.

On Tuesday September 1, the vast media machine went into action. Sound recordists strained their ears from the desolate coast of Scotland to the country towns of Cornwall. National attention was concentrated on the thousand-year-old cathedral of St. David's, in Pembrokeshire, to see what would happen to a priceless heritage. St. David's was right on the center of test pilot Trubshaw's flight path, as he climbed away from Fairford and headed for the north of Scotland to begin his Mach-2 run. The camera crews were alerted, pointing their telephoto lenses skyward; the sound recordists probed toward the north with their spindly microphone arrays. Anxious reporters tried to keep their eye on local inhabitants and birds, with an ear cocked for the expected bang. Just before 11 A.M. the message was flashed from the Ministry of Technology that Concorde was on its way, streaking toward them at 50,000 feet. Minutes passed before eager listeners heard what sounded like a gentle boom of distant thunder. It was a dreadful anticlimax for the newsmen. St. David's Cathedral was left safe and peaceful as Trubshaw shot past, fifteen miles off-course. "Ooops, Concorde off course shock," shouted The Sun on its front page. The international press was not amused, and many who knew of Trubshaw's generally poor opinion of the media wondered how a highly experienced test pilot could have made such an extraordinary error.

The Concorde was programmed to fly fifty supersonic flights down the west coast "boom alley," and soon protests were coming in. Wales felt aggrieved and rose up to complain about the infernal English machine. Wynford Evans of Haverford-west Council called on the government to abandon the tests shortly after they started. "I believe it was a deliberate act on either the part of the Ministry of Technology or the makers to be off-course over St. David's, so that monitoring equipment there could not give a proper reading," he said. He then added with Welsh shrewdness, "I think they deliberately misled the public in view of the fact that the world's press were present at St. David's; they could not afford a bad press." Concorde began to pick up very bad press, especially when it flew off-course, as it did again on October 3; no warning was given and villages were disturbed with unexpected bangs. As the *Western Mail* reported, "Cattle stampeded, buildings shook, and windows were shattered in West Wales yesterday as Concorde made its fastest supersonic flight down the Welsh coast." One farmer said that when he heard the bang "he felt as if there was something trying to rip his clothes off." In Cornwall there were complaints of cows aborting, walls cracking, and battery hens jumping up and down like Yo-Yos. For one person, it was almost like a poltergeist. "The windows rattled, the doors swung shut, and the dog didn't stop shivering all afternoon."

The boom tests were an appallingly ill-coordinated operation. Warnings never came, Concorde was off-course even when warnings were issued. Several times Concorde was early or late, dashing over Truro Cathedral and making a perfect sonic boom, all to no effect because the monitoring equipment was switched off. The only certainty was that there would be lots of pieces for the ministry to pick up, as 194 claims for damage compensation rolled in. The difficulty was assessing the legitimate ones. Often the ministry received ludicrous claims. A Pembrokeshire villager wrote for damages for a dozen jampots, claiming that they had exploded when Concorde flew over. Many poultry farmers said they lost eggs and that the boom had stopped their hens laying. The big headaches for the ministry were the hundreds of claims for cracked ceilings and glass windowpanes, none of which could be checked without large administrative cost. In many cases, particularly where farmers were concerned, the ministry tacitly accepted the claims at face value and paid up. However, one they did not pay was from a newly wedded Scottish couple from Oban. They claimed compensation for the cost of having a baby, since an untimely Concorde boom had interfered with their "rhythm method" of contraception.

The chances of the Concorde builders persuading the British government to allow supersonic overflight fell to zero after the boom tests. The tension among BAC executives visibly increased during the autumn of 1970 as they began to realize that the long silence on the part of the government and the increased sniping by the press could mean that Concorde might meet the same fate as its big American cousin. Early in 1971 an event occurred which shook the whole of the British aircraft industry to its foundation, spreading out to affect Europe and the whole aviation world. On 3 February 1971 British newspapers told the nation that their most renowned engineering company, Rolls-Royce, had gone bankrupt. The company whose products throughout the world were synonymous with the good name of British technology could no longer pay its bills, meet its workers' wages, or even settle the canteen accounts. Mary Wilson, the former prime minister's wife, who had made a name for herself as a poet, eloquently expressed the feelings of the whole country when she confessed that it was like "the loss of Gibraltar!" It was a traumatic shock for the government. Apart from the incalculable damage to Britain's good name, the company was supplying engines to thousands of airplanes and many of the world's air forces. One of the highest priorities was the Olympus development for Concorde; the other was the RB-211 for the Lockheed Tristar. The huge development cost and unforeseen technical problems on this engine were largely responsible for the Rolls-Royce crisis. It involved Lockheed, as well as Rolls.

Nobody in the Concorde team seriously believed that the British government would allow Rolls-Royce to collapse, but indirectly, the Rolls-Royce debacle was a very serious threat to Concorde.

The Heath government might be forgiven for regarding the aircraft industry with distinct coolness. It could hardly hold a high opinion of its management ability after the Rolls-Royce crash and having to keep it afloat on millions more of taxpayers' money to save the important Anglo-American deal or the Tristar. There would inevitably be fewer resources available for supersonic development should any difficult problems arise on the Concorde tests.

Keystone

LA GLOIRE

President Pompidou goes "one up" over Nixon, arriving in Concorde for the Azores Summit Meeting. The American leader admired the plane, but he was not allowed to fly in it.

The supersonic president, Georges Pompidou, accompanied by Henri Ziegler, chief executive of Aerospatiale, broadcasts to the French nation, flying at Mach 2 above the Bay of Biscay.

Aerospatiale

PROVING ITSELF

A much needed boost for the British image. Concorde flying at the Farnborough Air Show in 1971.

Anthony Wedgwood Benn, minister of technology and member of Parliament for Bristol South East, took his Concorde duties very seriously, donning full flying gear for a routine test flight.

Song for Europe   *The Observer*

18

The Mach-2 Tricolor

The Rolls-Royce–Lockheed operation managed to survive by the slenderest margin, yet another Anglo-American scheme was being set up with the avowed aim of killing Britain's other major aerospace project—Concorde.

A move was organized by environmentalists in New York to deprive Concorde of its most important route, the North Atlantic. This could be achieved by denying landing permission at Kennedy Airport on the grounds of excess noise. If Concorde could be stopped, then a major argument for the American SST would be removed. The two projects were linked, and the American environmentalists and politicians realized that they had an ally in

Richard Wiggs, the leading British opponent of Concorde. Although his movement did not have the stature or influence of the Coalition Against the SST, he had considerable nuisance value and regarded the Anglo-French plane as "a classic example of the Frankenstein syndrome. A monstrosity has been created beyond both the intentions and control of its creators and which is revealed as an anti-social menace." The British Anti-Concorde Project jumped at the idea of helping to destroy the European aircraft in New York. Ambitious New York Assemblyman Andrew Stein had decided late in 1970 to climb onto the environmentalist bandwagon in New York State. There were powerful political pressures behind the so-called airport noise lobby. Apart from the obviously affected residents, the huge acres of real estate surrounding city airports, like New York's, were becoming increasingly valuable building development sites—if the noise could be reduced. To many astute politicians, as well as voters, any reduction in decibels could be measured in thousands of dollars of development money. It had become an important national political issue that year and no one was surprised when New York led the way.

Promoting his cause and, by implication and association, that of the anti-SST and anti-Concorde lobby, Stein journeyed to England in the autumn to hear Concorde for himself. Holding press conferences in his suite at the Dorchester Hotel and making excursions into the wilds of rural Gloucestershire, he was pursued by cameramen and reporters. The natives of Gloucestershire, not unnaturally, were more than a little suspicious of what the well-heeled American was up to and reacted in a "very English and patriotic way" whenever Concorde was mentioned. He returned to New York to conduct his own version of what the English press suggested would be another Proxmire-style hearing.

At this point, the former minister of technology and M.P. for Bristol South East, Anthony Wedgwood Benn, decided to take up the challenge. Getting the *Sunday Times* to sponsor his trip, along with Robert Addley, Conservative M.P. for Bristol South West and the editor of the local Bristol paper, he set off for New York at the head of "The Bristol Concorde Mission." When the mission arrived, it set itself up in the Godfrey Hotel, and Benn urgently sought to tackle the press, muttering darkly about threats of a trade embargo if his appeal to reason failed.

At the same time, Richard Wiggs, leading another mission, hot-footed from Washington, where he had been lobbying at the Transportation Subcommittee hearings, and arrived in New York, issuing statements about the threat posed by Concorde. He urged the Americans to save the world from Concorde by banning it at New York.

It all looked like a twentieth-century revamp of Gilbert and Sullivan—a spectacle confirmed when the hearings actually began. The arena chosen for this curious exercise was a brown-tiled turn-of-the-century committee room "looking something like a public lavatory" in downtown Manhattan. Into this small, ancient, and noisy room scarcely 20 feet by 30 feet were packed a former British cabinet minister; a Bristol M.P.; a newspaper editor, Richard Wiggs; Proxmire aides, a presidential aide, and assorted environmentalists, together with a major contingent of press and television from Britain. The British public thought Concorde was on trial before the American people; in fact the United States press was conspicuous by its virtual absence. What purported to be a major arena of public controversy was in fact a single hearing set up unofficially by a junior member of the New York State Assembly.

Chairman Stein assembled his committee in a tiny room not designed for the hot lights of the TV cameras. Construction work going on outside made hearing impossible with the windows open. The session, which lasted all of two hours, began with Proxmire's aide rehearsing the now familiar anti-SST arguments. The first of the British witnesses, Richard Wiggs, promptly launched into a bitter personal attack on the man who had been responsible for Concorde, and who had consistently refused to see him while minister of technology. "Mr. Benn, in fact, only represents the builders of the Concorde and that section of the British Aircraft Corporation workers who seem to think they should be granted the privilege of continuing work on a machine which is both a prodigious financial lossmaker and an environmental monstrosity. If your bill has the effect of helping to kill Concorde, you will be doing the U.K. a great service," said Wiggs, claiming that "your bill has tremendous support in the U.K."

Benn's case rested more on philosophy than history. He reminded New Yorkers that Bristolians regarded their city as "the birthplace of America," invoking Cabot, the *Mayflower*, and even the S.S. *Great Britain*.* Through lack of cooperation by BAC, who rejected his suggestion to rename 001 "Great Britain," he could not develop his argument by pointing to the transatlantic "steamship of the air." He was as concerned about pollution as they were, pointing out with pride, "You can fish in the Thames before Big Ben. . . . For the Hudson and for the air above you, we wish you equal success." It was some time before he reached what many listening felt was the point of his peroration: "Before you discard, out of hand, the opportunity of improving aircraft by imposing impossible deadlines, join us in accelerating the improvement. Let's treat the problem with concern and effort; let's not turn the initials *SST* into an abbreviation for superstition."

Unfortunately the New Yorkers did not appreciate such a philosophic approach. "Man was not meant to live like an animal, cooped up," the Bristol mission were bluntly told. "He is supposed to open his windows and breathe some of God's fresh air and hear the crickets chirruping." Ironically, opening windows was what most of the people in the sweltering committee room wanted to do most at that very moment, but the roar of New York's traffic and construction work prevented it. Assemblyman Brewer launched into a performance that took even Chairman Stein by surprise with its ferocity. "Maybe the U.S. would be better off to become a second-rate nation than to go on sacrificing the flower of the nation's youth on the altar," continued Brewer, now striking a dramatic note that took the whole proceedings into a new dimension. It was some seconds before the astonished gathering realized that the assemblyman was denouncing President Nixon's handling of the war in Vietnam, not the SST. It was a strange climax to a curious event. *Sunday Times* readers were to learn about the occasion in Anthony Wedgwood Benn's weekend article, "My Fight to Save Concorde."

* The S.S. *Great Britain* was the world's first screw-driven passenger ship designed by Brunel. She was built at Bristol in 1843 where she is now preserved.

In fact it was the airlines who would be the final saviors of Concorde if they chose to be. The tests had proven successful and the manufacturers now felt sure that they could offer a safe plane, capable of doing what was originally specified. Although 16 airlines had placed options for 74 aircraft, the closer Concorde approached its design performance and entry into service, the harder it became to sell. In the eight years since Concorde was launched, the attitude toward air transport had changed. Flying had become a mass activity, and the airlines were dealing with an immense pent-up demand, reaching down to all levels in the community. Traffic grew steadily by 15 percent a year throughout the 1960s. Now bigger aircraft were needed for the future. While the Concorde was still under development, Boeing, with characteristic opportunism, had moved into the market of the 1970s with the 747 jumbo jet. Their breakthrough had as much to do with luck as foresight. In 1965 Boeing had lost the competition with Lockheed for the Pentagon's big C-5 military transport. As H. W. Withington put it, "When the C-5 contract went down I had a list of a hundred guys, and I said to Bill Allen [president of Boeing] you're going to need them." Allen listened to Withington's advice and deployed the team on designing a commercial airliner on the back of the failed military contract. It emerged as the 747, capable of carrying 300–400 people in armchair comfort over a 5,000-mile range.

The jumbo jet offered good operating figures and the ability to go for the cheaper end of the market. Speed, to the operators, was held to be subsidiary to lower fares and higher profits. The airline chiefs began to buy their fleets of jumbo jets, and the Concorde salesmen wondered if they would ever be interested in Concorde until the big new airliners could fill all their seats.

The big companies who had originally taken out options on Concorde began to show their coolness to the supersonic airliner, in spite of the thousands of computerized calculations, statistical models, and evaluations which BAC presented to them. Stories, leaked to the press, seemed to indicate that the major airlines, including BOAC, found the operating economics of the Concorde-sized SST less and less attractive as the time approached to turn options into firm orders.

Pan Am took the lead in "cooling" enthusiasm for Concorde.

The occasion they chose could hardly have been more appropriate or the location more ironic. *Time* magazine sponsored a VIP study tour of the Concorde. Influential congressmen, businessmen, and top airline brass were flown across from the United States. At the sumptuous Air France building in Paris on 7 February 1970, Henry Luce III of *Time* welcomed his guests to a magnificent lunch. Sparing no adjectives, he extolled the virtues of the coming generations of supersonic aircraft which would improve international relations with "instant visits." "We are not bringing know-how or capital or artful salesmanship," he hastened to add, lest his airline guests wondered where his loyalties lay; "instead we are bringing affirmation, praise, and perhaps an order book or two. The excitement of this visit is greatly heightened not just by the novelty of seeing Concorde itself, but by what it symbolizes of the future and what it implies for the spectrum of that future which we trust will be broad and varied and brightly colored."

Najeeb Halaby, then president of the world's most influential airline, Pan Am, however, took it upon himself "to bring some cold oxygen into some of the euphoria." After a polite tribute to what he termed "this fabulous group of gallant Gauls and brave British" for an "unquestionable tour de force," he continued: "It is one of the most fabulous stories of forced technological growth in the history of technology and of man. The flight testing has gone unusually well and when four hard-bitten, well-paid, clear-eyed, grizzled airline captains say it's well done, you know it is." It was only after he had carefully extolled the advantages for what he termed "the billion dollar show," as he liked to call the Boeing 747 (the description "jumbo" was avoided for reasons of imagery), that Halaby began to turn on the "cold oxygen." He questioned whether the public might find Concorde "old fashioned because of its constriction, back to the tube, you might say, from the living room." He began to reveal doubts on other sensitive areas like operating costs, passenger capacity, and maintenance expenses, all of which boiled down to a policy he described as "fly now, buy later." In a dramatic bid to avoid a decision, he suggested that Concorde should be shelved and developed into a larger airplane, whose economics would meet new airline demands. The British and French planemakers, still bearing the scars of their battle with the politicians and civil servants, winced when Halaby suggested, "For the long run, our brave British friends and our gallant Gallic partners and their parliaments themselves have a very tough question. Are you prepared to produce a very limited quantity of Concorde 1, and then face up to planning and financing a Super-Concorde, an airplane which will better meet the requirements of both passengers and airlines and will be superior to the Soviet and competitive with the U.S. SST?"

The proposal astonished some of his listeners, who remembered that Halaby had been responsible for President Kennedy's SST back in 1963 and now headed the company which had rushed in first with Concorde options. He was now rejecting the almost completed plane, and asking for a Super-Concorde to compete with an American design which might never arrive. There was a sharp anti-British backhand at the end of his performance. "It is wonderful and remarkable to hear the minister of transport talk of Concorde as a vehicle toward entry into the Common Market and the suggestion by implication was into a United States of Europe; if that is so, then surely part of the cost of developing Concorde is entente cordiale, being now 'entente Concordiale.' If he really means that, then surely the two governments can write off a very substantial portion of a two-billion development cost as the entry fee into the Common Market." The brazen temerity of an American businessman telling Britain and France to scrap a project on which they had worked for nearly a decade and to write off the gigantic bill as the price of Britain's ticket to Europe must have come close to provoking a diplomatic incident. Afterward, Geoffrey Knight, chairman of BAC Filton Division, icily remarked, "I feel something warm and wet trickling down my back." "That was no knife," Halaby interrupted, "that was a needle. And it was aimed lower than your back."

Concorde still possessed a sheet anchor which the government dared not move. It was a political plane, inexorably locked into Britain's Common Market strategy. Cancellation was unthinkable for a European like Edward Heath, while there was the slightest chance of Britain entering the EEC. In 1970 the omens were extremely good for British entry. The French government had become far more flexible and even encouraging. The difficult obstacles between Britain and Europe had been reduced to a manageable size. Almost within days of his election, Heath had called for a reopening of negotiations. By the autumn a team had been assembled under Geoffrey Rippon, which began a series of meetings lasting to the spring of 1971. For all the apparent progress, however, there was still the fear that France would veto the application at the last minute.

The British government did not want to cast the slightest shadow over the great Anglo-French Concorde project at such a delicate stage in the negotiations. On the other hand, there had to be some limit on the huge investment being made by the British government against what was appearing to be an increasingly uncertain market. The Concorde sales team spoke optimistically of selling anything up to 200 aircraft, which would bring a rousing £2,000 million contribution to each country's balance of payments. Hopefully, sales of this order would even repay the immense research and development bill, although both civil servants and manufacturers were cagey about this possibility.

The prime minister decided that the only way of dealing with Concorde was to "de-politicize" it, removing it from the political turmoil surrounding the Common Market negotiations, sealing it off from attack by political opponents in Britain. He was able to postpone the adoption of an official cabinet position on the project by throwing the whole issue at Lord Rothschild, the head of the Central Policy Review Committee. The donnish Rothschild had been coordinator of research for the mammoth multinational oil combine, Shell. Heath had called him into government service to analyze major problems facing the British cabinet and the criteria on which the government should attempt their solution. A small team of very high caliber had been assembled by Rothschild, who worked directly with the prime minister. Some time in early 1971 the team turned its considerable brainpower to an analysis of every facet of the Concorde program.

While the British "think tank" considered Concorde with slide rules and computers, President Pompidou decided to throw the full weight of the Elysée behind the enterprise. If Britain was indifferent and hesitant, France was in no way inhibited in supporting the aircraft designed to challenge American hegemony of the air. Plans were drawn up to show Concorde as a proud French achievement, not only in metropolitan France, but also in politically important areas like South America. Pompidou decided that he would be the first passenger to be flown in the splendid new airliner, whose superb engineering and magnificent design brought grudging admiration even from its bitterest critics.

On 7 May 1971, President Pompidou decided to take his first trip in Concorde. The tricolors flew proudly at Toulouse, and the two prototypes—one the French 001 and the other the British 002, flown over especially for the event—were lined up on the runway before the big crowd. For the British team it was a painfully embarrassing moment. Although the British press was querulously asking why Britain seemed disinterested in a project on which the taxpayer had spent millions, the prime minister had decided not to attend. Inevitably France annexed Concorde to her own propaganda advantage. Pompidou hurried straight past the British 002, with its crew standing beneath the needle-nose, and climbed aboard Turcat's 001.

Two armchairs had been installed amidships with cameras and microphones. President Pompidou made the best of his chances. Hurtling at twice the speed of sound ten miles high, he broadcast to the French nation, "From the technical point of view, the results have been achieved and the aircraft responds to the most ambitious hopes. From the point of view of money, the government has decided to pursue the project to the end. On the commercial side, the only uncertainties which remain and which do not depend on us I am sure will be overcome. How could anybody imagine that for the first time in history humanity will recoil before what is a spectacular and peaceful advance."

There were, however, some signs of hostility to the project in France, although the opposition could not be compared to the strength of the British feeling. *L'Express,* the magazine which had been started by the French radical leader Jean-Jacques Servan-Schreiber, struck a sour note in the euphoria, following Pompidou's Mach-2 presidential flight. It claimed that "Concorde is merely one of the last great grand designs of General de Gaulle, and one of the sole prestige projects which have survived him." Millions of Frenchmen would want to know why so much was being poured away on Concorde when the problems on the ground were very severe, with insufficient housing and bad public transport and pensions.

The French aerospace lobby merely dismissed Servan-Schreiber as being in the pay of the American aircraft industry. In fact, as a political opponent of the Gaullist government, Servan-Schreiber, together with other opponents, naturally singled out Concorde for attack as the regime's favorite status symbol. The attacks were not confined to Servan-Schreiber. In 1970, a major attack was launched in, of all places, *Paris Match*. In a devastating editorial, the magazine bluntly complained, "If it had been more closely examined its risks might have been judged out of all proportion to its benefits."

Even worse was to come with a leak in the French press of a confidential Gaullist report which attacked the whole rationale of Concorde. Written by the influential Charles de Chambrun, president of the UNR * foreign affairs committee, the report in the form of a very confidential letter to de Gaulle was printed in the radical magazine *Le Canard Enchaîné*, in September 1970. Occupying an influential position, de Chambrun had access to secret reports and his views had to be taken seriously. It was the most telling attack so far in France. De Chambrun claimed that France had thrown away the advantages which she had won in building the world's first medium-range carrier, the Caravelle, by concentrating all her energies and resources on Concorde. This was in bitter reaction to the failure to sell large numbers of Caravelles in the United States. In spite of the call by Air France for a stretched Caravelle, France had chased the prestige symbol of a supersonic airliner. This had played into the hands of the Anglo-Saxons. Even worse, the Anglo-French Supersonic Aircraft Agreement was an "agreement of dupes," because it allowed Britain to develop supersonic civil engines and sell them. Britain would gain more from engine sales than France could achieve from her engine know-how. De Chambrun castigated the manufacturers for their wild spending and the six program modifications between December 1962 and June 1968, with a plane going from 90 tons to 170 and a budget out of control. De

* UNR: Union de la Nouvelle République—the political party formed to support President de Gaulle.

Chambrun hinted that this was bordering on a scandal. Under the title "Les 5.000 milliards de la grandeur," *Le Canard Enchaîné* went on to point out that de Chambrun was warning his colleagues about the "impostures" of the new technocracy. He accused the technocrats of using the government to obtain huge credits for their favorite projects, and "once having got the money, escaping the system of Parliamentary control. They were short-circuiting any possible Parliamentary control, only submitting fractions of the problem, keeping well hidden their true objectives." For de Chambrun, this put democracy itself in danger.

The long letter from de Chambrun ended with the usual Gallic flourish, "Please accept, dear companion, the expression of my best sentiments." As *Le Canard Enchaîné* could not resist pointing out, they were "dear, very dear."

In general, the French people remained totally indifferent to these attacks on Concorde which they regarded as almost the antics of a lunatic fringe. As one top French Concorde executive put it, "Go and complain to any Frenchman about Concorde and he will push you off the pavement." The French could hardly understand Richard Wiggs' campaign, and when he took advantage of the *London Times* advertising service which guaranteed that any ad inserted in a London newspaper would also appear simultaneously in *La Stampa, Die Welt*, and *Le Monde*, there was some hesitation and embarrassment in France about carrying such an antipatriotic advertisement.

Certainly France had never shown any anxiety over Concorde's effect on the environment. Indeed it is regarded inside France as something of a joke. The French Air Force has never shown any hesitation in flying supersonically over France, and the famous case at Vézelay, where three people were killed because of the sonic boom, had more effect in Britain than France. The testing of Concorde at all supersonic speeds has taken place over many parts of France, the plane sometimes trailing a sonic boom from the Channel to the Mediterranean. According to Pierre Satre, the technical director of Aerospatiale, there are few complaints, or if there are, the gendarmes do not pass them on. In any case "you can only hear the bang in the country; the towns are far too noisy."

Of real concern to the French government was whether the British would keep their nerve. Fourteen days after President Pompidou's famous flight, there was an attempt to find out the strength of Britain's commitment. As the last set piece of the Common Market negotiations Edward Heath journeyed to Paris for a man-to-man session with Pompidou at the Elysée. It was an oral examination in Europeanism for the British prime minister, who was by now very good at the subject. The discussions ranged over an enormously wide area, from sterling to the role of Europe in the world. The two leaders ended their conversations with "complete identity of views as to the aim to be achieved." Concorde was certainly one of these aims.

By the end of June the champagne corks were popping in Luxembourg as Geoffrey Rippon's team drank a toast of celebration with their European counterparts. All that remained was for Heath to drive the legislation through Parliament, before he signed the Treaty of Accession on 1 January 1973. Concorde could now become not merely an affair between Britain and France but a question to be dealt with on a European level.

Although Britain's progress toward entry into the EEC was rapid, the government still delayed making a final decision on the future of Concorde. The occasional leak from the Rothschild "think tank" seemed to be encouraging. They analyzed the aircraft's economics in detail and assessed its impact on the whole field of advanced technology in Britain and Europe. Here they were moving in the realms of speculative rather than calculative assessment, but it was recognized that while "spinoff" is difficult to cost, the higher engineering requirements for everything from machine tools to avionics were having a stimulating impact in an important area of industry.

The arguments that weighed most heavily in the final Rothschild analysis and which clinched the recommendation made to the government were, first, the importance of the aircraft as a European project. Concorde had a far greater significance than would any conventional airliner, principally because it was fulfilling its role in building a base of technological cooperation with Europe. Moreover, if Britain were to withdraw, the political consequences—particularly for Anglo-French relations at a critical stage of the final negotiations to enter Europe—would be hard to imagine.

With Concorde cleared by the Rothschild think tank, Heath appointed Michael Heseltine the new Concorde boss, the complete opposite to the reticent Corfield who was famous for caution within the industry. Now it was Heseltine's task to get Concorde sold, and his impact was soon felt in the corridors of Weybridge and Bristol. Heseltine's dashing image and his ready use of the press and television to build up public confidence in the project soon earned him the title "Michael Brilliantine."

But as the new minister was to find out, winning orders for Concorde was going to be no easy matter. Apart from the increasing reluctance of the airlines to make any definite commitment to the supersonic and the worldwide recession in air travel, the American environmental lobby still threatened to make the aircraft unacceptable in the United States by fixing local airport noise regulations beyond anything that Concorde could reasonably be expected to meet. However, the British and French governments were now absolutely resolute in their determination to introduce supersonic airline services, and they knew they could force the pace. Both BOAC and Air France were state-owned airlines, holding an important competitive position against Pan Am and TWA. If they introduced a Concorde express service it would mount a serious challenge to American passenger traffic.

BOAC had been an early supporter of supersonic transportation, sitting on the Supersonic Transport Aviation Committee in the 1950s. The relationship between BOAC and the British government is an equivocal one depending very much on personalities at the top. Its relationship with the British aircraft industry has always been ambivalent, with a strong atmosphere of suspicion going back many years. The national flag carrier had always been closely connected with Concorde, but it had often played its own game against both governments and manufacturers. As a major world carrier, the airline had to fight for a share of the market against strong competition, especially on the North Atlantic, and mainly from the American airlines Pan Am and TWA. BOAC recognized its duty to encourage the national aviation industry, but it also had a primary responsibility to act as one of the world's most profitable and successful airlines. This depended primarily, but not solely, on the efficiency of its aircraft. Airline and manufacturers did not always agree on what was the most efficient aircraft; both had their own way of working out the figures. BOAC had consistently supported British aircraft in the past with the purchase of the Comet and the Britannia, but it had become skeptical about being a guinea pig for the British aircraft industry and having to pay the cost.

The airline had fought publicly to extricate itself from buying British VC-10s, and the Concorde's manufacturers feared that the same situation might repeat itself. This time the stakes were far higher. Not only was there a French connection, but Concorde was a vital part of advanced British technology. It was far too important to be left to the commercial decision of BOAC.

As Concorde became a more credible proposition for commercial aviation in 1970, the board of BOAC, led now by Keith Granville, knew that it would have no choice. Either Concorde would "go away," as TWA and the Americans hoped, or they would be pressed into operating the new airliner. BOAC showed little sign of wanting to start supersonic operations, even though Concorde proved itself capable of fulfilling its promised performance. There were suspicious press leaks from the anti-Concorde lobby that BOAC did not want the plane and that it had estimated that each one would lose the airline over £2 million a year, according to their own figures.

In a long and difficult series of negotiations, BOAC used every trick to win a favorable contract with the government. If they had to fly British then there should be some cover against losses. BOAC maintained that there was a problem of operating Concordes at the same time as jumbo jets. If Concorde were aimed at the first-class market it would surely hit the profitability of their regular airline traffic, making each jumbo more expensive to fly because of the loss of the high yield of first-class passengers. They also wanted to ask for a "stretched" Concorde, thinking that the present aircraft could never be profitable. The back-room teams at BOAC carried out a wide-range cost analysis based on many different assumptions. "We carried out an analysis of Concorde profitability based on six different assumptions," said David Nicholson, recent chairman of British Airways. "In one we lost a packet and in the others we made a thumping profit." In the end, two assessors out of three believed Concorde to be unprofitable, but the government wanted a different answer.

The British and French governments held the initiative in starting the ball rolling for world orders. Once they had pressed their airlines to buy Concorde they knew the world air travel scene would inevitably change. They prepared to "shotgun" the world's airlines into supersonic flight.

San Francisco Examiner

"If one SST traveling at twice the speed of sound can shatter 800,000 square feet of glass in one second, how many square feet of glass can four SSTs traveling . . ."

British Airways

SUPERSONIC SALESMANSHIP

Orders at last! Sir George Edwards happily concludes a sales agreement in 1972 with Keith Granville, chief executive of BOAC, for the delivery of five Concordes at a cost of 115 million pounds, including facilities and spares.

Selling the Shah. Michael Heseltine, Britain's minister of aerospace, joins the Shah of Iran in a Concorde flight during the aircraft's 1972 round-the-world tour. Iran Air has expressed an interest in three aircraft.

AP

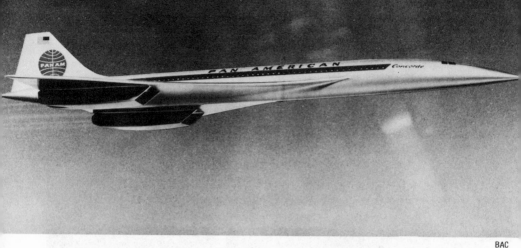

BAC

CALLING IT ALL OFF

The dream that would not come true: an artist's impression of Concorde flying in Pan Am livery.

Charles Lindbergh throws his prestige against the SST and campaigns to stop civil supersonic operations.

AP

Charles Seawell, chairman of Pan Am, killed off Anglo-French hopes of capturing the U.S. market by cancelling his Concorde options in January 1973.

Pan Am

Charles Tillinghast, chairman of TWA, followed Pan Am's example. He condemned Concorde's "dismal economics."

TWA

"Now, costing on this aircraft is simplicity itself—just think of a number and keep doubling it."

19

"Hitting a Brick Wall"

Three weeks before the crucial Pan Am decision on Concorde was due, a top-level sales team led by Geoffrey Knight landed at New York's Kennedy Airport. Knight, the ex-marine who had masterminded the drive to sell Concorde, was in no doubt about the magnitude of the task facing his team. The Pan Am decision was critical; if the largest international American carrier endorsed the Concorde with firm orders, the rest of the world's airlines would fall into the basket like a pack of dominos. There was one forbidding obstacle to any successful deal: the airlines had been badly hit by the stagnation in passenger traffic on the North Atlantic which had hit all airlines in 1970. To make matters worse, Pan Am passenger traffic failed to grow for the first time in many years, just as they were introducing their jumbo-jet fleet which was doubling airline seating capacity. These factors, together with other anxieties about management and efficiency, meant that the company was on the verge of bankruptcy. In spite of Pan Am's historic interest in Concorde, the chances of the American company finding £1,000 million for even a small supersonic fleet seemed out of the question. As one of the sales team put it, "We knew we couldn't sell to Pan Am because of their financial position, so we realized that there was absolutely no chance of them saying 'yes, we will buy' on January 31," the date of their option deadline. "What we tried very hard to do was to get them to extend their option decision to a later date." Impressively English, Knight's ready sense of humor and incisive manner had given him essential access to the American airline bosses. They "liked his style," which owed more to David Niven than the usual American salesman. Even the French had accepted without demur that Knight was the right man to be the Concorde "supersalesman."

When the team assembled in Knight's suite at New York's plush Hotel Pierre, the three British, one French, and two Americans held the first of many strategy meetings in their makeshift headquarters. Outside, the bare trees of Central Park seemed incongruous in the springlike sunshine of the warmest January in living memory. Someone remarked that it was a favorable omen. The team realized they were going to need it; following another year of huge losses, Pan Am's bankers had just agreed to continue their massive $280 million loan to keep the airline afloat. The American press and public still held an equivocal view about supersonic transport. It was two years since Congress had killed off the Boeing project and the United States was very cool toward a European successor. There was talk of landing restrictions and prohibitive noise regulations being imposed by Congress.

The newspapers had been full of stories about "The Bird That Won't Die" or "America's SST: Sleeping Monster or Dead Duck?" Senator Proxmire had been busy holding another set of Joint Economic Subcommittee hearings in Washington, just to keep up the political pressure against a possible revival of the Boeing project. President Nixon had managed to squeeze a small contingency fund to keep the SST study alive, but Boeing had finally given up hope. Just before Christmas they dismantled their second huge model SST and packed it up for shipment to a Florida museum. The local Seattle paper remarked acidly, "Proxmire killed America's first-generation SST. Its mock-up on public display will serve as a monument to his shortsightedness." In fact, the latest of Proxmire's hearings had been squarely aimed at the Concorde.

He had found a new ally. The veteran air hero, Charles Lindbergh, had fired off a broadside against SSTs in an article to *The New York Times.* "My personal conclusion is that the regular operation of SSTs in their present state of development will be disadvantageous both to aviation and to the peoples of the world. I believe we should prohibit their scheduled operation on or above United States territory as long as their effect on our overall environment remains unsatisfactory." Because he was an important figurehead on the board of Pan Am, many assumed that other directors shared his view that it would be best for all concerned if Concorde would quietly go away.

BAC was also chasing the second major American airline, TWA, but if the chances with Pan Am looked gloomy, the prospects with TWA looked far worse. Their finances were a good deal healthier than Pan Am's; but in a significant report in *The Wall Street Journal* TWA's chairman, Charles Tillinghast, cast extreme doubts over any early supersonic purchase by his airline. According to the report, British airlines had attempted to create chaos "with their cheap North Atlantic fares that summer" which Tillinghast believed "perhaps eliminated whatever slim chance" remained that the United States carriers would be able to afford to purchase Concorde. In any event, Tillinghast found it "difficult to see anything that would lead us to make an affirmative decision." As if to emphasize the finality of the American position, he said he was "certain that Pan Am can't and won't decide in favor of the plane." The "can't" was taken to be a reference to Pan Am's well-known financial difficulties. They were not their own masters; the giant corporation was virtually a hostage to the consortium of bankers bailing them out.

Knight's men immediately addressed their attention to Pan Am's bankers.

Just before 10 A.M. on the morning of January 18, the team left the neo-baroque of the Pierre for the glass and chrome modernity of the First National City Bank on Park Avenue. The Concorde men were meeting some of the hundred bankers flown in from all over America. It was all a "very friendly chat over coffee and biscuits" before the audience filed into the auditorium and the presentation began.

The arguments and case for Concorde's profitability were moved with logic and precision. "Selling an airplane is not a simple business," one of the presenters later confessed; "to put it crudely, you have to convince an airline that if it doesn't have the plane it's going to lose money." Now that they could predict what was going to happen to Pan Am's traffic once BOAC and Air France were operating Concorde on competitive routes, the presentation was much easier. To back up their case they produced the most powerful argument of all: a market study recently conducted in America which showed that even at increased fares, business traffic opted for the fastest airplane. The survey had been undertaken by Market Facts Inc., and their findings showed that most business travelers currently traveling at economy fares in subsonic jets would pay up to 40 percent more in fares to fly in Concorde.

The presentation had seemed to go very well, and lunch with the bankers was an enthusiastic and "very democratic affair." The long and apparently friendly meal was followed up that evening by a reception held at the Pierre, timed to coincide with the arrival in New York of British aviation minister Michael Heseltine.

Back amid the trompe-l'oeil pilasters of the Pierre, "the atmosphere became very mellow." Even the more pessimistic members of the team started shortening the odds on the private betting book they were keeping on the final outcome.

Selling the bankers was one thing, but securing an actual order from Pan Am was another.

Pan Am's vice-presidents, technical managers, and engineers had paid frequent visits to the British and French plants over the years, including one famous visit by an aged senior pilot who almost "bent" Concorde in trying it out. But detailed discussions on purchasing did not begin until very late in the day. "Pan Am did not seriously begin evaluating Concorde until no more than six weeks before the decision" was BAC's view. "They did not get down to the short strokes until a week or a fortnight before the deadline. More important, they were still changing their minds on the last day." It was this haste to meet an artificial deadline that the Concorde team knew was endangering their hopes of a sale. In the BAC view "someone at the very senior level decided that once and for all they had to be told which way to go, and that a decision had to be made." The reason given by a senior executive of Pan Am was simpler: "We had an evaluation team of about ten which had been working on Concorde for months. We had made a decision that enough company time and money had been spent on Concorde evaluations, and there were immediately pressing decisions which had to be made about whether to order more 747s." The rush seemed unnecessary to the Concorde men, who felt that their chances would be made better by a "more sensible selling situation." It seemed a little unfair to them that Pan Am, having created the option situation back in 1963 to suit its purposes, was trying to use it to force a final decision. Pan Am "was fundamental to Concorde." "If we sell to Pan Am then everybody would have to react," was the view of the team. But the converse was equally true. If they failed to sell to Pan Am, then "we were faced with a hell of a public relations problem."

The major problem that faced Geoffrey Knight in selling the Anglo-French supersonic was convincing skeptical airlines that in spite of its higher price (nearly twice that of the 747) and bigger operating costs, it really would make money for the airlines. BAC executive John Isles rationalized their difficulties in trying to sell Concorde to the apparently reluctant airlines, explaining, "Every aircraft has been bought, historically, on a basis of lower operating costs. Here they were confronted with an aircraft which, for the first time, had higher operating costs. There was no historic precedent that could be used to justify it. Concorde was faster and more expensive; the precedent was for aircraft to be faster and less expensive." The question was would the doubling of speed and the halving of time offset the extra cost of operation and create an attractive prospect for business traffic. The salesmen believed that their market surveys and computer models of airline operations proved that Concorde could be profitable to operate. But their airline audience was skeptical. They had been caught before rushing into the wide-body era with the huge jumbo jets, which although they cost 30 percent less to operate had demanded massive investment in airport plant and equipment. The sudden increase in carrying capacity meant that thousands of seats had been for sale for years with nobody to fill them. "This disastrous effect on airlines over the last three years on the financial front has hurt Concorde terribly," was the view of Isles; "to my mind it all stems from the hasty purchase of that one airplane, the Boeing 747."

The Pan Am negotiations had their own curious style; Knight and his men knew that it was going to be difficult getting to see the right people at Pan Am. Of all airlines they had encountered, they found great difficulty in gaining access to senior staff at Pan Am. Of course, as one of them pointed out, "To say that we, as manufacturers of Concorde, or Boeing, or any of the manufacturers can tell a large airline their business would be wrong. They would be affronted by it. All we can hope to do is 'to spur their thoughts.' "

It was hard for members of the Concorde team to communicate with Pan Am. More than one member of the team would have been very happy to have been "put through the wringer" for a face-to-face confrontation. Instead of that, they "sat in the Pierre and waited for the phone to ring. It was very much up to us to engineer meetings and to try to find out what they were doing." It was left to the individual members of Knight's team to ring up their opposite numbers to fix lunches and meetings. "Although the two teams never met officially at any one time in the negotiations, we each did it separately." Often, the individuals on the two sides would meet for lunch in smart, dimly lit New York restaurants, like the Cheval Blanc, over large scotches and steaks. The Concorde men collected snippets of information gleaned by "subtle or very direct" questioning. Through these, they tried to piece together what was happening in the Pan Am building several blocks away. The Americans were used to this poker game. They sat in air-conditioned executive suites, shirt sleeved and sporting their ruby-set fraternity rings like an old school organization. To BAC it became more and more like fencing in the dark.

At last a pattern began to emerge. Pan Am's main concern was the high purchase price of $30 million and the manufacturers' projected operating costs. The initial optimism began to fade after long days trekking between the Pierre and the Pan Am building. Even the receptionist's smile greeting them on the forty-fifth floor became noticeably "more and more strained the more often she saw us." The Concorde men began to realize that "something quite startling had to happen."

It all came down to a crucial series of decisions for Pan Am. Neither they, nor anyone else, had any experience of supersonic operations. Confidence was needed for such a decision, and for a number of reasons, not least Pan Am's current financial plight, the airline distrusted the supersonic performance figures. Concorde had always come within 1 percent of its predicted performance, and the manufacturers saw no reason to doubt that this would be translated into the production aircraft. But Pan Am's evaluators were skeptical. An error of 5 percent would rob a supersonic of half its passenger capacity, with disastrous financial results. Full reserves were another bone of contention. FAA regulations had been based on the United States SST which had never flown. As a result of flight experience on Concorde, the British felt that the American demands were very high. But persuading the FAA to modify its hypothetical rules for lack of hard evidence was a tough job. There was a further major difference over whether the Concorde would reach its cruising altitude in a smooth climb or in a series of steps. The so-called step climb was necessary with subsonic jets because of air traffic problems, but Concorde would operate well above them, and a fast climb out would save 3,000 pounds of fuel on any trip. Against a total payload of only 25,000 pounds, this represented 300 miles of extra range or another 10 passengers. The cruise climb had already been accepted by the European air traffic authorities, but not by the Americans.

In the face of these mounting objections the Concorde team began to wonder whether the "buy American" policy of United States airlines was enforcing itself behind the scenes. They began to experience a "feeling of helplessness." Every argument was subjective; and they were never given the formal opportunity to argue against the case as a full team across a table with the Pan

Am team. "I knew roughly what their thinking was but had not been given anything to attack," was the way in which one of the BAC executives summed up his feelings.

Just as the Concorde team in New York was believing it really was "up against a brick wall" another bombshell made their task even more difficult. On Sunday January 20, *The London Observer* carried front-page headlines, "U.S. Airlines Turn Down Concorde." To many it seemed a stab in the back. *The Observer* had for years adopted the role of Concorde's most determined critic. Every single piece of evidence which could be accumulated by its correspondent, Andrew Wilson, against the aircraft—some of the evidence ridiculous—had been used in an almost religious hostility toward the project. The fact that *The Observer* was anti-Concorde did not dilute the impact of the article, which had clearly been based on information leaked from Pan Am's board. It gave the impression that the board had already taken the decision not to buy Concorde because it failed to meet four out of five criteria on range, service capability, passenger comfort, and operating costs. It only qualified on speed. "I am told," continued the well-briefed report, "that the figures used in Pan Am's analysis were 'extremely conservative.' " The article was datelined New York and went on to spread more gloom about the possibility of Concorde ever being allowed to land in the United States. "To add to the difficulties—not to say crisis—facing the British and French makers with the impending cancellation of 17 to 23 strategically placed orders, a new move will be made next week to restrict Concorde operations by BOAC and Air France in the United States. A bill being introduced in the New York State legislature by Republican sponsors will fix sideline noise limits at New York airport at 108 decibels—four decibels lower than the promised Concorde noise level."

The press story appeared on the same day that Sir George Edwards, now the chairman of BAC, left London airport for New York. Rumors spread like wildfire that he was on a last-ditch mission to save the situation. When he landed at Kennedy Airport he told reporters with a grim determination, "If the options were being canceled, I would not be here."

The Observer report was painfully near the mark. But no board decision had been made. As a matter of policy it was left to the management of the company; the board would only be involved should purchase be recommended. This was well known to the team in New York, but clearly had been overlooked by *The Observer*, which had overstated the finality of the matter. Reaction to the carefully leaked information caused Pan Am considerable embarrassment, but their denials that no decision had been made did not halt press speculation that cancellation was imminent. This did not stop the *London Daily Express* from calling on the president of the United States to "smooth a path for the airliner."

The reaction of Concorde men in New York was angry. "What we really wanted now was to get that Pan Am order, not just because of Concorde, but because we would be screwing Andrew Wilson." This sentiment was shared by many people back in Britain, judging from the flow of letters supporting Concorde that appeared in the press. Some papers talked of "The Great American Double Cross" and in New York the salesmen tried to tackle "the brick wall of Pan American's lack of enthusiasm."

Across the world, Concorde was flying into trouble of a very different kind. The first British prototype was on its way to Johannesburg for "hot and high" performance trials at the high-altitude Jan Smuts Airport. Piloting the plane was the director of flight operations and chief test pilot for BAC, Brian Trubshaw. He was being hunted to South Africa by delegates from the British anti-Concorde lobby anxious to organize demonstrations against the plane at Johannesburg. At Luanda in Angola, Trubshaw flew into a scene that surpassed even the worst that the Anti-Concorde Project could do. As he taxied Concorde for takeoff, two flags fluttered out of the cockpit window, a Union Jack and what Trubshaw believed to be the Angolan flag. The result was a near riot. An airport car screamed up to prevent takeoff and the famous British pilot found himself hauled before officials. The flag that Concorde had been flying as a courtesy gesture to Portugal was in fact the flag of the rebel "Popular Liberation Movement for Angola." After paying a hefty fine out of his own pocket for the mistake, Trubshaw awkwardly marched back to the aircraft, which eventually took off after some hours' delay. It was not long before an instant mob of outraged Portuguese citizenry was crowding into the gardens of the British consulate at Luanda with banners declaring "Down with Concorde" and "We support the I.R.A." BAC officials described the mistake as a "shopping error." Before the plane left Bristol, a junior official of BAC had been sent to a local ship's chandler to collect the flags for the tour, and of the two flags which the storekeeper had produced for Angola he had chosen the more attractive one.

The "hot and high" trial in New York reached fever pitch. It was a very different situation from the BOAC negotiations which had also been tough. "Every dealing with BOAC had been a whacking big confrontation," recalled a BAC executive, "but our assumptions which may have been optimistic got a fair hearing against BOAC's views which we believed to be pessimistic. Every opinion had a force, except for price and performance; nobody knew for certain, as the airplane was without precedent." While the team was sweating out the last few days before the deadline, *The Observer* kept up the pressure with another broadside which announced that not only had Pan Am made its decision but that it was demanding the return of its deposit money. In Parliament, the aerospace minister, Heseltine, assured worried M.P.s that no decision had yet been made. Parliament sent its best wishes to the sales efforts being made in New York. The minutes ticked away to a decision that now seemed inevitable.

Meanwhile the Pan Am chairman, William Seawell, left New York for an IATA conference in Geneva, leading to increased speculation that the Americans had already turned their back on Concorde. Substantial rumors were also filtering through to the Pierre H.Q. that TWA had already written their press release to coincide with the expected cancellation. This smacked of unfair collusion.

At the eleventh hour, a last-minute attempt was made to save the situation and to persuade Pan Am to hold off a final decision for ninety days. BAC proposed to lease the initial Concordes to Pan Am. This was dispatched with BAC executive Derek Johns directly to Seawell in Geneva. On receiving the document, Seawell held a long telephone conversation with New York to discuss the proposals. It failed to have any noticeable effect on the decision. As one Pan Am vice-president remarked, "If it was an offer to give the plane away if we would fly it, then it would hardly have convinced us that this Concorde had good economics."

On the afternoon of January 30, the Concorde men in New York had made their last ploy to persuade the airline's evaluation team to hold on to their options for another ninety days. But the odds were against them. "For a U.S. airline to take up or continue options in that political situation was going to involve them in a major PR problem. With the combination of a violent environment lobby, a 'buy American policy,' together with the economic difficulties of the airlines, both Pan Am and TWA would have bought themselves a load of trouble. They really wanted to stave off a decision for one or two years," was one BAC opinion. Others felt somewhat bitterly, "Where there's a will there's a way—and there was no will in Pan Am because of the airline's financial situation."

That afternoon the Concorde sales team assembled in the suite at the Pierre, laying odds unenthusiastically on the final decision. "We all knew that Geoffrey Knight would be 'called to the presence' that afternoon and had made specific arrangements." In the likely event of an unfavorable decision, Knight's departure would be down the service elevator and out the back door. This was to avoid a confrontation at an awkward time with the world's press. On the fateful day, one of the team recalls that they "had lunch together in the Pierre; it was particularly memorable because we had the best scampi I have ever tasted. The day before the decision, we had made up our minds that there was nothing further we could do to change what was coming, so we just waited. When the news finally broke, I heard it on the phone from Geoffrey who thanked us for all our work and told us not to be too disappointed. I put the phone down, kicked a few things, and swore a few times to let off steam. Then I went and joined the others to go out and get sloshed."

Camera Press

SOVIET SST DISASTER

The TU-144, with its modified airframe, a few minutes before its disastrous crash at the 1973 Paris Air Show.

Spectators watched as it broke up above the small village of Goussainville where the crew and eight people were killed. The cause of the crash will never be truly known but it was thought to have been caused by a photographer falling onto the controls.

Camera Press

BAC

CONCORDE OVER AMERICA

Concorde's first flight into the United States, 20 September 1973. Crowds line up at Dallas-Fort Worth airport to see the supersonic airliner for themselves.

On the runway at Dulles International Airport, Washington. Concorde traveled from Texas to Washington in record subsonic time, before flying home to Paris in 213 minutes.

BAC

EGG OF
S.S.T.
(EXTINCT)

AVIATION MUSEUM

MAKE IT
FRIED,
OVER,
WELL
DONE!

Denver Post

20

"Oh Perfidious Columbia!"

"American rejection of Concorde has put supersonic travel on the shelf, most of the U.S. industry believes—and it will gather a lot of dust before it is taken off again." In welcoming the "thumbs-down" rejection given by the almost simultaneous rejection of Concorde by Pan Am and TWA, the *Mobile Press* of Alabama was not alone. Its views were echoed by newspapers across the United States and shared by millions of Americans, among whom were numbered more than a few airline executives. They waited for the world's leading airlines to fall in behind the influential American giants in damning the commercial prospects of the European supersonic. Concorde would be banished from the skies. No one believed that Britain and France would carry on building the aircraft at over $60 million apiece "to wait on the shelf" for potential customers. It looked like the end of all prospects for supersonic travel in the foreseeable future. It was not just the environmentalists and Senator William Proxmire who drew comfort at the prospect; many airlines flying half-empty jumbo jets which were years away from repaying their investment could feel a little more confident in their future balance sheets, now that the threat of the supersonic appeared to be receding.

There were some Americans who were not prepared to let dust gather on the supersonics. President Nixon, ever jealous of United States prestige, was determined to keep the SST project alive and coolly asked for $46 million for continuing NASA research. In private—if not in public—the financially troubled American airlines were relieved that the Concorde had suffered such a humiliating rejection. Perceptive executives wryly confided that they had now found themselves in the same anti-SST camp as their enemies, the environmentalists, who were now busily reinforcing their groups throughout American suburbia to fight any attempt to establish supersonic travel or revive the American SST.

The environment lobby received support for their stand from the American National Academy of Science. A few weeks after the Pan Am decision this distinguished institution issued a report which had, in fact, been prepared eighteen months earlier on the possible threat of the U.S. SST to the upper atmosphere. The group of top-level scientists led by Gordon J. F. Macdonald, a well-known meteorologist, expressed anxiety over the possibility of damage to the ozone layer by high-flying supersonic airliners. Macdonald's nine-man committee, after several days' deliberation, had claimed that the stakes were high; a "5 percent decline in ozone would produce at least 8,000 extra cases of skin carcinomas and melanomas per year in a population the size of the white population of the United States." It called for more investigation of the SST threat. Hypotheses such as this continued to keep alive the indignant ardor of citizen groups mobilized against the "menace of the SST." Paradoxically, at the same time billions of dollars were voted by Congress to build a fleet of supersonic bombers.

The American press showed little sympathy for the bruised feelings of Britain and France. They seemed rather naïvely surprised by the sudden anti-American backlash in Britain's press. "Oh Perfidious Columbia" was the ironic headline of *The New York Times* report filed by its London correspondent, Anthony Lewis. "It was well known," wrote Lewis, "that the British harbored no envy of the world role played by the United States." Generally the people of England were quite content to "cultivate their garden," but "the decision by America's two overseas airlines not to buy the British-French supersonic airplane has evoked here a reaction worthy of Colonel Blimp at his most blustery. Nations, like individuals, it seems, may harbor resentments in their unconscious hidden feelings that at some point will burst out." Maintaining that Britain and France had become deluded by Concorde, a plane nobody wanted, Lewis concluded: "It is sad that so much of Britain's limited resources and so many of her hopes have gone for so little in the way of reality. Americans are not in a position to criticize. . . . But we know that eventually reality makes its claims. Scapegoats run out. Illusion has to stop."

The right-wing British *Daily Express*, which reflected the strong pro-Concorde feelings of its owner, Max Aitken, an ex-R.A.F. Battle of Britain pilot, drew a great deal of comment in the American press. Under the headline "The Great American Double Cross" the British newspaper declared: "Let's face it, the Americans dislike intensely even the thought of buying British planes. And they would cheerfully kill off the British aircraft industry if we were mad enough to allow them."

The *Milwaukee Journal*'s London correspondent, Edwin Roth, replied by saying that the British were suffering from "the ridiculous conviction" that the world owed Britain a living. The Concorde rejection was "another bad blow for Britain's much damaged national pride."

Yet there were still a number of American journalists who did not regard the Anglo-French achievement as a failure and who could not tolerate the crowing of the environment lobby.

"The 'eco freaks' time would be far better spent attacking the American car than rare airplanes and solitary pipe-lines in remote places," observed Don McLean of the *Indianapolis News*.

Bob Considine of the *Baltimore News American* agreed. "Ceremonial sarsaparilla probably flowed like champagne in the offices of Senator Proxmire and other antagonists of the next stage of the air transportation art—supersonic travel—when the word came that a few companies were canceling their intentions of buying the British-French Concorde.

"The mostly self-declared defenders of the nation's allotted share of ozone hailed the cancellations as the fruit of their own endeavors. Actually the American carriers—most of whom have been having a hard time financially—simply decided that their stock-holders would raise hell if more millions were spent on new equipment during a period when the companies are still paying for their subsonic jumbos. . . . The detractors of the SST," he went on, "are a special breed whose ranks include many who are as concerned about the environment as Daniel Webster was when he decried the ravages brought about by 15 mile an hour steam locomotives." Considine pointed out that Senator Proxmire's state built more outboard motors than any other state in the union and was, therefore, guilty of polluting America's lakes and rivers with exhaust fumes. Furthermore, he cast doubt on some of Proxmire's witnesses, one of whom "had previously distinguished himself as an authority by attributing the great Northeast electrical blackout of some years ago to 'flying saucers.' "

Proxmire ignored such jibes and moved on to settle the fate of Concorde. In early March 1973, his Senate Joint Economic Committee made its report describing Concorde as "a commercial failure." He claimed that Concorde testified to "the consequences of political interference in commercial decisions that we ourselves will disregard only at our peril." The senator's report demanded that there should be no American SST until environmental hazards had been eliminated. Moreover, the committee believed that private funding was essential to a successful SST project and cast serious doubt on President Nixon's need for $42 million for supersonic research.

Across the Atlantic the Concorde's makers took stock of their shattered marketing strategy. Their sales campaign had been based on the domino theory of "sell to Pan American and the rest will fall in line." Now that the two biggest American airlines had given a resounding "NO," a dominolike collapse in reverse seemed highly likely. Of the American airlines only Eastern and Braniff were left with the pretense of holding options, and the former was expected to relinquish its position. Everyone expected that the state-owned British Overseas Airways and Air France, who had already converted their options into orders, would stay with the project. But their nine airplanes would mean a ludicrously small and enormously expensive manufacturing operation. If no other customers came forward the British and French governments would seriously have to face abandoning the exercise.

In the domino collapse of February 1973, one crucial airline still remained undeclared on Concorde: Japan Air Lines. As one of the world's most efficiently managed and profitable carriers, JAL was a major competitor to the Americans on the Pacific and polar routes. Together with Qantas, the Australian carrier, it occupied an important place in the Concorde sales strategy, made even more critical by the American rejection. If JAL and Qantas could be held in the game—even without options—they might yet push the reluctant United States carriers into the supersonic operation. By a strange twist of fate JAL was due to renew its option interest a month after Pan Am, and the world's press focused on the dealings in Tokyo. The French had a sales team in Japan working around the clock to persuade JAL's board not to desert the project. A senior JAL spokesman had already said that the American decision set "good guidelines for other airlines." It was time for reinforcements, and part of the British sales force from New York was sent on to Tokyo. "It seemed when we arrived that we were in for a repeat performance," recalled one of the Britishers who commuted back and forth from daily strategy meetings at the French embassy to JAL headquarters. "It was the same figures, the same 'our calculations' against their analyses that we had had to face in New York. The only difference was that being typically Japanese everything was more formal, more correct and polite."

After days of endless presentations and argument the British admitted that they had done all they could. Tea was being taken with their Aerospatiale colleagues in the ornate reception room of the French embassy in Tokyo when the news came. "We were

expecting the worst when an official came in and announced that
JAL were not going to come out against the Concorde." Intense
diplomatic activity, particularly by the French, had "persuaded"
the Japanese minister of transport to issue firm instructions that
JAL would maintain its interest in Concorde, for the time being.
It was not exactly a victory for the British and French teams, but
at least it was a morale-boosting consolation for the failure in
New York.

Having shored up the Pacific front and prevented a "Japanese
embarrassment," the manufacturers now felt safe to drop the
idea of an option list. Its use over the years had been to allow the
airlines to "wait and see," rather than to place firm orders.
Invented to suit the convenience of Pan Am nearly a decade
earlier, it was ironic that this originating airline had turned the
device into a humiliating indictment of Concorde's prospects.

In March 1973 Concorde appeared to be at the nadir of its
fortunes, yet it was extremely unlikely that Britain and France, in
spite of a series of high-level investigations, would abandon the
project. Britain's prime minister, Edward Heath, was not celebrated for his ability to compromise, and having decided on a
pro-Concorde policy he showed every intention of keeping the
scheme in existence. He was also strongly pro-European and had
evolved a close working relationship with President Pompidou,
who had personally identified Gaullist prestige with Concorde's
technological promise. Pompidou had eased Britain's entry into
Europe and Heath was determined not to endanger the new
entente. As long as France was determined to continue the
Concorde project, Heath would support his ally.

Thus the British and French civil servants, backed up by the
manufacturers and technocrats, began to devise a new strategy
to save Concorde. The mainspring of their plan was a determination to confront the American airlines with the stark choice of
either purchasing Concorde or losing all their high-yield first-
class passenger traffic in a commercial aviation war with Britain
and France. First, however, the British and French planners
realized that every attempt had to be made to restore confidence
in the aircraft. An energetic public relations campaign was drawn
up with the avowed aim of showing that Concorde was here to
stay and could perform outstandingly well on the world's air

routes, particularly those into the United States. At the same time, the French and British governments insisted on a thorough review of the airliner's capabilities to see whether its performance could be improved sufficiently to attract new airline customers.

The public relations offensive opened with a New York press briefing in early May, when BAC revealed to the media for the first time the dramatic result of its market research survey into travel preferences of American businessmen. The work had been carried out by the reputable New York company Market Facts. Their comprehensive opinion samples proved that supersonic travel would attract a large percentage of this important market. The business travelers were shown comparative subsonic and supersonic timetables and offered a choice of fare structures, ranging from first class plus 20 percent on all-first-class planes to a mixed configuration offering both first class plus 10 percent and coach plus 20 percent. The results were even better than the Concorde salesmen had predicted: "Concorde can capture between 40 percent and 84 percent of the overseas business market originating in the U.S." Not only that, but the supersonic would actually generate more traffic since "the availability of Concorde will increase the volume of overseas business travel from the U.S. by 12 percent."

The encouraging and potentially explosive conclusion drawn by the researchers was that Concorde could not only siphon off almost all of the first-class traffic on the key Atlantic and Pacific routes because of its halved journey times, but it would also capture a large slice of the economy-fare market too. "Some 70 percent of the economy passengers interviewed were prepared to pay a 40 percent higher fare to fly in a one class Concorde and around 80 percent indicated that they would move up to a mixed class Concorde sold 20 percent above today's economy fares."

At the briefing BAC announced their intention of widening the SST's market appeal. Too much attention had been concentrated on the prestigious North Atlantic run. There were other possible routes where the airliner's speed could be a great money spinner for any U.S. airline. One suggestion pushed by the manufacturers was a high-speed shuttle from New York to Miami. There would be a "no frills" approach and the plane would seat 140 rather than 108 passengers. BAC officials announced that they were redesigning the interior of aircraft to induce a "wide-bodied" look. To undermine American nerve, stories were also leaked that British Airways was dreaming up new services such as a "cut-price" supersonic standby in which passengers could join a standby list at coach fares for Concorde. There would also be streamlined VIP services, "offering Concorde flyers separate entrances, checking, baggage handling and customs, to match the halved journey time." Word was spread that Iran Air was negotiating the purchase of two Concordes for the Cannonball service along "the Kissinger route from Paris to Peking." Concorde's great marketing potential began to be exploited by British Airways, who talked of day trips to Europe, with a 5:30 P.M. start from New York, putting the passenger in London at 9 P.M. "body time" and 2 A.M. local. As one journalist noted, this schizophenic splitting of real and "body time" had problems. "The terminal and the roads are empty. You're in a hotel bed by 3 A.M. local time, when both your body's clock and the local environment spell sleep. At 10 A.M. London time (5 A.M. body time) the traveler can be on his feet for a full working day before the 6 P.M. Concorde flight back to New York which lands the traveler back in New York at 4:30 P.M. local time."

It began to become clear to the United States aviation industry that there would be no quarter in the battle to get Concorde onto the commercial air routes. If the Concorde market research was correct then Pan Am and TWA knew that they could incur losses of some $200 million worth of business annually when supersonic services began in 1976. The American airlines were in no mood for bad news. In the first half of 1973 they were suffering from the advance effects of what was beginning to look unmistakably like recession, and discussions were under way between United, TWA, and American to rationalize routes.

American airline bosses were blaming the Boeing 747 jumbo jet for their economic troubles. Many executives rued their purchase of the extra seating capacity offered by the jumbo jets at a time when passenger growth seemed to be stagnating. "I feel pretty stupid sitting here with all those big airplanes so soon," confessed American Airlines president George A. Spater. He spoke in the knowledge that already some of America's brand-new jumbos were being mothballed on a desert airfield in New Mexico to await the arrival of better times.

In this atmosphere BAC turned its fire on the 747. Speaking at an international conference in London, Geoffrey Knight, BAC's vice-chairman, declared, "It is the economics of the 747 that is in dispute, not those of Concorde."

Even beneath the studied indifference of the American airlines there were signs that the American SST lobby had not capitulated entirely. On May 26, Senator Barry Goldwater drew the attention of Congress to the progress of the Anglo-French plane. He asked that the case made in the *Arizona Republic* editorial "SST? Mais Oui" be entered on the *Congressional Record*. "Setback has been the name of the game for the British French combine building the supersonic Concorde airliner. Environmentalists have muddled its name with unsupported allegations; airlines have dropped purchase options, and U.S. congressmen are trying to have even a test hop to our shores banned." But it pointed out that the Concorde project was still alive and that the Market Facts survey indicated high latent demand for faster travel. The editorial concluded, "The SST seems to be going through the same economic and scientific trauma American aviation endured in the late 1940's."

The Concorde manufacturers began to sense a slight thaw in the United States attitude toward their product. The FAA, although it had, as expected, banned supersonic flight over the continental United States in April 1973, did not display any hostility toward the aircraft. If the Anglo-French plane were to serve U.S. cities, however, it would have to throw off the "Frankenstein syndrome" of a monstrous potential environmental threat.

New questions of SST safety dramatically arose to worry both the environment lobby and the supersonic engineers from an unexpected source. On Sunday June 3, a crowd of 300,000 spectators at the world's premiere air show, at Paris Le Bourget airfield, watched test pilot Mikhail Koslov bring the huge TU-144 down toward the runway after a ten-minute demonstration flight. The elegant delta-winged airliner looked like Concorde's sister airplane and was the pride of the Soviet aircraft industry. Suddenly within a few feet of the runway, Koslov turned on the full power of the Kuznetsov engines and soared into a climb. Many of the experienced fliers and aircraft experts watched spellbound as the great airliner climbed into the sky at such a steep angle that its full configuration could be clearly seen against the Paris sky. An Italian test pilot shouted, "E andanto" ("It's going in") as the plane suddenly pitched over at the height of 7,000 feet and dropped in a steep dive toward the earth. Below lay the small French village of Goussainville, and the pilot fought to bring the big delta out of its dive; but the strain on the airframe was colossal. Suddenly the left delta wing snapped off at the wing roots, and there was nothing Koslov could do. There was a spurt of flame as the aircraft began to break up. Within seconds and before the vast crowd the plane hit the ground killing its crew of five and spraying flame and debris over the small village, killing eight people.

Immediately, the anti-SST lobby demanded to know whether there was an intrinsic design fault common to all SSTs which had led to the disaster. But nobody seemed sure what had happened, and the atmosphere of international cooperation was not improved by charges that U.S. intelligence men had picked up key parts of the smoking wreckage, for secret analysis as a clue to a Soviet supersonic bomber based on TU-144 know-how. It was not until a year had elapsed that the Franco-Russian inquiry exonerated the TU-144, claiming that "no anomaly could be uncovered either in the construction or in the general functioning of the aircraft and its systems." The environmentalists, however, used the incident to cast doubt and dismay on all SSTs.

By mid 1973 the terrors posed by the sonic boom had receded and there were two outstanding environmental charges leveled against the aircraft: first, there were the suspicions that the plane would endanger the upper atmosphere; second, the plane would be very noisy.

There could be no final answer to the frightening charges about SST damage to the upper atmosphere until the large-scale study by the Environmental Protection Agency had been completed. Over 1,000 researchers were involved in a team led by Dr. A. J. Grobecker, manager of the Climatic Assessment program. Satellites, high-altitude balloons, sophisticated ground equipment, as well as a fleet of aircraft including Concorde and the U-2 spy plane were deployed to investigate how Concorde's engine emissions would affect the stratosphere. Would they lead to ozone depletion or some other harmful effect? The subsonic effect of current jetliners at altitudes about 30,000 feet was also under review in the most exhaustive study ever done in this field.

Noise was a very different problem, and much was known about its damaging effect on people. It had become a hot political issue in many parts of the United States, particularly among those living close to airports. One U.S. agency estimated that some 15–20 million Americans were affected to a greater or lesser degree by the noise of jet engines. The main opposition to noisy aircraft was concentrated in Los Angeles and New York. In Los Angeles millions of dollars had been spent rehousing and razing the homes of some 2,000 people living near the airport perimeter. In 1973 the air traffic control of the Los Angeles airport was reorganized so that landing and takeoff by noisy 707s could only take place over the sea. New York also boasted highly effective anti-noise groups including the Town-Village Aircraft Safety and Noise Abatement Committee (TVASNAC), which published a provocative newsletter and lobbied congressmen. Another group, the National Organization to Insure Sound Controlled Environment (NOISE), called for strict limits to be imposed on airline operators. The hostility to noisy aircraft had grown so much that airport construction and expansion were seriously delayed in many United States cities.

Although the new generation of wide-bodied jets were very much quieter, this only magnified the problem of the first-generation jets like the 707; and the Concorde used the same type of turbojet engine. It is hardly surprising that Franklin W. Kolk of American Airlines bluntly stated, "There will be no SST until this is straightened out."

The United States anti-noise groups deeply distrusted their protector, the Federal Aviation Agency, responsible for establishing noise levels. They believed the agency was playing a waiting game, in the hope that supersonic operations would gain acceptability in America. As early as 1969, the FAA had issued a regulation known as FAR Part 36, which stipulated that all new generation jet aircraft would not be allowed to operate if their noise level exceeded 108 EPNdB * on approach, takeoff, and on the airfield itself (sideline noise).

The Tristar, DC-10, and 747 could all approach this level but according to the Environmental Protection Agency over 90 percent of American airliners exceeded these limitations. Concorde was in this category. Yet the FAA, according to its numerous critics, did little to enforce its own standards.

On landing, measurements showed that Concorde made slightly less noise than the Boeing 707 (115 EPNdB against 120 EPNdB) but it was noisier on the airfield and on takeoff. The reason was simple. Concorde had been designed, like the 707 and DC-8, for the airline operating conditions of the 1960s. When they embarked on the project in 1962, the Concorde design team had accepted the International Civil Aviation Organization's resolution that "supersonic aircraft should not create a noise level exceeding the level then accepted for the operation of subsonic aircraft."

Now, with the requirements of the environment-conscious 1970s and '80s, there are extremely difficult technical problems involved in suppressing the roar of Concorde's turbojet engines. Jet engine noise is caused by two main factors: the high pitch of the machinery rotating inside the engine casing and the roar generated by the high-speed expulsion of hot gases into the cooler atmosphere. The new generation of jet engines owe their quietness to the fact that large fans rotating less fast, and therefore more quietly, move a larger volume of air more slowly through the engine to give more thrust. But Concorde's engines have to operate at supersonic regimes where big fan jets would be less efficient. The Olympus engines derive their high power from driving a smaller volume of air at much higher velocity. They are consequently noisier than the big fan jets and as the manufacturers admit, "Conventional silencing techniques for subsonic aircraft proved to be economically disastrous when applied to Concorde." Different silencing methods have been applied. Larger engine intakes and other devices have been tried and high hopes were placed in a complex system of retractable

* EPNdB: Effective Perceived Noise measured in Decibels. This is a system of noise measurement used for environmental purposes in which the noise reading is corrected for tone acceptability (PNdB) and duration.

spades inserted in the jet exhaust. The promises of early labora-
tory tests, however, have not been proved in practice. The
manufacturers are up against special and difficult problems:
"While it would be technically unsound to promise further noise
reductions, there is an on-going program which is seeking new
ways to reduce overall noise levels. Its main elements are, long
term developments of silencing methods, identification of internal noise sources and their suppression, flight techniques." New
takeoff and landing patterns, utilizing Concorde's high rate of
climb and maneuverability, have shown that the ground noise
can be cut by as much as 60 percent.

Concorde presented the FAA with a difficult situation. Although public opinion was hostile to the introduction of noisy
foreign supersonic airliners, the FAA could hardly insist on their
prohibition from American airports while large fleets of 707s and
DC-8s were still operating throughout the world. A ban on
Concorde would be interpreted as American protectionism and
would play into the hands of those who, like Henri Ziegler, called
for a greater resistance to the U.S. industry's penetration of
Europe. Moreover, the FAA, aware of its responsibility to
encourage the U.S. domestic industry, could hardly introduce
regulations that would entail the expenditure of billions of dollars
by American airlines on jet engine "hush kits." There were too
many potential "Penn Centrals of the air" for further bank-
ruptcies to be risked. The FAA wanted a gradual adaptation of
FAR 36 over several years, but would the people wait? Already
Assemblyman Harris of New York had introduced a bill into the
state legislature which would prohibit the operation of all aircraft
making noise in excess of 108 EPNdB. He also proposed that
"aircraft presently in service in New York would not be affected
by this legislation, only supersonic aircraft which exceed 108
EPNdB would be barred from using our airports." It was, the
British and French felt, a question of one law for the subsonics
and another stricter one for the Concorde.

In the summer of 1973 the FAA was called upon to declare its
position on the SST when it was announced that Concorde would
visit North America. If aircraft noise worried the citizens of New
York, Los Angeles, and Chicago suburbs, the Texans had no such
fears. In keeping with its tradition of doing everything in the

grandest style, the Lone Star State planned to open the world's biggest airport at Grapevine, midway between Fort Worth and Dallas. Here on a 17,500-acre site, served by a ten-lane highway, the Texans had decided to build a jetport of the future. There would be giant 11,000-foot runways big enough to handle any kind of aircraft, and passengers would be whisked between the large terminals in mobile lounges. Construction teams were working around the clock to finish the $700 million scheme in time for its autumn inauguration. What better inauguration could there be than to invite the world's fastest airliner to the world's biggest airport? For the Concorde it was a godsend. Already there were plans to fly Concorde from Paris to Rio, but the question was how the aircraft could enter the United States. Now the Texans were ready to extend a welcome and an application for landing permission was filed at the FAA.

The antics of the Texans did not meet with approval everywhere. The *Columbus Evening Dispatch* complained: "Hucksters who are seeking to drum up publicity for next month's opening of the new Dallas–Fort Worth International Airport are applying despicable pressure on official Washington. These 'do-it-bigger-and-better' Texans have invited controversial British-French Concorde to park on their tarmac. . . . Concorde is a discredited, gangly bird. It deserves no special perch." In Texas the attitude toward Concorde's impending visit was different—traditional hospitality mixed with curiosity. Glenn Shelton of the *Wichita Falls Record News* wrote, "That big British French turkey the Concorde will fly to America next month for the opening of the big new Dallas–Fort Worth Airport. It will loaf along over the Atlantic at about 1400 miles an hour. I'd certainly like to traipse over and see this supersonic monster and see how it compares with the glider I flew in World War II."

The Concorde manufacturers were determined to seize every advantage of their Texas breakthrough. The trip was meticulously planned; Concorde 002 was selected as the plane for the job, flown by the flamboyant French pilot Jean Franchi. The plane would accomplish two tasks on one mission. As well as flying into the United States, it would also fly to Caracas, showing the Venezuelan airline, VIASA, the value of its high speed. The first leg of the journey would be from Paris to Las

Palmas in the Canaries. The next stage would be a supersonic dash across the South Atlantic to Caracas, carrying the Venezuelan minister of transport and the president of VIASA. After a short stay in the Venezuelan capital the plane would fly across the Gulf of Mexico to Dallas–Fort Worth. A large team would be carried in the thirty seats placed on board 002, ahead of the test equipment. Journalists and opinion formers from the American press, including executives from Braniff (important potential customers), would be flown to Caracas in a slow subsonic 707, then whisked back to the United States in Concorde in half the time.

The journey went according to plan. Taking off from Paris Orly at 0930 hours, Concorde reached Caracas in 6 hours and 25 minutes, including a 44-minute refueling stop at Las Palmas. In Caracas the sleek supersonic attracted numbers of sightseers, and on leaving, Franchi made a slow, low-level flight over the city, before flying on to Dallas–Fort Worth in 3 hours. A few minutes before eleven o'clock on September 20 the first supersonic airliner landed in the United States.

Concorde's arrival in Texas was very nearly more spectacular than anybody would have wished. As Jean Franchi came over the horizon and made his approach above the heads of the admiring crowds, he suddenly pulled up Concorde's needle-nose. To everyone's amazement the plane shot up to 3,000 feet in less than 20 seconds, engines blasting at full throttle. A small red Cessna had been spotted full of photographers, just three miles ahead of Concorde, in the middle of Franchi's flight path. "It was a high risk incident," commented one airport official. "There were a few seconds to respond and react. It could have been another story." Franchi was more laconic; when asked how he reacted to the control tower directive, he merely said, "They asked me if I can move very fast. I told them *I sure can!*"

The Texas press gave Concorde a royal welcome. "Everyone agrees Concorde's a show stopper," wrote the *Dallas Times Herald*. The 400 newsmen from other parts of the country were also impressed. "First SST Zips in to Texas Sized Welcome," said the *Pittsburgh Press*. France and Britain had sent their strongest Concorde team. The two heads of the manufacturing companies, Henri Ziegler of Aerospatiale and Sir George Edwards of BAC, were there to meet Texas dignitaries and to talk business with Braniff, backed up by a strong sales and PR team. Even the British embassy had sent officials to help persuade the Americans of Concorde's virtues. One was seen to wince when Jean Franchi, asked his opinion of Texas, took a look around and said, "You seem to have plenty of concrete out here." Maggie Kennedy of the *Dallas Times Herald* found that one of the most impressive members of the visiting Concorde team was stewardess Anna Leygues. Under the headline "Beauty Flies on Concorde," she told how Anna, a former French beauty queen, had been carefully selected for Concorde duty and wooed away from husband and child in the interests of duty. "I love Concorde," said Anna, and went on to tell how all the considerable arts of French hospitality were to be available for its passengers. The champagne would be superb and would accompany a typical continental breakfast. Dinner might be caviar, duck with celery purée, potatoes, and a tray of eight or nine French cheeses. There would be "an absolutely elegant French pastry for dessert." The plush interior deeply impressed even the hardened American maintenance men. One strode down Concorde's aisle, sat down in one of the luxurious armchair seats, and, leaning back, said, "Man, this is really it. Real leather!"

In the three-day run up to the airport's official opening, Concorde stole the show. Thousands queued up to see her, and the elegant jet flew two supersonic trips, carrying American VIPs over the Gulf of Mexico. Hundreds of newsmen attended the successful press conference, chaired by Braniff chairman Harding Lawrence, and then filed through 002's long fuselage. Thousands of well-heeled Texans and the visitors from Europe attended a charity ball on the eve of the inauguration and walked out on to the tarmac between dances to look at the graceful airliner parked in the warm Texas night. Many of them subscribed to the verdict of Governor John Connally, who believed Concorde to be "the most beautiful plane in the world."

On September 23, with the success of her Texas visit behind her, Concorde sped to Washington, covering the 1,000-mile trip in 1 hour and 58 minutes at subsonic speed. The administration which controlled Dulles International Airport placed no hindrance in Concorde's way, but Washington's welcome was cooler than that of Texas. The *Washington Star News* wrote, "We trusted that if it *had* to go to Texas, at least it wouldn't come here." It then went on, "We've scotched the bird, not killed it, and it's going to take the best efforts of Americans to resist the blandishments of those who, in the words of one British airline official, want to convince us that the plane 'is not the monster many people think it is. . . .' On Wednesday it's supposed to return to Paris—non stop in three hours 44 minutes. Bon voyage. Don't hurry back."

Such press reaction did not deter President Nixon from demonstrating his strongly pro-Concorde attitude by awarding the Harmon Trophy for aviation to Brian Trubshaw and André Turcat for their work in bringing Concorde through its flight test program. Nixon told them encouragingly, "Supersonic transport planes one day will be an accepted means of intercontinental passenger travel." Support for the presidential line also came from his FAA administrator, Alexander Butterfield, who remarked, "Concorde will be certified in the U.S. about the same time that it wins certification in Britain and France." The chairman of the Civil Aeronautics Board was equally impressed. "There is no question about it being economically operative in its first years," he said.

Suddenly everything seemed to be going Concorde's way, and Sir George Edwards could not resist the opportunity of telling the Americans a few home truths. Speaking at a U.S. aviation industry lunch he said: "We are a long way out in front. I promise you we are not going to muff this chance. We are not going to lose our lead. There is not the slightest sign of either government losing its nerve." He almost relished the awkward position of the American industry over the SST. "Political decisions have taken away your belt," he said, "and with Concorde we now propose to see that situation through to its usual interesting end."

Then in an aside, Sir George revealed that for all the talk of "strong nerve," the French and British governments would be delighted to see American involvement in their SST. "You don't stand a chance of catching us. The only hope you have is to join up with us."

Having said that his door was always open for an American visit to discuss a supersonic arrangement, Sir George left Washington on a record-breaking Concorde flight home. It was the first North Atlantic crossing by a supersonic airliner, completed by Franchi in a staggering 213 minutes. It is not surprising that the *Washington Post*, reflecting on Concorde's North American adventure, concluded, "Concorde Visit Achieves Objectives."

The British *Daily Express* was forgivably more ecstatic when it cried, "213 Minutes to Glory!"

Sir George Edwards' "chance aside" on United States participation reflected a growing concern by Britain and France on how to find the apparently endless resources needed not only to keep Concorde going, but also to improve its appeal for the world's airlines.

In June the French government appointed René Bloch, a distinguished French aerospace engineer and chief of the French guided-weapons establishment, to make an independent survey of the aircraft's capabilities and any changes that might make it more marketable. At the same time the Concorde Directing Committee issued CDC Directive No. 102 to the manufacturers which called for "an estimate of the gains to be expected with regard to range, payload and operating costs." The study would also have to pronounce on the implications for the present fleet of sixteen aircraft. "We were given carte blanche and £3 million to come up with suggestions as to what should be done," said one BAC engineer. The $64,000 question—or, in the case of Concorde, the $64 million question—was, what would persuade the airlines to buy?

First the design team ruled out the possibility of a new "super" Concorde. "It just wasn't on," said a member of the committee. Also they knew that many improvements, scheduled to be included after the first forty production aircraft, had been cashed in to make up payload deficiencies on the entry-into-service plane. Most airlines buy an aircraft for their critical sector. If they meet the requirements on this yardstick of performance they can then be used on any other route. For an important customer like Japan Air Lines the critical route was the "great circle" flight from Anchorage to Tokyo. But Concorde, designed primarily for the North Atlantic, could not make the distance with an acceptable and profitable payload. Similarly for Pan Am, if Concorde's range could embrace Frankfurt and Rome, it could become a far more attractive proposition on the Atlantic routes.

Three possible changes were envisaged to give Concorde a reasonable chance of bringing about a victory in the domino game. Plan "AIR1" would entail adding an extra full tank in the tail of the airliner, giving it an extra 200-mile range. This could make all the difference to Pan Am and JAL. A more ambitious plan, "AIR2," would provide not only the extra tank but also modifications to the engine, leading to an improvement in thrust. Then the "AIR2B" version would provide wing modifications. "We put them together in flow charts to see what would happen if certain things took place in the domino game. It was clear that if you sold the key airlines, everything would tumble out from there," said one BAC executive.

While the new plans were being studied, the British Committee of Public Accounts once more criticized the management of the project. In July it deplored Concorde's "startling escalations" in expenditure. The M.P.s were also angry because the Department of Trade and Industry insisted on keeping the true costs of Concorde secret. They had provided a report with asterisks and blank spaces where key figures should have been presented. The M.P.s were incensed, but the government would not budge, maintaining that it was vital to keep various parts of Concorde expenditure secret for commercial reasons.

This cavalier behavior angered the House of Commons, but the minister, Michael Heseltine, was determined not to reveal the true costs in the complex wheeling and dealing that was going on with the airlines. The asterisks stayed.

In spite of the success of the American visit, the press began to question the success of Heseltine's sales strategy—there were no new orders.

Once again there were mutterings in the British press about impending cancellation. These were given a new impetus following the Yom Kippur war and the Arab oil blockade of late 1973. Faced with growing fuel costs, the airlines were all in deep trouble. Fares were increased, profits fell, and there was a 20–25 percent cut in services around the world. Three years' expansion of the industry had been wiped out, with large-scale redundancies in the United States.

The new doubts over Concorde gave fresh ammunition to its

critics. In *The Observer*, Andrew Wilson attacked the project, and revealed the confidential minutes of a secret meeting of the manufacturers, which had called the aircraft "unsellable." Claiming access to the minutes of the committee charged with appraising the aircraft's future, Wilson blew as many "secrets" as he could. The major alterations to engines and wings could not become effective for six years, according to one expert at the session; and the plane would be "a very expensive package." The present aircraft could not be altered, and the noise measurements made on 002 had been "very disappointing."

The criticism of *The Observer* was supported by the pop daily *Sun*: "We must KILL the Concorde," it announced, together with the news that "there can only be one possible reason for pursuing this stubborn policy. . . . The Government are set on keeping the French sweet, at any price. . . . It is better to have Pompidou looking down his nose at us than to have the flying white elephant looking down its droop snoot at the futile millions we are pumping into it. . . . Sadly there is only one sentence on Concorde. The death sentence. It must be pronounced sooner rather than later."

Everything now turned on the next fatal meeting announced for early 1974 between Michael Heseltine and Yves Guéna, French transport minister. But before that occurred, Prime Minister Heath and his government were ousted in an election fought in the face of power cuts, the three-day work week, and Britain's worst economic crisis since the war.

FIGHTING FOR SURVIVAL

British cabinet minister Anthony Wedgwood Benn addressing BAC and Rolls-Royce workers at Fɪl-ton during the cancellation crisis of 1974. The assembly plants of the British Concorde can be seen in the background.

The construction facilities at Aerospatiale's Toulouse complex, showing two of the sixteen Concordes being built.

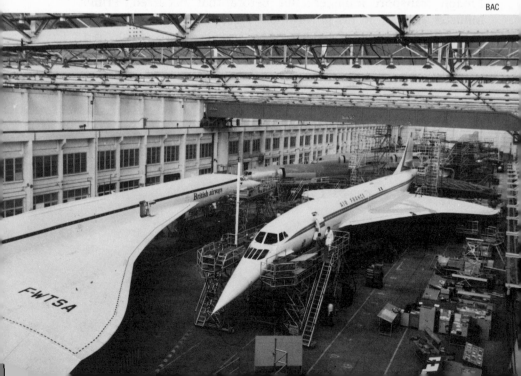

BAC

KEEPING IT OUT

Concorde takes off for a double Atlantic crossing from Boston's Logan International Airport on 17 June 1974. The round trip was completed in under 8 hours.

Representative Lester B. Wolff, New York Democrat and leading campaigner to prevent Concorde operations in the United States, covering his ears during a replay of Concorde's noise at an FAA Environmental Impact hearing in Washington, April 1975.

AP

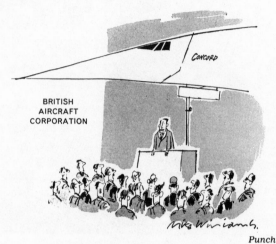

Punch

"Now remember lads, the taxying trials were a great success, so if all else fails she'll make a pretty good taxi."

21

"A Decision of Wisdom and Hope"

The British general election of February 1974 took place in the bitter atmosphere of a miners' strike which threatened to bring down the British economic and political structure. In addition to the grave industrial unrest, the world energy crisis resulting from the Yom Kippur war had placed Britain in a perilous balance of payments situation. Whoever won the election would introduce strong economic measures entailing a close scrutiny of government spending. For the British people, the future appeared grim, with little rise in the standard of living until the late 1970s. Pundits began to speculate on whether there would be a repeat of the 1964 Concorde farce when the Wilson cabinet had decided to axe the project at their first cabinet meeting, only to be frustrated by the French. Now, a decade later, France was no less intractable. Yves Guéna made the position clear at a press conference on February 19.

"The true problem of Concorde," he said, "is to determine how many machines to build." Although sixteen were in production for nine firm orders and five options, "we are going to propose to our British partners the start of production on numbers 17, 18 and 19. That would be a decision of wisdom and hope."

This would have only a small effect on employment, according to the minister. He then went on to say that "we are not opposed to the addition of a supplementary tank of 4,500 kilos which would increase the range of the supersonic." This would only be practicable on planes after the tenth but even the French did not believe that work should start on a new engine and modifications to the wing. Doubts had begun to appear, even in France.

Le Figaro sadly noted that "the quality of two countries at every level has, since the beginning of the program, led to a regrettable absence of decision-making and an unhappy propensity to compromise."

The man who now faced the Concorde decision was Anthony Wedgwood Benn, a leading member of the Labour leadership who was, perhaps, more familiar with the airliner's problems than any other minister. The energetic minister, who now preferred to be called by the more egalitarian name Tony Benn than by his full name (which, he felt, reflected his aristocratic origins) greatly strengthened his position in the Labour party since he had last been responsible for Concorde in Harold Wilson's 1964–70 government. Benn was now a leading advocate of a left-wing philosophy embracing a populist form of socialism which would allow participation by the workers in decision-making.

He also believed in extending public ownership over a far greater slice of British industry and in backing radical workers' cooperatives where capitalist enterprise failed. Yet Benn had fought hard for Concorde and he also represented the key "Concorde constituency" of Bristol South East. His presence in Parliament depended upon Bristol votes and their main interest was the continuation of Concorde. Yet, during the election, Benn had carefully avoided any specific commitment on the aircraft.

"It is the Labour party's hope and desire that the Concorde project should succeed," said Benn, but he qualified his remarks by saying, "Nobody is in any doubt that a project of this kind must be determined by its marketing prospects."

When Prime Minister Harold Wilson returned to Downing Street, Tony Benn, as expected, became secretary for trade and industry. He immediately called for a thorough report on Concorde. The press, sensing a dramatic decision, were met with the noncommital "I will brief myself fully and then make a statement." On March 18, just over two weeks later, Benn stood up to address the House of Commons. Wearing a blue tie emblazoned with a tiny Concorde, he made a statement that was to deliver the most devastating and embarrassing blow against the supersonic project. Claiming that he was giving information which his predecessor Tory minister, Heseltine, had refused in the interests of sales prospects, Benn proceeded, to the delight of the project's opponents, to fill in the blanks and to remove the asterisks in the Concorde account.

As Benn himself admitted, the figures were "much worse" than he ever expected and, with the manner of a doctor pronouncing a hopeless case, he hoped the House would understand that he "had tried very hard to help Concorde succeed." None of the £1,070 million development costs, of which Britain would pay half, would ever be recovered in sales. To make matters worse, even though the manufacturers expected to sell 130 Concordes by the 1980s, there would also be a substantial production loss amounting to £200 million on the fleet of sixteen under construction. Furthermore, the production loss could increase, the more Concordes were sold, amounting perhaps to £250 million on one hundred production planes. Sales were extremely difficult and noise was a major problem. "It is uncertain, as yet, whether the aircraft will prove acceptable at New York [Kennedy], Tokyo or Sydney," declared Benn, He then made possibly the most damning and, regarded by many BAC men, the most treacherous statement of all: that British Airways did not expect to make a profit on their supersonic operations; worse, that "British Airways estimate that the operation of Concorde could substantially worsen their financial results, possibly by many millions of pounds a year." Surely this had to be the end of Concorde.

Benn gave a press conference immediately after his Commons statement and then departed for Bristol to explain his action to his irate constituents. In the face of such evidence, the press lost no time in calling for the axe. Newspaper editors sensed that finally this was the moment of truth Concorde could not escape. "Concorde Shocker," chimed the *Sun*, proclaiming "a grim set of shock figures last night set the scene for grounding Concorde *permanently.*" *The Guardian* lost no time in calling for summary execution. In an editorial titled "Britain's Flying Overdraft," it declared, "Concorde may have been a brave venture but it is a bad bargain. Thanks to Mr. Wedgwood Benn, we now know a lot more about its badness than we did before the election and the news is about as dismal as it could be. . . . In effect, not even the loyalest or most starry-eyed airline executives can be expected to buy Concorde unless the price is subsidized, which means, within limits, that the more we sell, the more we have to pay." Other newspapers drew the same conclusions. It seemed that it was only a matter of time before the Wilson government administered the death blow.

But the French government remained studiously calm, a warning that any thought of cancellation would meet with customary Gallic intransigence. The French Ministry of Transport let it be known that it did not share Benn's "gloomy analysis" and that "there is nothing that incites us to pessimism."

If Benn had hoped to stimulate a democratic debate about the plane's future, he could hardly have achieved greater success. Industry workers and executives sensed that the most decisive battle had, at long last, arrived. They immediately began to fight back.

Lord mayor of Bristol, Wally Jenkins, requested Prime Minister Harold Wilson to meet a delegation of city leaders. Meanwhile, the trade unions exploded into frantic action. French trade unionists were invited to coordinate plans; others rushed to an emergency meeting of leaders of the Confederation of Shipbuilding and Engineering Union holding their annual conference at Eastbourne on the Sussex coast. The union's leader, Hugh Scanlon, a powerful figure on the left of British politics, was called into the battle. It looked like another fight in which the unions would be ranged against the British government.

Ron Nethercott, regional secretary of the Transport and General Workers Union, charged into the fray. "Time is against us," he said. "If Concorde is to be kept going, Tony's going to need all the support he can get to save Concorde in the budget." Admitting that Benn's news had been gloomy indeed, Nethercott went on to say, "But we want to say a big thank you to him for telling us the truth."

If Benn's objective was to protect Concorde, he had approached the problem in a strange way, particularly in the face of powerful figures in the Labour government such as Home Secretary Roy Jenkins and the new heavyweight Chancellor of the Exchequer Denis Healey, who were determined to kill the project. Benn naturally found himself on the opposite side of the cabinet table to these right-wing Labour leaders. He was opposed to them not only on various points of socialist policy but also on the Common Market and, now, on Concorde. But once in Bristol, Benn seemed to lose his Westminster pessimism. "To the people of Bristol," he said, "Concorde is not dead. Supersonic travel will come and it is up to the workers, trades council, and townspeople to keep it alive."

On March 20, perhaps the most dramatic meeting in Concorde's long history took place. Eleven thousand workers—designers, engineers, draftsmen, fitters, and mechanics, as well as office girls, secretaries, and management executives—gathered in the huge hangar at Filton. As they waited for Benn, one report described the atmosphere as "curious, to say the least. It was light headed, frivolous, confident almost." The levity was apparent from the start when a shop steward asked for everyone to put what they could into the collection buckets coming around for the "Save Concorde" campaign. There were roars of laughter when he announced that the stewards were to meet for strategic discussions in the Anchor pub immediately afterwards.

Yet many at the meeting believed that Benn had come not to cancel Concorde, but to build himself a popular base for protecting the project and the jobs of his constituents against his rivals in the cabinet, Jenkins and Healey.

In spite of Bristol's defiance, the newspaper columns reflected the growing conviction that Concorde would be scrapped; and, as usual, there were letters from irate Britons blaming it all on the United States.

"There must be no sharing of the technological advantages and engineering progress of Concorde with America. The American aerospace industry has long since waited to secure just these advantages," wrote A. W. B. Hester of Chandler's Ford, Hampshire, in *The Times*. Lord Orr Ewing, defending Concorde, cast doubt on Benn's figures and claimed that "these figures bear all the signs of preparation by the civil servants and do not appear to have been compiled after consultation with the industries involved." The pro-Concorde lobby believed the books had been well and truly cooked.

There was, however, no shortage of critics. "Now that it seems clear that the only purpose of continuing with the Concorde project is as an extension of the social security system, might it not be cheaper to pay those concerned for not producing it, just as in America, farmers have been paid for not cultivating the land?" asked B. T. Buckle of Horsell Park, Surrey. For his part, Professor G. C. Allen of Cobham in the same county claimed that "it would be inexcusable if this highly competent body of men should continue to be engaged at vast expense to the taxpayer in the manufacture of a product that no one wants to buy."

The Observer, true to form, lost no time in crying, "We must stop Concorde now." They claimed that Benn had justified the long campaign of their air correspondent, Andrew Wilson, who "has been warning successive governments since 1963 of the folly of proceeding with Concorde." Surely, asked *The Observer*, we should not go on building planes at £30 million apiece for a nonexistent market just to keep workers employed in Bristol. As for Anglo-French relations, surely a "sterile technological project to which Britain had been held hostage for twelve years could not be regarded as a suitable basis for an international partnership or the price of consolidation of Britain's membership of the EEC."

Summing up, in what it believed might be the last in a long series of doom-laden editorials to kill Concorde, *The Observer* said, "Already, over these last 12 years, Concorde has caused ugly developments in our political life. First, there was the official attempt to suppress the truth about the damage it would do to the environment; then there was the deliberate concealment from Parliament on supposedly 'commercial' grounds of Concorde's true costs and there was the attempt by the plane's manufacturers to portray the critics of this whitest of white elephants as traitors to Britain's interest. Concorde must be stopped and stopped completely. . . . Later, it will be necessary to hold a searching inquiry into how Concorde came to be started and why it was so long sustained."

The most immediate threat to the project was Chancellor Denis Healey's national budget. On Tuesday March 26, the chancellor, in the middle of his long diatribe on the nation's economic health, at last provided a marker. He chided the House and the whole of Britain in a paternalistic tone: "We must avoid spending large sums of money and skilled manpower on projects which use high technology and are unlikely to bring an economic return." He said that Concorde was now under review in consultation with the French government and, "meanwhile, in framing my budget proposals, I have not allowed for any expenditure on development or production beyond the existing program." The Concorde manufacturers breathed a sigh of relief: there was still time to save the airliner.

Amid warnings from *The Daily Express* that the French were planning to "go it alone" if Britain pulled out and threats of drastic strike action from the unions if there were cancellations, Benn visited Paris for a meeting with Achille Fould, the new French minister of transport. The expected confrontation never took place; the meeting was an anticlimax with all decisions delayed.

Benn explained that the ministers had reviewed "the respective positions of their governments in the context of a wide survey during a very friendly discussion." France still wanted to press ahead but Britain hesitated. *The Observer*, guessing at the decisions reached at the meeting, boldly announced, "Concorde will die within three months." This time, the anti-Concorde lobby was determined not to be cheated on legal grounds as had happened in 1964. Benn was reputed to have taken a scrap of paper with him to Paris which was an exchange of letters between himself and Chamant, France's minister of transport, in

1970. This was believed to have cleared Britain of any legal responsibility for compensation in the event of unilateral cancellation for lack of commercial viability.

Taking advantage of the delay and indecision, the aircraft industry's campaign to save Concorde began to reach its peak. It extended across two countries and involved the total industry from the board room to the shop floor. The industry's workers sensed a plot to kill Concorde emanating inside the civil service, aided and abetted by certain factors inside British Airways. They believed that figures had been cooked up to show their plane in its worst possible light. The industry knew that the civil servants, always trying to save money, were their natural enemies, but they were deeply angry over the attitude of British Airways, who were damaging the aircraft's sales prospects by publicly requesting an operating subsidy. They believed that British Airways wanted to rid themselves of Concorde, even though they had contracted to buy it.

The industry moved with united force on both sides of the Channel. It was too late for political niceties; the unions would be supplied with information by the management to pressure the ministers, and the management would tolerate threats of sit-ins and strikes if it meant keeping Concorde in being.

The most interesting development came, not from the predictable battalions of unions and management, but from the middle rank of executives and professionals whose careers were tied up with the future of advanced British technology. For too long they had been listening to the knockers and the politicians who were likely to put them out of work. Now, as they met daily over lunch in BAC's company restaurant, they realized that the only way to save their future would be to fight. Plans were drawn up to lobby M.P.s and opinion formers. There would be car stickers and leaflets but, most important of all, the professionals would present factual arguments about Concorde's performance and potential with an integrity and authority no advertising or PR firm could match. It would be "straight from the horse's mouth." Under the name of CASE, Campaign for Supersonic Engineering, the professional and middle management opened their energetic campaign. They zeroed in on the House of Commons.

In presentations to M.P.s, the ornate neo-Gothic committee

rooms of the House of Commons soon echoed with the jargon of high technology. CASE claimed boldly that "Concorde will make money." The marketing men stated that, with operating costs based on an aircraft price of £18 million with £5.2 million in spares and a utilization of 3,300 hours a year, Concorde could turn in a profit on a break-even load factor of 48 percent.

The team also argued that the sale of forty-one Concordes abroad would contribute £630 million to the British balance of payments. This figure would be even higher if savings on the purchase of American jets by British Airways were taken into account. The investment to date, the engineers argued, had been greatly exaggerated. Only £60 million a year had been spent by Britain since the start of the project. This was small beer compared to the other large British subsidies on railways, shipyards, and nationalized industry.

CASE also developed the Concorde argument on a different level. The £535 million spent on Concorde development was £535 million invested in U.K. technology. New technologies had sprung from aviation research: heart pacemakers, miniature motors for artificial limbs, blind and deaf aids, the toughest glass in the world, high-strength materials, new oils and synthetic fluids, as well as innovative manufacturing techniques. Also, high technology paid off; the export of one Concorde was the equivalent to the export of 30,000 cars or a million bicycles.

The CASE pamphlet ended with a plea that Britain should not abandon Concorde. It pointed out that the U.S. government had indirectly financed the Boeing 707 with its support for military programs and "the United States government has already spent more money on supersonic airliner research than has been spent by the United Kingdom: they are merely awaiting a suitable opportunity to build their supersonic airliner."

CASE made a profound impression on the debate by the quality of its presentation and argument. Its papers became an important part of the cabinet discussion on Concorde. But another paper was soon to drop on the desk of the secretary of state for trade and industry which he had to take very seriously. Compiled by the Confederation of Shipbuilding and Engineering Workers Union, the special report carried the considerable muscle of one of Britain's most powerful unions, which was also a major influence in the Labour party. Assembled with the help of BAC's junior management, the CSEU argued that Concorde's "techno-logical achievements are unparalleled and have recently been assessed as comparable to that of the U.S. moon program."

Then the union argued that Britain was relying far too much on past achievements and that her record aerospace exports were composed largely of spares and secondhand aircraft. "We cannot believe that a government, least of all a Labour government, would rely on military aircraft to enable the industry to survive. Yet, the cancellation or limitation of the Concorde project would mean just that. If Concorde were canceled, it would mean 'the slow garroting of the whole aerospace industry with all of its 200,000 employees, decades of skill, and billions of government investment.' "

The study threw considerable doubts on the civil service figures and stated that an overall costing of cancellation would have to take in many more factors including the extra redundancy pay to match the skill of aircraft workers, losses to rates and corpora-tion tax, decline in investment, and the need to invest in replacement projects.

The report underlined the catastrophic economic effect on the South West of England of Concorde cancellation which would be "the atrophy of social life leading to a decline in educational standards" as prospects for work in an industry characterized by its adventurous technology became replaced by the hope of "secure routine clerical employment in the glass-fronted office blocks of insurance and banking houses; the only area where jobs are being created. Any idea that Concorde workers will happily turn their skills to making aluminium prefabs cannot be ration-ally projected by those who claim to understand the modern aircraft industry."

The report also surprisingly adopted a Gaullist line, claiming that Britain would forfeit her standing in Europe and that "any government who fails to guarantee Britain's lead in supersonic transport that has been bought and worked for over the last 12 years will have to boast that it down-graded the industry to become the most advanced collection of aerospace subcontract firms in the world."

Was all this worth throwing away when Concorde development represented only one six-hundredth of public expenditure for the current year? "Can the government really argue that, for every £600 of public expenditure, it is not worth spending £1 to successfully launch the most advanced civil aircraft in the world?"

After summarizing the case for continuing the project, the CSEU bluntly suggested that "it would not passively allow the cancellation or run down of this important project."

The union argument was received sympathetically by the ruling Labour party. Although Healey and Jenkins still wanted to kill the project, the thought of bringing such devastating unemployment throughout the industry, leading to widespread strikes, made even the anti-Concorde hawks pause for thought. The trade unions and the unknown attitude of the French led the ministers to realize that the price of getting out might be far higher than the costs of staying in the project. In the House of Commons, sixty Labour M.P.s, taking note of the mounting union pressure, signed a motion warning the government against precipitate action. If it came to a vote on the floor of the House of Commons, it was by no means certain that the government could carry the day in moving cancellation.

Then, once again, Fate entered on the side of Concorde. Any careful timetable leading to a decision was dramatically disrupted when, on the evening of April 2, President Pompidou died. He had been the foremost supporter of Concorde in France and had even fought a presidential election with the call "For Progress, Concorde and Pompidou." Now another delay occurred, as the French ruling establishment began to fight among themselves to capture the presidency, and the turmoil of another election campaign began. For three months, no high level discussions at ministerial level took place between Britain and France.

The new president of France, former Minister of Finance Giscard d'Estaing, and his prime minister, Jacques Chirac, certainly showed no intention of canceling Concorde.

Across the Channel, the move to cancel Concorde was losing its momentum and the attitude of the trade unions was becoming harder.

One trade union leader declared that, if the government should scrap the project, "there will be a very vigorous policy of retaliation moving from passive resistance to outright resistance." Now BAC threw its weight behind the campaign to keep Concorde.

On May 23, BAC issued a booklet, "The Common Sense of Concorde." Over half a million copies were printed and circulated to M.P.s and the public. The cost of cancellation, according to BAC, was not the government's £80 million but a staggering £600 million, far more than Britain had already spent; £200 million would be in redundancy and compensation, while £400 million would be claimed by France in compensation. BAC maintained that "on simple financial grounds alone, it is self-evidently less expensive to the exchequer to carry on." It reminded the public and taxpaper that "the present Concorde not only meets all its airline guarantees but does so handsomely."

It also went on to claim that, once Concorde had become established, "a gradual orderly development would inevitably lead to success, and the aircraft would continue to be made and sold for the rest of this century and beyond."

The pressure for a pro-Concorde decision from the government mounted. On May 23, hundreds of aircraft workers journeyed to London to demonstrate outside No. 10 Downing Street, where the cabinet was believed to be discussing their Concorde policy. Ministers were barracked and heckled as they arrived and a petition was handed in for the prime minister's attention, with 1,000 French postcards in support. Once more, however, the British government ducked the decision. It was impossible to form any conclusion until Giscard d'Estaing's government had established itself in office. By now, however, the facts presented by Benn in the House of Commons had been completely clouded with argument and dispute. They had, in fact, been effectively discredited.

The anti-Concorde lobby, however, fought on. Energetically striking at Concorde anywhere in the world, Richard Wiggs was tireless in persuading American environment groups that Concorde was almost dead and calling on them to fight for a ban on the plane in all United States airports. He sought to damage Concorde at the highly sensitive point of foreign sales. In May, when BAC issued a statement that it was extremely delighted with the progress of negotiations with the Shah of Iran for the purchase of two aircraft, Wiggs issued a counterblast "to all cooperating groups in the U.S., U.K., and France" that the BAC statement had "little real significance" and that it was merely being "used here for propaganda purposes." He urged immediate action, in case there was a possibility of an Iran Air order. "Can we ensure," he asked, "that Iran Air receives a number of letters on the problems facing any attempt to operate commercial SSTs into United States airports and also letters from London and Paris, pointing out that commercial Concordes will not be welcome there?

"Another point that some might like to refer to is that the Shah of Iran, during the recent oil crisis, was reported as having said that oil is too precious to burn." Wiggs, urging that supporters should lobby the man at the top, obligingly enclosed the Shah's address:

> His Imperial Majesty Mohammad Reza Pahlavi Aryamehr,
> Shahanshah of Iran,
> Saadabad Palace,
> Tehran,
> Iran.

According to *The Express*, Wiggs was not alone in trying to stop the Iran deal. One of the top civil servants in the Department of Trade and Industry had, apparently, tried to stop the sales mission leaving for Tehran. Terry Walker, one of Bristol's Labour M.P.s, took up the charge, calling on the government to mount an inquiry. "I know there are many civil servants in the Trade and Industry Department who are against Concorde. They are inadvertently helping the Americans waiting for Concorde to collapse."

Concorde's manufacturers, BAC and Aerospatiale, had one great asset in the battle for survival. Now that the first two prototypes had completed most of their flight tests, the manufacturers possessed the longer-range test aircraft capable of flying airline routes. They could now show people all around the world not only Concorde's superb aerodynamic shape but also its extraordinary speed and ability to operate airline schedules.

From May 27 to June 18, Concorde 002 flew a series of flights across the North and South Atlantic operating on a typical airline-type timetable. A substantial number of seats were offered on these trips to American and European businessmen to give them a foretaste of Mach-2 travel. Between May 27 and June 5, Concorde 002 flew five round trips between Paris and Rio via Dakar, at an average time for the outward and homeward journey of 6 hours and 50 minutes. On the last day, with true panache, the plane flew from Paris to Rio and back in a single day, with just 46 minutes' turn-around at Rio. The operations proved that Concorde could keep exceptionally good airline times with variations in the journey time of only a few minutes because of its flight path high above the weather.

On June 13, 002 was ready for the North Atlantic. However, it was not to be as trouble-free as the South American run. The U.S. environmentalists were on the alert. The publicity success of Concorde's Texas trip made them determined that the plane should have no chance to touch down. Already, strong political pressure had been brought by the French and British governments on the FAA for landing permission at JFK, New York's airport, but this had been resisted.

The New York Port Authority would only allow Concorde to land if it could produce a noise level below 112 EPNdB. The FAA did not force the issue. The political figure who led the opposition to Concorde landing, Congressman John W. Wydler, said, "I am pleased that there will be no landings or takeoffs at JFK because the plane, in its present configuration, is extremely noisy and its landing would set a precedent to which I object. In fact, I voted against an American SST on the grounds that it was too noisy. It would be ironic to have our own airports used by foreign SSTs which are even worse."

If New York would not accept Concorde, Boston would; but the aircraft did not escape the inevitable attack from environmentalists. When Massport (Massachusetts Port Authority) let it be known that the supersonic airliner would be visiting the city's Logan Airport, a case was brought before Federal Judge Frank H. Freedman arguing that the plane could not land since the Department of Transportation had yet to issue an environmental impact statement clearing it of any damage to the human environment. After three hours of argument, the judge decided against the charge and Concorde was free to land in the United

States. On June 13, thousands of Bostonians crowded to see the "big bird" fly in.

Concorde received a hearty welcome at Boston's Logan Airport. Edward J. King, Massport executive director, said he was "perfectly delighted to see the wonderful Concorde here at Logan." But there were protests from community groups who believed Concorde was being used in "mindless expansion of airports."

Edward J. King commented that "I was on the field when it landed and it did not appear that the Concorde made much more noise than the conventional jet plane which landed before it." Concorde then took off for Miami, which it reached in 80 minutes.

On June 13, with typical publicity flair, Aerospatiale flew Concorde 002 from Boston to Paris and back in the same time as it took a jumbo jet to make the crossing one way. Even this did not convince some American columnists.

Jim Dance wrote: "If the assorted politicians, airport people, press and substitutes aboard the flight had their say, they would probably ride Concorde every time. But, of course, they were not paying for the trip." The thirty-three guests ran the gauntlet of electronic hardware "like getting to the Pullman diner through the kitchen" and they were given champagne, Concorde ties, and Dior perfume. But, with a Concorde seat costing $570,000 against $70,000 per seat on a 747 or DC-10, "the blending of Anglo-French imagination and know-how is not exactly a bell-ringer in the cash register department."

On June 30, the *Cleveland Plain Dealer* attacked Washington for helping the Anglo-French manufacturers in their last-ditch attempt to popularize the aircraft. This, however, appeared to be violating the law since there was doubt about Concorde's environmental impact. "Until the day that the SST can be shown to operate without adverse effects, it would not be so terrible to rely on sluggish subsonic jets."

To some Americans, Concorde was clearly a new and exciting aviation challenge. Many in the U.S. industry could not understand the curiously half-hearted approach to such a splendid aircraft by the British government. Their views were summed up by *Aviation Week*'s editor, Robert Hotz, who had made the supersonic flight from Boston to Orly. He accused the British of being fuzzy-minded about Concorde. "Even now," he wrote, "the future of Concorde balances on the decision of a group of fuzzy minded Labour ministers whose past record of folly on technological decisions is unsurpassed. It would make no sense nor save any money for Britain to withdraw from Concorde now."

The inner conflicts simmering inside the British cabinet about whether Concorde should be continued suddenly burst into the open. On Thursday May 2, Lord Beswick, Anthony Benn's assistant and minister of state at the Department of Aviation, summoned journalists to an impromptu meeting. He gave a background briefing on Concorde in which he clearly named Chancellor of the Exchequer Denis Healey as the villain of the piece. He accused him of being "totally prejudiced against the industry and of having published phony figures." In Beswick's view, Healey had wanted to cancel Concorde in his budget but had been stopped only by fear of the French reaction. Now the figures had been challenged and looked very different. Beswick then attacked *The Observer* for continuously attacking the plane and publishing phony figures.

Although the press conference was off the record, this was more than *The Observer*'s anti-Concorde aviation correspondent could take. He was stung into publishing a full report, much to the embarrassment of Beswick and the government. This hardly helped matters in the cabinet and there were angry accusations against Andrew Wilson for breaching press confidences.

Although the national airline, British Airways, had been blowing hot and cold on Concorde, there were still very powerful voices inside the corporation who did not want the airliner. On June 1, in perhaps their last attempt to persuade the British government to abandon Concorde, British Airways issued a devastating report in which the corporation forecast that operation of its five-Concorde fleet could reduce profits by up to £25 million a year. David Nicholson, writing to Peter Shore, the secretary for trade, maintained that Concorde was really an experiment and there should therefore be a large subsidy from the government. The £25 million loss would be made up of £16 million on Concorde and £9 million on subsonic jets. Even in the most favorable circumstances, Concorde could just about break even but it could also mean a substantial loss in parallel subsonic services. "The undoubted advantages of Concorde's capability in terms of speed and time saving tend to be offset by its narrow tolerances in performance, noise characteristics and other features."

The report ended by stating that all at British Airways "share the excitement inherent in a great step forward in aviation technology but we believe that the financial strength and viability of British Airways are our over-riding concern."

The manufacturers immediately protested to the government, and a strange confrontation took place in which Peter Shore, the secretary of state, conducted a debate between BAC's salesmen and British Airways planners, who had so often criticized the aircraft. For several hours with the minister in the chair the BAC management pitted their facts and figures against the airline skeptics. "We came away thinking we had at least convinced the minister," said one BAC executive, after the unprecedented meeting.

The British Airways report deeply shocked BAC and confirmed in the minds of many workers and executives throughout the industry that British Airways would stop at nothing to kill the national plane. "They are doing exactly what they have done to all our other aircraft," said one executive bitterly. Help came from a colorful and unexpected source, the buccaneering Freddie Laker, Britain's most successful independent airline operator. Within hours of British Airways' decision, he said publicly, "If I could have the same terms and conditions as British Airways, I would be prepared to operate Concorde and would make a profit." There were five tailor-made routes for the plane, according to Freddie Laker; these were New York, Toronto, Miami, Caracas, and Rio de Janeiro. On these runs, Laker Airways could clock up a profit of almost £6 million. British Airways rejected this proposal saying that, of course, anybody could make money out of supersonic flight—if they operated supersonics only.

Bernard Levin, the acerbic columnist of *The Times*, joined the row: "British Airways, having calculated that it will face a loss of £25 million a year if it should be compelled by the government to put the Concorde into service, I see that Mr. Frederick Laker claims that he, on the contrary, could make an annual profit of £6 million instead. That's nothing. A man I met in the local over the weekend said that, if he were allowed to operate the Concorde, he could make a profit of £150 million a year, whereupon the Major declared that he could make a profit of £870 million a year and old Mrs. Gilligan, downing her fourteenth port and lemon, insisted that she could make a profit of what she just had time to call 'millions and millions and millions and trillions and trillions and trillions and trillions,' before she slumped insensible to the floor."

The reason why Concorde still existed was, according to Levin, because "the two major parties are in it up to and over their ears: that ministers, both Labour and Conservative, have hornswoggled Parliament and the nation for a decade, that everybody involved has the goods on everybody else, that the proceedings have come to resemble one of those international bicycle races in which nobody is willing to take the lead and the competitors dawdle for three quarters of the way until they are in danger of falling off their machines."

Andrew Wilson worked to expose the Concorde lobby workers in both industry and politics and pointed out how they had effectively discredited British Airways figures. Freddie Laker's figures had been prepared for him by BAC, he argued; a *Daily Mail* journalist reported that they had been cooked at Epsom Racecourse on Derby Day by Geoffrey Knight of BAC and Freddie Laker.

The Concorde story moved to a climactic crisis which many expected and hoped would be fatal. Everything now turned on the meeting to be held between Harold Wilson and President Giscard d'Estaing in Paris on July 19. The mini-summit was to discuss general matters between Britain and France but, particularly, the renegotiation of Britain's Common Market membership. Concorde was a major item on the agenda.

Having reviewed the project, France still maintained an unwavering course. Rather than cut back production from the sixteen aircraft already in the pipeline, she was advocating that the two countries should keep the production lines turning over a little longer by raising the number of aircraft to be produced to nineteen. Assuming that Iran and China took their six aircraft, this, together with British Airways and Air France orders, would make a total of fifteen planes on order altogether, leaving a reserve of four. Long-dated material could be ordered and early components assembled. The advantages of ordering another three planes, in the French view, was that not only would the labor force be kept in being but, should Concorde prove a great success on entry into service, there could be an unforeseen demand from airlines for the plane and it could take two years for the manufacturers to wind up production again.

Prime Minister Wilson had little choice. With a powerful section of the British cabinet determined to axe the project and Chancellor Denis Healey already declaring that he had made no provision for Concorde in his budget, how could the prime minister agree to move entirely in the opposite directon by increasing Concorde production? It would require Wilson's considerable political balancing skill to keep the project in being.

On July 19, the two leaders got down to business. The French were highly apprehensive that Prime Minister Wilson would pull the rug out from beneath the whole supersonic enterprise and that what had started as a bid to build a European challenge to the United States would end in a major division between two of Europe's major powers.

The long arguments, detailed papers, and high-pressure lobbying since Benn's March statement had had an effect on the battle lines inside the cabinet. To the relief of Giscard d'Estaing's ministers, the president learned that Concorde would not be canceled by the British. On the other hand, Britain had no intention of either modifying or of building more aircraft until some significant new factors emerged, namely more foreign countries. The French were disappointed that Concorde modifications were ruled out and that production should be halted at the sixteenth aircraft, but they said nothing, preferring to face the difficulty of redundancies at Toulouse rather than the far greater problem of a British pull-out.

The aviation industry, after its bitter fight, had saved the project, but only for a limited period. Concorde would now go into service with British Airways, who would have to stop complaining from the sidelines.

But as one BAC engineer understandably asked, "Is it a lease of life, or the slow death?"

HARD-LEARNED LESSONS

The full-scale mock-up of the Boeing 2707 SST.

NASA continues experiments on improved supersonic airliner design, ready for the time when the United States decides to build an SST.

SUPERSONIC SUPERPOWERS

Prototype of the North American Rockwell supersonic B-1 swing-wing bomber being developed for the U.S. Air Force. The number of large military supersonics will far exceed world commercial SST fleets.

Soviet SST assembly plant at Voronezh. The TU-144 has spearheaded Russia's overall supersonic capability and know-how.

"We use these if we cancel Concorde!"

The Politics of the Ostrich

In the summer of 1975 prospects began to look brighter for Concorde for the first time since the Pan Am rejection eighteen months earlier. The spectacular record-breaking Atlantic flights followed by the Paris go-ahead decision included an unexpected bonus from the Shah of Iran. In spite of the Anti-Concorde Project's letter campaign, the Shah at the end of a $5 billion shopping spree for new technology in France let it be known that he intended to order three Anglo-French suspersonic airliners. In return, a grateful French government laid on a Concorde to fly the Shah home. The Paris–Tehran flight of 2,624 miles took just 2¾ hours, three hours less than a Boeing 707. The significance of this time saving was not lost on the delighted Iran Air officials who greeted the Shah with a red carpet at Pahlavi Airport. The Persian airline would now stand alongside British Airways and Air France in spearheading supersonic travel. The Shah, determined to use his oil riches to promote his country to the forefront, planned to establish direct air services to the United States, and Concorde's great time-saving advantage was an essential element in these plans. Iran Air had traditionally close operational links with Pan Am, and there was a possibility that the Americans might operate the Concorde after all, by means of the Persian connection. The rich Iran Air could operate Concorde for Pan Am.

There were excited rumors in the British media and official denials from New York and Tehran. The Shah was not yet ready to reveal his full plans. But with the British Labour government now officially supporting the Concorde, British Airways reflected this change of mood. "From a stance of only two weeks ago of damning the Concorde with a series of financial statistics designed to show that it could not make a profit," *Aviation Daily* noted with surprise that it had "changed 180 degrees to the point where Chairman David Nicholson is now publicly saying the airline wants Concorde and 'the sooner the better.' He is taking large advertisements in leading British national daily newspapers singing the praises of the aircraft and saying that it is going to be a great addition to the British Airways fleet. A more remarkable somersault can hardly have been seen in the world aviation industry in the past 25 years."

The French, who had never shown such inconsistency in backing the supersonic airliner, withdrew the 001 Concorde prototype from flight test operations to prepare it for enshrinement alongside Blériot's historic machine in the Musée de l'Air. The British were more phlegmatic; their first prototype 002 was also due for retirement from the test program. After bowing out with a special low-level flypast of British seaside resorts, it met with a potentially disastrous undercarriage failure on landing. Ironically, this was the first major mishap on the test program, but the aircraft was saved from serious damage by a brilliant two-point landing executed by test pilot John Cochrane. Unhappily, no museum or airport rushed forward to offer a permanent resting place for the "lame" aircraft. It was patched up and pensioned off for ground duty and taxiing trials.

British public opinion, which had never fallen below a 56 percent vote in support of the project even in its darkest hour, now began to rally. Encouraged by the bullish attitude of British Airways and by support from a government facing the prospect of an autumn election, public and press painlessly swallowed the news that the cost of the progam would inevitably rise owing to inflation. It looked as though the £12 per head for every man, woman, and child that it was estimated Concorde would eventually cost would secure the prestige of giving the world its first supersonic service early in 1976. But the future prospects were not so bright for the workers at Bristol. They knew that the program for production which had been drawn up to build hundreds of aircraft had now been cut back to an initial sixteen. In the absence of any Anglo-French agreement to start work on the next batch in coming months, work on the production lines would begin to disappear early the following year.

It was rumored that Prime Minister Wilson, with characteristic political adroitness, had arranged for "cancellation at long range." He had secured French cooperation in his forthcoming bid to renegotiate Britain's Common Market terms by agreeing to produce sixteen aircraft, but at the same time the government had seemed to accept the arguments to wind down the project slowly. On the other hand, if no new orders were forthcoming, everyone connected with the project knew that Concorde's production life would be very short indeed.

The heady days when the Concorde salesmen predicted that orders for two hundred aircraft would keep the production lines busy for ten years had long since vanished. Now even the most optimistic would only predict a maximum sale of thirty to seventy aircraft. Most believed that no further orders would be placed until the airlines had had a chance to assess Concorde's performance in service; at the very earliest this would not be before 1976. It was now highly important to show that Concorde was politically and environmentally acceptable to operate from the major United States airports.

High-level diplomatic activity at Washington could smooth the passage of FAA certification for U.S. operations, but the manufacturers had to deal with the environmentalists now trying to prevent local airport authorities from agreeing to Concorde landing rights. Playing an increasingly vocal role in the campaign directed at local congressmen and the state legislatures were groups like TVASNAC (Town-Village Aircraft Safety & Noise Abatement Committee) and the Metro Suburban Aircraft Noise Association on Long Island, New York. This last group, which draws its membership from the long-suffering communities around Kennedy Airport, was determined to make a stand against the Concorde, its logo showing an upraised arm clutching a sword menacingly pointed at an aircraft. They were, however, less directly hostile than the fifty-three-year-old New Yorker Lorna Zeller, who had been arrested for taking pot shots at aircraft landing at a runway.

The environmental groups soon went to work on the Concorde. They claimed that the port authorities were "under very heavy pressures from high offices in Washington and London to allow this very noisy craft to use JFK's facilities." In its October bulletin the Metro SANA thundered, "Since little Nigeria stood up to those who would increase the noise pollution of people living around airports, and since British Airways is still planning New York service, we can assume that they consider the United States less concerned with the health and sanity of its citizens." The subsequent press coverage conveniently overlooked that Nigeria's refusal to sanction a supersonic stopover in Lagos had less to do with noise than the politics of Black Africa's campaign against apartheid. New York Governor Hugh Carey assured the electorate that he would "vigorously work to ensure that the Port Authority does not permit supersonic aircraft to use the airports under its jurisdiction unless dramatic improvements are made in the planes to bring them up to standard." Congressman Wydler, not to be outdone, publicly warned the FAA and the Environmental Protection Agency (EPA) about accepting the Concorde under current noise criteria, adding significantly, "It would be ludicrous to stop construction of an American SST because of noise problems and then allow a foreign SST to operate in its place." Xenophobia was playing a part in the mounting campaign.

In the face of this environmental flak being fired by the East

Coast airport communities and the political row brewing in Washington, the British and French manufacturers decided to take the initiative. The French were instrumental in deciding that Concorde 002 should be sent on an immediate tour of the Americas to knock down some of the fallacies being propagated in the American press. If the East Coast airports were hostile, then Concorde would "Go West." Concorde's Boston trip had proved to be a massive crowd puller. Getting through the traffic jams to the airport had taken thousands of eager sightseers longer than the supersonic flight across the Atlantic. Concorde was its own best ambassador when it came to putting the environmental argument in proper perspective. The ability of people to perceive fractions of a decibel might be endlessly disputed in Washington, but Concorde's landing and takeoff had raised nothing but cheers from crowds, who could not tell the difference in noise levels from those of everyday subsonic jets.

The French supersonic spectacular was launched in October when Concorde 002 left Paris to fly via Gander in Newfoundland to Mexico City, in a big sales pitch that would take in San Francisco, Los Angeles, and Anchorage before returning via Lima, Bogota, and Rio de Janeiro to Paris. It was a pitch aimed particularly at airport and local officials. One member of the French Concorde delegation was blunt: "We have no choice. The airlines for the moment are not showing any interest. So the best thing we can do is fly the plane around the world and develop passenger interest."

The West Coast trip proved to be a brilliant public relations success. The impact of the environmental lobby proved far less than anticipated; protests were far outweighed by favorable press and television reaction, typified by the blaring headline in the *Oakland Tribune*, "France's SST Hard Act to Top," and by the thousands of members of the public who came to see the "Big Bird."

The only hitch in the program was that San Francisco's flamboyant mayor, Joseph L. Alioto, had to decline his supersonic flight, not because he was worried about "questions from people who think Concorde is going to destroy the world" but because he was anxious not to violate the local constitution which banned officials from taking free transportation from transportation companies. His mayoral integrity was protected by his cousin Frank, who led a party of VIP travelers on a junket that began with a trip to Mexico City, where, after a lavish reception at the French embassy, they were feted at one of the best night spots—at the French taxpayers' expense. When they were flown back to San Francisco by Concorde in record time the next morning, they were all "under the weather." According to the gossip columnist of the San Francisco Chronicle, "The plane took off from Mexico at around 6 A.M. and only three hours earlier several illustrious San Franciscans were living it up in a flamenco joint, the most vocal being the Mayor's cousin Frank Alioto. 'Bring on the broads,' Frank kept shouting and the party's British hosts took him literally. In the name of public relations, they went outside and rounded up five hookers, whose appearance seemed to shock Frank. 'I've never cheated on my wife in my life!' he announced, heading for his hotel. 'Stuck' with the 'broads,' Bill Chester, Airports Commissioner and Vice President of the ILWU, at least had the manners to buy them a round of drinks."

At Los Angeles, car parks were jammed by spectators anxious to get a glimpse of the needle-nosed aircraft. Far from believing that Concorde would destroy the world, the Californians loved Concorde. Ruth Ashton, a TV reporter who was sampling opinion at the airport, told viewers, "Everybody was oohing and aahing," people were "thrilled, it's beautiful, just like a bird. We didn't talk to anyone today who thought the noise was excessive." In fact, the new two-segment steep approach had shown the airport officials that Concorde could land at a noise level of 102 decibels, which was well inside the 115-decibel limit.

On another TV program Arthur Kelly, veteran airline operator and president of Western Airlines, stated, "I think that when they fly this plane over the North Atlantic, then this airplane is going to be a money maker and it's going to affect the first-class market as radically as anything that has ever happened in the history of aviation." Kelly, a respected member of the U.S. airlines' hierarchy, had flown to Ancorage and back. He was even more blunt in an interview with the Cleveland Press: "When the Concorde and perhaps the TU-144 begin the destruction of the first-class service on the subsonic jets across the Atlantic and on other international routes, the U.S. will again wake up to the fact that while certain people in our country decided to stop progress, the rest of the world didn't."

This was music in the ears of BAC and Aerospatiale. The warning to the U.S. airlines was echoed by Richard Fitzsimmons, a senior executive of McDonnell Douglas, who commented, "What if the passengers buy Concorde's high speed? What if their load factors are 90 percent—as happened with the British Comet? Then the Concorde will make money and hurt the economic balance of the whole system." "Hurt" was an understatement. In 1973–74 Pan Am and TWA carried four times more lucrative first-class Atlantic traffic than British Airways or Air France. In 1974 Pan Am earned more than $70 million for its precarious finances from this remunerative traffic. In 1976 this would be in danger of being siphoned off by Concorde.

After the West Coast trip, the American aviation industry began to sense the biggest challenge to its supremacy in a quarter of a century. But now, unlike the 1950s, when the Comet 1 had introduced the world's first jet service, the U.S. was not building a rival aircraft.

Now the stakes were incalculably higher, affecting not only the future of the European and United States aerospace industries but also the technical and economic relationships of two of the leading nations in the powerful EEC trading bloc. Concorde was within an ace of proving itself a winner. It was only months away from airline service where it could cause a revolution in air travel comparable with the first jets.

The long evolution of Concorde has been a strange and fascinating saga reflecting the constantly changing political and economic pressures of our present world. The course of its development has raised many fundamental issues about the control of technology in a democratic society.

In 1962 when the Concorde project was launched in the splendor of London's Lancaster House, it was an appropriately lush setting for a scheme that conformed to the most fashionable theories of the day concerning the growth of technology. Britain and France then unquestioningly accepted the arguments for seemingly limitless and inevitable advance; technology was virtuous in its own right. "Man will go faster, whether you believe that or you don't," said one British cabinet minister responsible at the time for launching the supersonic transport. This summed up the view of the world's aerospace industry, and it was an assumption with which, at that time, the public agreed. There was certainly no question of or mechanism for consulting the people on matters of advanced technology. This was considered a matter for scientists, and only very few elected representatives could grasp the facts.

The arguments for supersonic passenger flight, presented by the Royal Aircraft Establishment at Farnborough, who were cast in the role of assessors, reflected an almost blind faith in technological products. "A successful supersonic aircraft would not only be a commercial venture of high promise, but would also be of immense value to this country as an indication of our technical skill." This attitude was shared by similar research establishments around the world. As Farnborough's ludicrous attempts to estimate the costs and their rudimentary market forecasts show, the main aim was to build a faster and more impressive airliner than anybody else. In this respect, Concorde was probably the greatest—and certainly the last—indulgence of Britain's aviation technocrats. Throughout the 1940s and 1950s they had experimented with a dazzling array of different prototypes in seeking a way to build an unassailable technological lead for the British industry in post-war aviation. Their conceptions were often brilliant, like the Comet 1, the world's first jet airliner, and the Viscount turboprop, but too often limited resources were squandered on projects like the Brabazon and Princess Flying Boat which could not have—and did not—find markets. When Concorde was launched, it had an announced development budget in 1962 that was far in excess of any previous project and that was known to be "phony as hell" inside the industry. Indeed, one of the reasons for Britain and France forming a partnership was that neither believed they could afford it alone. But they also hoped to take a leaf from the American book by creating a much bigger market produced by the two nationally owned airlines.

Concorde was also started for reasons of legitimate national interest: to wrest the technological initiative in aerospace from the United States. The British and French technocrats had watched the American industry inherit the jet airliner market pioneered by European technology. British jet-engine know-how and airframe developments with the ill-fated Comet and later with the Caravelle had given the European nations a brief experience of leadership in aviation. The Comet disasters and the take-over by the American industry when it introduced the Boeing and Douglas jets left the European industry a long way behind. To prevent total U.S. colonization of the skies, Britain and France decided that their best chance lay in raising the stakes in the "technological roulette game" by doubling the speed of airliners. If they were first and fast enough, they could stake out a clear market share in the next generation of airliners.

The United States was expected to respond to the challenge and rush into the supersonic gamble. How much would she stake in the contest for leadership? Originally most of the opposition to the Concorde came from politicians fearful that any American SST would rapidly overtake the European effort in speed and size. They were not wrong, at least in the early days of the "great SST race." American industry, at that time tackling the technological goal of putting a man on the moon by 1970, believed itself capable of building a bigger and better SST than Concorde. Spurred on by pressure from Juan Trippe of Pan Am and Najeeb Halaby at the FAA, President Kennedy committed the United States "to develop at the earliest practical date the prototype of a commercially successful supersonic transport *superior* to that being built in any other country in the world." The stakes in the roulette game were raised even higher; the American SST was to be faster than Concorde and nearly twice the size.

The "superior" SST was to take the resources of American technology "beyond the state of the art" into the realms of new materials, structures, and engineering techniques required to build a commercial aircraft from titanium. There was no question that, given the time and resources, it could be done; but given the conditions of the SST race, the need for federal funding, and the commercial conflict built into the program, it proved a disastrous gamble. When an impatient Congress, responding to public pressure, axed the SST, it had become a far more modest venture. Its size and speed had fallen and it had cost the American taxpayer more than the Concorde. At least the Anglo-French governments had a plane for their money.

Now, well over a decade later, with the American SST nonexistent except for a series of models in a NASA wind tunnel, the Anglo-French aircraft industries believe that Concorde is still the essential spearhead in the attempt to break the U.S. domination and near monopoly of Western commercial aircraft construction. According to Henri Ziegler, who built up Air France after the war and was chief of Aerospatiale, "We are in an absolutely crazy situation. Today in the Western world the U.S. represents only 51% of the total aircraft market. Europe represents 26%. But industry-wise we have let the Americans push us completely back until we are in danger of being pushed out entirely. In aircraft production terms we have dropped progressively down from 10% to a mere 6½%. They are working like hell to completely destroy the independent European aircraft industry."

The aircraft industry is particularly important to Europe because Europe is the nonsocialist world's only major aerospace producer apart from the United States. Its emphasis on high technology is an essential stimulus to the technological and industrial growth of an advanced industrial nation. Equally important for Europe, aircraft construction calls for high engineering standards and a heavy input of skilled labor per ton of raw material used. The export of each $60 million Concorde airframe can bring a return equivalent to the export of 30,000 cars or one million bicycles. Furthermore, aerospace is a key defense industry, essential for European security and political independence.

Since the end of the Second World War the increasing scale, competitiveness, and aggression of the United States aerospace industry has made it increasingly difficult for Europe to foster its own industry. Although it might be argued that the Europeans have fared less well in the West's "free market" for aircraft because American planes are better or even less expensive, the record shows that there is no such thing as a free market in aircraft. Selling planes is a highly political business. National interest, prestige, and diplomatic position are often at stake. European aircraft manufacturers understandably complain about the "cowboy" methods employed by U.S. sales teams who are often backed up by military missions and the State Department. The French claim that this is exemplified by the all-out way in which General Dynamic's YF-16 fighter was pushed against its European competitors in the NATO fighter competition. Frequently, it seems, the Americans do not seem to share a common political interest with Europe in aerospace. The Concorde is perhaps the most significant example.

What exacerbates the situation is that the U.S. aerospace industry is deeply protectionist about its own domestic market. American airlines simply *prefer* their own national product, and it is almost unheard of for a European aircraft to be sold to them in any number. A major factor is the steep 5 percent tariff on European aircraft imports into the United States which virtually prices any foreign competitor out of the market. The Americans, however, are free to sell their products in European markets without this burdensome tax. The federal government also stands ready to fund research in the military field that can spin off into commercial aircraft. Both the Boeing 707 and 747 were initiated through defense contracts, but the SST was not, which is perhaps significant in the light of its subsequent failure. However, the supersonic swing-wing B-1 bomber is a major defense program that many U.S. aviation experts see as the foundation for a future all-American SST.

It is hardly surprising that many British and French observers believe that the controversy about Concorde in America and the reluctance of U.S. airlines to accept it are part of a great conspiracy to destroy the European aviation challenge and its future survival.

Certainly there is more than a suspicion, particularly in France, that Pan Am's and TWA's decision to drop Concorde was designed to ensure that the United States industry retain its world monopoly. Why, they ask, should Pan Am have supported the plane and maintained a major part in its development and modifications only to totally withdraw at the last and critical moment? It would have cost them little to maintain their option interest in the same way as the Japanese and Australians. The equal finality and deliberate timing of the TWA decision are quoted as yet further evidence to support the conspiracy theory of the U.S. airlines.

The British are typically more sanguine and reserve their judgment. Although they accept that Pan Am's financial situation was a convenient excuse for dropping Concorde (less so in the case of TWA), they see that the U.S. airlines for the first time run the risk of losing technical leadership to British Airways and Air France. More important, they risk the loss of at least two-thirds of first-class traffic worth nearly $60 million annually on the North Atlantic alone. As one senior Pan Am executive maintained, their decision was "a calculated gamble." With over $40 million at stake, were the U.S. airlines gambling that their decision might "kill off" the Anglo-French supersonic? As one BAC executive complained bitterly after the negotiations, "They could have made it work if they had willed it." After all, they had done precisely this with the Boeing 707, the early models of which were flown by Pan Am even though they could not cross the Atlantic without an intermediate fueling stop. The question is, would they have made the same decision if the first supersonic airliner had been American rather than European?

The American airlines' decision has led to a deliberate "talking down" of Concorde operations. Little mention is made of the point shown up by all the marketing surveys done in the United States about the supersonic's great appeal because it slashed long flights in half, saving passengers the fatigue of "red-eye" subsonic international flights. Far more play has been made of the apparently "dismal" economics of supersonic flight. This off-the-cuff verdict, thrown out at a press conference by Charles Tillinghast of TWA, is hotly disputed by the Anglo-French manufacturers who claim that their plane is a victim of the reckless rush into wide-bodied jumbo jets. These, in the face of international recession, falling traffic, and rocketing fuel prices, have left the world's airlines with a glut of unfilled seats, unprofitable load factors, and balance sheets dropping into the red.

Once "uneconomic" Concorde flies, the indications of market research in America and Europe show that between 40 and 50 percent of all international business traffic will migrate to the supersonics at first-class-plus fares. It may cost the airlines more per seat in terms of aircraft depreciation and fuel to fly passengers supersonic, but Concorde will be easier to fill and the return per seat will be more profitable than the subsonics. But Concorde's financial benefits to the airlines have to offset losses on the profitable first class and business traffic from the jumbo jets. However, the European manufacturers do not regard the "convenience" of airline balance sheets or corporation politics as a valid reason for halting the development of faster air travel. When Concorde goes into service on the world route, it will be an interesting test of the American citizens' loyalty to see whether they will support their "half-speed" airlines.

The American airlines may have taken the course they did to test the resolve of the British and French to press ahead with Concorde in a commercially hostile situation. The U.S. industry has often sensed a divided attitude in Europe toward both American competition and the need to maintain an advanced aircraft industry. This view can only have been reinforced by the political crises that periodically beset Concorde. The whole project was, and is, dependent on a fluctuating set of political premises. One of the principal reasons for initiating the scheme was to build a European unity through technology as opposed to the nineteenth-century technique of tariff walls and customs unions. As the British cabinet minister Wedgwood Benn maintained, "European technology meant finding something big and dramatic and exciting which was within your capability and doing it." In the early days, the British and French governments undoubtedly saw Concorde in this light and created an exclusive "little common market" of their own to build the airliner. The Germans, Dutch, Italians, and other members of the European Economic Community were not involved initially and subsequently showed little enthusiasm. Concorde, conceived as a plane for the Paris/London–New York route, held no attraction for Lufthansa, Alitalia, and KLM once the option system collapsed. Unlike later aviation projects, Concorde was always viewed as a private "Anglo-French affair" rather than a Common Market project. Even now, much to the fury of France, which sees itself as the principal leader in a "buy European" strategy, the state-owned airlines of Belgium, the Netherlands, and Italy follow the stubborn policy of Lufthansa in providing the U.S. industry with its richest market outside the United States. "They are not linked with the interest of their communities. They are happy to buy Boeings" is the bitter comment of one senior Airbus salesman, disappointed that Europe's own wide-bodied jet transport was not making headway against the Lockheed Tristar and McDonnell Douglas DC-10.

Yet Concorde has been used as an effective political weapon in cementing Britain to the Common Market. Ever since de Gaulle's famous *"Non"* to British entry in 1963, Concorde has been regarded by the French as a token of British faith in the principle of European unity. Once Concorde has proved itself in airline service, this "diplomacy" may well be used to persuade other European airlines to fly supersonic and play a part in any future developments. The other members of the EEC will be seeking concessions from Britain and France in the future; the price of cooperation and understanding on butter or ball bearings may include support for Concorde.

There is now a danger that if the discrimination against Concorde continues, France in particular may try to persuade the EEC to agree to a protectionist barrier against the United States aerospace products in the same way as European aircraft are discriminated against in America. In the French view a "buy European" policy may be the only way to save their advanced industries from becoming mere subcontractors. The British have, so far, been more flexible, believing it is better to trade even on a subcontract basis, as in the case of the Rolls-Royce RB-211 engine for the Lockheed Tristars.

The protectionism of the U.S. aerospace industry is understood by the European planemakers, but the sometimes hysterical "protectionism" voiced by the environmental lobbies is a different matter. This crusade was determined to stop at nothing to "blockade" the European SST from landing at American airports.

Wild environment "scare stories" have been written up in exaggerated detail by journalists keen to exploit the "good copy" about the sonic boom, radiation hazard, ozone depletion, skin cancer, and the deafening noise Concorde was supposed, rumored, and calculated to cause. Very few American newspapers had the honesty to caution their readers, as the Indianapolis News did in 1973, that the "Eco Freaks Do as Much Harm as Good." Columnist Don Maclean pointed out that by going for an all-out attack on SSTs and Alaska pipelines there was a danger that the real polluters like the motor car were being ignored. The reason, he explained, was that "SST planes have more glamour and therefore more publicity potential than less mundane but polluting devices. . . . The chief villains when it comes to messing up our environment are not the new things coming along—the SST, the new pipelines—it is the old established systems. The motor car for one . . . is there any reason why we have to have 375 horsepower engines in our cars, engines which use up natural resources exorbitantly and put excessive amounts of pollution in the air? . . . Not only that, but bigger cars create bigger junk heaps which clutter the landscape. Big cars use more gas which means more pipelines and bigger oil tankers, which cause bigger oil slicks. Big cars require bigger roads and more of them."

Compared to cars, aircraft in general and the supersonic Concorde are remarkably clean. The supersonic discharges into the environment only 5 pounds of pollutant per 1,000 miles traveled as opposed to the 50 pounds or more of a typical car. The smog of Los Angeles and Tokyo is the tragic memorial to the unbridled freedom given to the internal combustion engine in the name of mobility of the individual—another example of the old adage that it is always harder to stop something that is established than something new.

The "SST Cancer Peril" and Concorde's effect on the ozone level have given rise to what one American columnist dubbed "ozonitis." "It is highly contagious," he mocked, "and is carried by zealots who pull facts out of context and twist them to support their own theories. The cancellation of the American SST is mute testimony to the lethality of the malaise." Whatever else the great "ozonitis" scare has to its credit, it at least persuaded the U.S. Department of Transportation to launch a massively organized multimillion-dollar "Climatic Impact Assessment Program." The result of the best scientific analysis and hundreds of thousands of hours of computer data gathered, ironically, from Concorde flights, balloon soundings, and minutely accurate sampling of the upper atmosphere showed, "Operations of the present-day SST aircraft and those currently scheduled to enter service (about 30 Concordes and TU-144s) cause climatic effects which are much smaller than minimally detectable." Moreover, the CIAP report published in December 1974 cited other causes which were equally, if not more seriously, damaging the upper atmosphere: "aerosol sprays and industrial sources of dust and carbon dioxide." The *Houston Post* wryly commented under the headline "NO BANG, JUST PSST" that men, women, and children of the world were doing more to destroy ozone by punching aerosol buttons than the effect of Concorde. "We all do it. And with each poof, we are throwing one more minuscule dart into the ozone that saves our lives. It seems an inglorious way for the human species to end."

No matter what the scientific evidence proves, there will always be a body of public opinion which, with a rationale more in keeping with medieval alchemy than the twentieth century, will cling to its cherished myths. The fanaticism of a certain section of the American anti-SST lobby was determined to keep up the Concorde blockade at all costs. When in November the British 002 landed in Bangor, Maine, after an incredible 2 hour 55 minute flight from England, pilot John Cochrane accepted that the arguments would continue. "The aircraft has been sur-rounded by so much controversy," he told local newsmen, but added with his typically Scottish homespun sense, "People will just have to see the craft in action before they realize that it's just another airplane."

One of the local people who did see the aircraft in action was elderly Mrs. Dorothy Grayu. Her views cut straight across the controversy about Concorde noise and must have struck an echo in many Americans. "It was just marvelous. It's progress. That's what I would call it."

The mainspring of the environmental opposition is that super-sonic airliners might be the embodiment of progress for some, but the symbols of a technological advancement in the wrong direction for many others. The history of the Concorde and the other SSTs raises important questions about the management, control, and application of national scientific and industrial resources. The issues surrounding the aircraft have made people aware for the first time of a totally new area of politics—the politics of technology. Fundamental to the new politics was the choice that industrial society made about what priority it allo-cated to technical growth and what priority it gave to the environment. At stake were important factors such as the public's right to question governmental and political decisions made in an area which might drastically affect the quality of life for everyone.

The American SST was under development and Concorde had started its first test flights when the politics of technology began to surface. Almost overnight the world became aware that it faced possible environmental disaster as a result of unchecked industrial growth. The Europeans had unconsciously become accustomed to living with this idea for years, following the experience of the first industrial revolution. But in the late 1960s Japan and, more importantly, the United States suddenly became alarmed about the consequences of uncontrolled growth. This feeling, which began with the pollution of lakes and rivers, was compounded in the popular mood of the American public, disillusioned with the Vietnam war. It has since been compounded by the feeling of desertion during the Yom Kippur war and the energy crisis following the Arab oil blockade in 1974. For the first time in history the poor nations were able to hold the rich to ransom. It is not surprising that people no longer identify progress with the blind pursuit of a higher standard of living that brings little pleasure or satisfaction to the quality of life in densely polluted cities.

Idealists naturally want to escape to a Utopia where technology is carefully controlled and regulated. Just how an accustomed standard of living can be maintained in such a circumstance is often glossed over. The 15,000 Boeing workers thrown out of their jobs in Seattle at the time of the cancellation of the SST would no doubt willingly have accepted a little pollution in return for work. The lines at the welfare office were an eloquent testament to that. It would be wrong to credit the environmentalists with the "honor" of defeating the Administration over the SST in 1971. They did not achieve this alone, although they created a powerful groundswell. First, Boeing had overreached itself in trying to build a "superior" Mach-3 titanium swing-wing SST for 300 passengers. By the time they were on their third design and had spent a billion dollars, the public and the politicians had lost confidence. Second, in the judgment of well-placed observers, the Boeing company itself was half-hearted in its commitment to the supersonic project. It was uncharacteristically slow in manning the barricades to defend it, and some high-placed officials privately welcomed the final cancellation with relief. Financially, Boeing could have foundered on the same rocks that almost wrecked Lockheed on the Tristar project. Third, the environmentalists found themselves in the same political camp as the powerful and astute Senator William Proxmire of Wisconsin, who was a dedicated opponent of the SST on financial grounds. His January 1971 report, "SST Is on the Skids," claimed that "Concern for the Environment Does It," but his previous campaign had been run as a crusade against federal spending.

With the SST canceled, the environmentalists and Senator Proxmire have turned their fire on Concorde. In spite of the subsequent environmental uproar about climatic changes and skin cancer, by 1974 $2 billion in federal funds had been poured into America's supersonic B-1 bomber program. By 1980 no fewer than 240 of these swing-wing supersonics, each bigger than Concorde, costing more than $76 million each, will be roaring across the very stratosphere that a handful of European airliners were purported to be destroying. It is a curious irony, as the influential *Wall Street Journal* pointed out.

British environmentalists, organized as the Anti-Concorde Project, have been no less dedicated in their efforts to cancel their own supersonic and have received encouragement and coverage by a number of equally dedicated journalists. But their impact has been considerably less in Britain than in the United States. A curious "special relationship" with the U.S. anti-SST lobby has been forged and representatives have been skillfully deployed at various Washington and New York hearings, accredited in a mysterious way as representing the views of the British public. Although they have always claimed to speak for British opinion, surveys have shown that home support for the project has always been greater than 60 percent. Yet anti-Concorde spokesmen have always been on hand to tell the American press, television, and congressional committees that the British public is looking to the far-sighted Americans to put an end to the reckless adventure.

The environmentalists on both sides of the Atlantic may well have served interests with motives different from their own. In attempting to blockade Concorde in the United States, they are erecting a protective shield around the very same military-industrial complex they profess to despise. Not only has the supersonic B-1 bomber program gone ahead almost unnoticed, but their actions in blunting the European challenge will merely enable the American industry to increase its already powerful domination of air travel unchecked. Such a situation is hardly likely to encourage good relations between Europe and America at a time of international stress. Washington has certainly been aware of this and has tried not to act like a "xenophobic banana republic" in spite of a vocal minority of American opinion which appears to insist that it should.

The CIAP report has put the environmental issue into its true perspective. Dr. Groebecker, a leader of the scientific group behind the report, has aptly commented that the SST "was merely a pimple on the environmental problem." In March 1975 the FAA, on the strength of the report, recommended that Concorde and the TU-144 should be allowed to operate in the United States. It considered that the only environmental threat was airport noise, although this was at or below the level of the first generation of subsonic jets. The FAA decided that since it was impractical to insist that all the 707s, DC-8s, 727s, and DC-9s currently operating should be expensively modified to bring them within the stipulation of FAR 36, it could only be fair to allow Concorde to escape the strict noise requirements. U.S. subsonic jets will continue to operate for many years and the "incremental cumulative noise imposed on airport communities" from the relatively few SST flights would, in the FAA's opinion, pass unnoticed. Concorde was, therefore, likely to represent a minor threat to the environment!

The environmentalists, led by Senator Proxmire, immediately protested at what they regarded as FAA treachery. The hearings, convened by the Administration in April to sound opinion on its proposed agreement to supersonic operations, attracted droves of lobbyists, perhaps sensing that this was the last chance to stop Concorde. On the opening day demonstrators paraded in Washington, calling for an SST ban. They were undeterred by the FAA's carefully worded warning that a refusal to allow British Airways and Air France Concorde operations could "raise substantial issues under international law and could have foreign policy implications." Britain and France were accused of diplomatic tricks, with Congressman Lester Wolff of New York maintaining, "We must face the unpleasant truth that, while legal, scientific, economic, and moral logic all combine to fly in the face of the recommendations favoring Concorde, the unpleasant specter of diplomatic blackmail hovers over all we say and do here." The FAA was even accused by Congressman Joseph Addabbo of New York of mounting a "charade" and that the agency did not care to "unduly rile friendly nations which have invested great sums in producing these planes, although these same nations limit hours of air traffic into their airports."

The French and British manufacturers resisted this strong American political attack with only limited success. They relied very heavily on presentations of scientific evidence to prove that Concorde was not a menace to the upper atmosphere and that its noise levels could be well controlled on takeoff, especially with a 25-degree bank immediately after takeoff. This, however, merely brought the countercharge that this maneuver, although completely safe in European eyes, would endanger thousands of American lives. Inevitably, the manufacturers, supported by the formidable power of British and French diplomacy, found themselves combating Richard Wiggs, leader of the Anti-Concorde Project. The veteran campaigner and his supporters had somehow found sufficient funds to fly to Washington and New York, where Wiggs inevitably claimed to speak on behalf of the British people. The New York congressmen, in spite of other evidence, gave him the benefit of the doubt. After two days of emotional charge and countercharge the FAA hearings ended with a warning from Proxmire that he would seek to introduce legislation to ban Concorde on noise levels. The whole circus then moved to New York for yet more hearings before the far more hostile New York Port Authority. Once again, the placards were out, and British viewers plainly saw Governor Hugh Carey on television leaving his options open on the question of whether Concorde should land. Thus local American politics seemed to be taking the initiative dangerously away from the central government in Washington. The risks of this action, particularly to relations between the United States and Europe, should not be underrated. A ban on the aircraft that has taken almost twenty years to develop could not be permitted by Britain and France. Local environmentalists would be responsible for influencing the future of European technology, one pillar of the West's strength. Should the American Administration prove unable to allow Concorde flights, it will be seen as a form of technological isolationism by the most powerful technological nation in the world. This would plainly be ludicrous, and the world's leading power would be pursuing the politics of the ostrich.

By indulging in a noisy witch hunt the environmental minority is clouding far more significant issues raised by SST development. The international contest to build supersonic airliners which started in the early 1960s succeeded in demonstrating the technological brilliance of the advanced industrial nations but was motivated by a political thinking far more in tune with the age of the dreadnought than the era of rapidly accelerating technology. But now, after almost fifteen years of development, the American SST has disappeared and Concorde has become greatly significant to the future of French and British industry. Notions of prestige have been replaced by new considerations of political and economic importance which can vitally affect the relations between Europe and the United States and indeed the future role of Europe in the wider world. Having produced Concorde, the Europeans believe that their ability to build such excellent aircraft together with their growing unity will enable them to challenge the long-established American monopoly of the world's aerospace industry.

Banning Concorde from the U.S. will be a major setback for the European aerospace industry and perhaps one more step down the road of what Harold Wilson called "industrial helotry," since this vital European industry will survive only on American terms. With such important issues at stake, rejection of Concorde on the grounds of "environmental protectionism" could lead to European public opinion and industry demanding greater protection of their own advanced industries, particularly aerospace. This could have a damaging effect on the West at a dangerous time.

The truly revolutionary impact of Concorde has been concealed amid all the charges and countercharges over the SST thrown up by rival political lobbies. As supersonic scheduled services spread around the world, the impact of a new generation of air travel will be plain to see. The first generation of subsonics had an immense effect on the world's political, economic, and cultural life. The greater efficiency and comfort of flight, together with the slashing of airline timetables, had a great effect on decision-making in the world of business and politics. The jet liner also opened up new areas of the world for people to visit and led to a boom in tourism, mingling peoples and attitudes.

Concorde will now speed up this process. It will have an even more profound effect on decision-making. The European centers will be within a day trip of New York and the eastern seaboard. Japan and Australia will become closer to the U.S. and Europe. Perhaps the most notable feature of the approach to Concorde operations has been the attitude of the rapidly developing countries of the Middle and Far East. China, Singapore, Iran, and many Arab countries have all expressed great interest in supersonic services. They know their countries will benefit from the rapid exchange with the advanced countries of politicians, opinion formers, technicians, businessmen, scientists, and others who all affect the complex working of the global community.

Communist China may be following the example of Russia, where airlines have been highly developed to overcome the absence of ground communications over vast distances. Russia is pressing the TU-144 into service to link farflung Vladivostok with Moscow and to take key workers to any part of the economy where they are needed. For Iran the advent of Concorde will mean that this booming, oil-rich country will be able to open an express route between East and West. Tehran will be athwart this communications corridor, which will bring Iran new opportunities for industrial and political influence. The Eurasian land mass as a whole will be bound closer together by supersonic travel. Concorde and TU-144 will play a leading part in this development. It would be ironic for the United States, which has gained so much from the introduction of the subsonics, to cut itself off from the world developments in a technological huff.

In the next decade the world will see whether Concorde can achieve its promise and whether the great investment made by Britain and France will be justified. Whatever the result of this colossal gamble, it is unlikely that a project like Concorde will ever be started in quite the same way again.

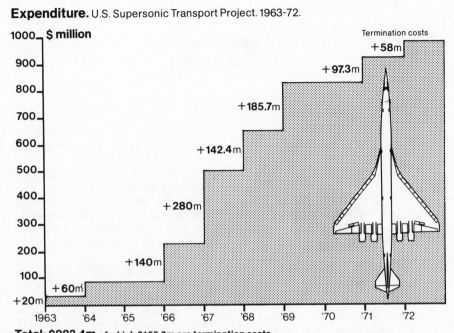

Expenditure. U.S. Supersonic Transport Project. 1963-72.

$ million

Termination costs
+58m
+97.3m
+185.7m
+142.4m
+280m
+140m
+60m
+20m

1000 · 900 · 800 · 700 · 600 · 500 · 400 · 300 · 200 · 100 ·

1963 '64 '65 '66 '67 '68 '69 '70 '71 '72

Total: $983.4m of which $155.3m are termination costs.
To this total should be added $52.3m private investment.
($38.1m from Boeing and $14.2m from airlines, sub-contractors, etc.)

Source: FAA

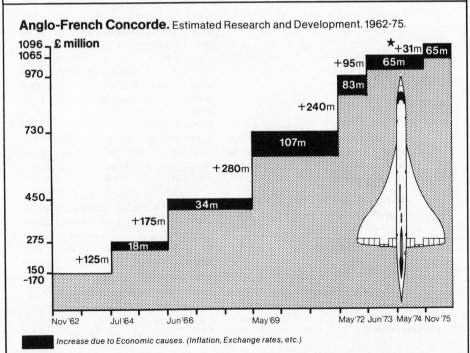

Anglo-French Concorde. Estimated Research and Development. 1962-75.

£ million

*+31m 65m
+95m 65m
83m
+240m
107m
+280m
34m
+175m
18m
+125m

1096 · 1065 · 970 · 730 · 450 · 275 · 150 · -170

Nov '62 Jul '64 Jun '66 May '69 May '72 Jun '73 May '74 Nov '75

■ *Increase due to Economic causes. (Inflation, Exchange rates, etc.)*

*In addition to this sum an R & D estimate of £1,070m was announced in March 1974. No estimate for Economic causes was given.

Appendix 1
The Treaty

Treaty Series No. 3 (1963)

Agreement

between the Government of the
United Kingdom of Great Britain and Northern Ireland
and the Government of the French Republic

regarding the Development
and Production of a Civil Supersonic
Transport Aircraft

London, November 29, 1962

[The Agreement entered into force on the date of signature]

*Presented to Parliament by the Secretary of State for Foreign Affairs
by Command of Her Majesty
January 1963*

The Government of the United Kingdom of Great Britain and Northern Ireland and the Government of the French Republic;

Having decided to develop and produce jointly a civil supersonic transport aircraft:

Have agreed as follows:

ARTICLE 1

(1) The principle of this collaboration shall be the equal sharing between the two countries, on the basis of equal responsibility for the project as a whole, of the work, of the expenditure incurred by the two Governments, and of the proceeds of sales.

(2) This principle, which shall be observed as strictly as possible, shall apply, as regards both development and production (including spaces), to the project considered as a whole (airframe, engine, systems and equipments).

(3) The sharing shall be based upon the expenditure corresponding to the work carried out in each country, excluding taxes to be specified by agreement between the two Governments. Such expenditure shall be calculated from the date of the present Agreement.

ARTICLE 2

The two Governments, having taken note of the agreement dated 25th October, 1962 between Sud Aviation and the British Aircraft Corporation (B.A.C.), and of the agreement dated 28th November, 1961 between Bristol Siddeley and the Société Nationale d'Etudes et de Construction de Moteurs d'Aviation (S.N.E.C.M.A.), have approved them, except in so far as they may be in conflict with provisions which are the subject of agreement between the Governments.

ARTICLE 3

(1) The technical proposals, which shall form the basis for the joint undertaking by Sud Aviation and B.A.C., comprise a medium range and a long range version of the aircraft.

(2) The Bristol Siddeley-S.N.E.C.M.A. BS/593/3 turbojet engine shall be developed jointly for the aircraft by Bristol Siddeley on the British side and by S.N.E.C.M.A. on the French side.

ARTICLE 4

In order to carry out the project, integrated organisations of the airframe and engine firms shall be set up.

ARTICLE 5

A Standing Committee of officials from the two countries shall supervise the progress of the work, report to the Governments and propose the necessary measures to ensure the carrying out of the programme.

ARTICLE 6

Every effort shall be made to ensure that the programme is carried out, both for the airframe and for the engine, with equal attention to the medium range and the long range versions. It shall be for the two integrated organisations of the British and French firms to make detailed proposals for the carrying out of the programme.

ARTICLE 7

The present Agreement shall enter into force on the date of its signature.

In witness whereof the undersigned, being duly authorised thereto by their respective Governments, have signed the present Agreement.

Done in duplicate at London this 29th day of November, 1962 in the English and French languages, both texts being equally authoritative.

For the Government of the United Kingdom of Great Britain and Northern Ireland:

JULIAN AMERY.
PETER THOMAS.

For the Government of the French Republic:

G. DE COURCEL.

Appendix 2
Sonic Boom

When an aircraft is flying at supersonic speeds changes in air pressure are generated from each discontinuity of the aircraft's contour which coalesce into a bow and a stern wave. These shock waves are propagated from the aircraft in the form of a cone with its axis centered on the aircraft's flight path (top). When these shock waves meet the earth's surface their passage is marked by a slight rise and fall in atmospheric pressure which is heard as a sonic boom, a sound that can vary from a low rumble to a loud crack.

The area on either side of the flight path which is exposed to the sonic boom is limited by refraction caused by temperature gradients within the atmosphere and may be further modified by such phenomena as wind (bottom).

Both overpressure and the rise time vary with distance from the aircraft. The characteristic double boom is heard only in a zone narrower than the width defined by the calculated "cut-off" rays. Between this inner zone and the theoretical edge of the boom carpet the boom becomes a dull rumble.

U.S. Department of Transportation
Federal Aviation Administration
Concorde Supersonic Transport Aircraft
Draft Environmental Impact Statement
March 1975

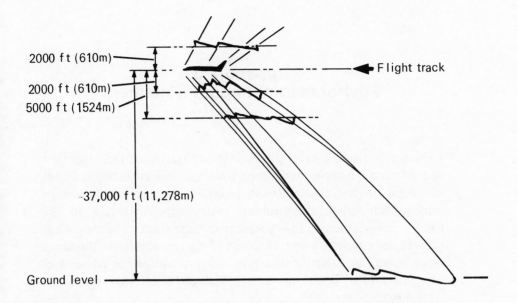

2000 ft (610m)

2000 ft (610m)
5000 ft (1524m)

37,000 ft (11,278m)

Flight track

Ground level

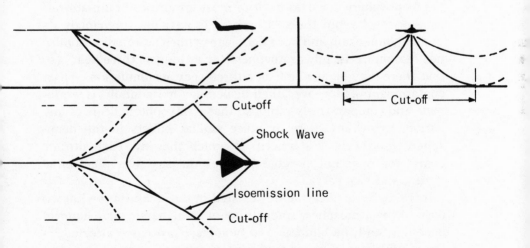

Cut-off

Cut-off

Shock Wave

Isoemission line

Cut-off

Appendix 3
Environmental Impact Statement

During the discussion of the supersonic transport (SST) project in 1970, the question was raised whether impurities from flights of aircraft high in the stratosphere could alter the proportions of atmospheric trace constituents with harmful results to the earth's environment. The question is important because, while they make up only a tiny fraction of the atmosphere, the trace constituents in their natural proportions control the balance of life-giving heat while blocking lethal radiation that otherwise would reach the earth's surface.

Flight in the stratosphere (typically above 12 kilometers or 39,000 ft) is of concern, while flight in the troposphere below is not. The reason is that, through turbulence, storms, and rainfall, the troposphere cleanses itself of most impurities in a matter of days or weeks, but the stratosphere is virtually stagnant in its vertical dimension and does not cleanse itself so rapidly. Impurities remain in the midstratosphere for as long as three years (so that there may be as much as a three-year accumulation of past contaminants). Moreover, their dispersion, horizontally, is worldwide and comparatively rapid, so that stratospheric fleets of any nation, flying anywhere, produce similar effects in the hemisphere (northern or southern) in which they fly. High-altitude commerce over Europe contaminates the sky over the United States, and vice versa.

In 1970, large uncertainties existed in our quantitative knowledge of the atmosphere's constituents, its dynamic and chemical behavior, and the climatic and biological processes affected by the atmosphere. Thus, at that time, there was no valid scientific basis for judging where, in the range from entirely negligible to truly significant, the conjectured effects of stratospheric flight might fall. There was simply not enough knowledge from which to draw the needed scientific conclusions.

During the congressional debate in July 1970, legislation introduced by Senator H. M. Jackson directed the Department of

Transportation to mount a federal scientific program to obtain the new knowledge needed to judge how serious the conjectured effects might be and to report its results to the Congress by the end of calendar year 1974. This report of findings describes the results of the ensuing program.

The Department's Climatic Impact Assessment Program (CIAP) has drawn on nine other U.S. federal departments and agencies and seven foreign ones. It has also drawn on the individual talents of some 1,000 investigators of numerous universities and other organizations in the United States and abroad. It has necessarily encompassed a wide range of science and technology.

A special committee of the National Academy of Sciences and the National Academy of Engineering was organized to review the work of CIAP and to form an independent judgment of the results, on which the academies will issue a special report. The committee members have worked hard on the problems throughout two years of CIAP.

CIAP has yielded a harvest of new scientific data, and has progressed considerably in drawing the data together into a better understanding of the cause-and-effect relations between aircraft effluents in the stratosphere and environmental impacts. Serious uncertainties still exist, but their magnitude has been reduced substantially so that useful conclusions are now possible.

The task of CIAP has been to reach scientific conclusions, which can be used for establishing approximate technical and operational standards that will assure a chosen level of atmospheric quality in the course of the future development of air travel. To achieve this objective, the process of establishing and meeting standards should start now because of the long lead times involved. Only through such standards can future large-scale development of SST operations, by any nation, avoid significant adverse environmental consequences. Moreover, only through such standards can the continued evolution of the subsonic fleet alone avoid similar consequences.

While the environmental pollutants from aircraft described in this report are important, they are by no means the only causes of the final effects noted. Some examples of other causes are: aerosol sprays and industrial sources of dust and carbon dioxide.

Principal Scientific Conclusions

1. Operations of present-day SST aircraft and those currently scheduled to enter service (about 30 Concordes and TU-144's) cause climatic effects which are much smaller than minimally detectable.

2. Future harmful effects to the environment can be avoided if proper measures are undertaken in a timely manner to develop low-emission engines and fuels in step with the future growth of stratospheric aviation. These measures include:

   a. The development of new engine technology leading to lower levels of nitrogen oxide emissions (which involves a lead time of 10 to 15 years for development, fabrication, certification, and introduction into service of the new engines).

   b. Use of jet fuels having a sulfur content smaller than that in current fuels, through the application of state-of-the-art desulfurization processes.

3. If stratospheric vehicles (including subsonic aircraft) beyond the year 1980 were to increase at a high rate, improvements over 1974 propulsion technology would be necessary to assure that emissions in the stratosphere would not cause a significant disturbance of the environment.

4. The cost of carrying out the measures in conclusion 2, including the operational cost of compliance, is small compared to the potential economic and social costs of not doing so.

5. A continuous atmospheric monitoring and research program can further reduce remaining uncertainties, can ascertain whether the atmospheric quality is being maintained, and can minimize the cost of doing so.

Executive Summary
Department of Transportation
Climatic Impact Assessment Program
December 1974

Appendix 4
Concorde in Operation

ACHIEVED FLIGHT TIMES

	Concorde Hr : Min.	Subsonic Hr. : Min.	Statute Miles
Washington, D.C. - Paris	3:33	7:30	3840
Boston - Paris	3:09	6:30	3440
Paris - Boston	3:08	7:40	3440
Boston - Miami	1:31	2:50	1260
Paris - Caracas via Las Palmas	6:04	11:10	5260
Rio - Paris via Dakar	6:35	11:30 redeye 13:30 via Dakar	5730
Toulouse - Dakar	2:35	*4:45	2280
Beirut - Toulouse	2:29	*4:30	2140
Darwin - Singapore	2:29	4:15	2080
Manila - Tokyo	2:18	4:00	1860
Manila - Darwin	2:20	4:00	1980
London - Tehran	3:52	5:30	2740
Bahrain - Singapore	3:52	7:50	3930
Singapore - Bahrain	3:40	7:40	3930
Bahrain - Fairford	4:12	*6:30	3220
Buenos Aires - Rio	1:50	2:50	1240
Paris - Cayenne via Sal	5:35	*8:00	4180
Toulouse - Tehran	2:36	*5:50	2860

Estimated Non Stop Time (No Direct Flight)

Timetable

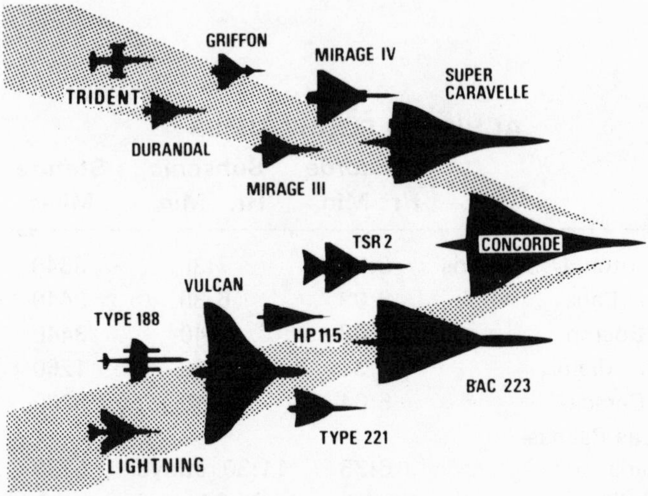

Background Experience

	Max. Tow. lb.	Approach EPNdB	Sideline EPNdB	Takeoff EPNdB	1977 Fleet size
Concorde	400,000	114.9	113.1	117.8	Under 20
707-320	332,000	120	108	114	550
DC8-50	315,000	118	106	114	180
DC8-61	325,000	117	103	117	
Other 1st generation subsonics	258,000 to 335,000	noise levels comparable to above . . .			300
747-100	710,000	113.6	101.9	115	280
747 Latest	775,000	107	98	108	

Noise levels in EPNdB relate to FAR 36 measuring points.

Noise Levels, 1977

Index

A-300 Airbus, 181, 275; roll-out of, 1–9
Adams, Arthur, 128
Addabbo, Joseph, 282
Addley, Robert, 199
Aeroflot, 60, 63, 152
Aerojet Company, 185
Aeronautical Research Institute of Sweden, 36
Aerospatiale, 1, 2, 5, 8, 139, 190, 208, 228, 238–39, 256, 258, 269, 272
Airbus, 181, 275; roll-out of, 1–9
Aircraft Committee of Directors, 77
Aircraft Magazine, 117–18
Air France, 9, 12, 63, 64, 67, 80, 203, 210, 216, 220, 228, 261, 264, 272, 274, 281
Air Registration Board (Britain), 162
Aitken, Max, 226
Alioto, Frank, 268
Alioto, Joseph L., 267–68
Alitalia, 275; use of U.S. aircraft, 3
Allen, Professor G. C., 249
Allen, William, 144, 149, 189, 202
American Airlines, 37, 231, 234
Amery, Julian, 48, 49, 51, 52, 53, 57, 59, 67–68, 72, 82, 83, 84–85, 89, 92, 97, 126
Anderson, Clinton, 188
Anglo-French Supersonic Aircraft Agreement, 39–52, 72, 73, 75, 79–80, 82, 107–8, 110, 207; British attempt to withdraw from, 86–100, 135–36, 244–45, 265; final breakthrough on, 50; first contacts toward, 44; negotiations for, 45–51; signing of, 51–52; U.S. intervention in, 48–49, 90–91, 93
Anti-Concorde Project, 123, 128, 130–31, 161–62, 175, 199, 221, 263, 280, 282
Ashton, Ruth, 268
Association of Supervisory Staffs, Executives, and Technicians (ASSET), 99
Avco Company, 185
Aviation Daily, 88, 104, 264
Aviation Week, 258–59

B-1 (supersonic bomber), 273, 280, 281
B-47 (bomber), 21, 31
B-58 Hustler (bomber), 31–32, 125, 126
B-70 Valkyrie (bomber), 30, 32–34, 70, 71, 118

BAC-111 (airliner), 84, 91
Bank of England, 88
Beggs, 180
Bell XS-1 (rocket-plane), 21, 124
Benn, Tony. *See* Wedgwood Benn, Anthony
Beswick, Lord, 259
Bisplinghoff, Dr., 148
Black, Eugene, 49, 62, 70, 71
Blackwell, Miles and Richard, 14–15
Blériot, Louis, 264
Blériot Memorial Lecture, 78
Bloch, René, 241
Bluestreak (rocket), 49
Blum, Leon, 99
BOAC News, 68
Boeing Company, 15, 30, 32, 35, 46, 48, 63, 68, 71, 271, 275; layoffs, 189, 279; use of German technology, 20–21
Boeing Dash 200. *See* Boeing SST
Boeing Dash 300. *See* Boeing SST
Boeing 707, 21, 30, 34–35, 60, 63, 67, 150, 235, 236, 238, 252, 263, 273, 274, 281
Boeing 727, 281
Boeing 747, 6, 169, 192, 202, 203, 217, 218, 231, 232, 234, 235, 258, 273
Boeing 2707-100. *See* Boeing SST
Boeing SST, 143–52; Ad Hoc Committee report against, 169–72; adoption of delta wing, 151, 168, 185; airframe, 145; cost of, 152, 168, 169–70, 173, 176, 178, 185, 189; defeat of, 166–90, 214–15, 279–80; design of, 112–15, 118; Nixon support of, 168, 169, 171–74, 182, 185, 186, 188, 189, 214–15, 225, 227; Proxmire Committee hearings on, 176–82, 199, 214–15; unveiling of mock-up, 112–14; use of swing wing, 114–15, 118–19, 144–46, 148, 150–52, 168, 185, 279; weight problems, 146–49, 185
"Boulton Paul Affair," 138–39
Brabazon, Lord, 19
Brabazon (prototype aircraft), 19–20, 87, 159, 270
Braniff Airlines, 228, 238, 239
Brewer, Assemblyman, 201
Bristol Aircraft, 40–41, 81

McDonnell Douglas Aircraft Company, 269, 276